D. L. Snader.

THE DESIGN OF WALLS, BINS AND GRAIN ELEVATORS

BY

MILO S. KETCHUM, C.E.

M. Am. Soc. C. E.

PROFESSOR-IN-CHARGE OF CIVIL ENGINEERING, UNIVERSITY OF PENNSYLVANIA ; SOMETIME
DEAN OF THE COLLEGE OF ENGINEERING AND PROFESSOR OF CIVIL ENGINEERING,
UNIVERSITY OF COLORADO; CONSULTING ENGINEER

THIRD EDITION—REVISED AND ENLARGED

SECOND THOUSAND

TOTAL ISSUE, SEVEN THOUSAND

McGRAW-HILL BOOK COMPANY, Inc.

239 WEST THIRTY-NINTH STREET, NEW YORK

LONDON: HILL PUBLISHING COMPANY, Ltd.

6–8 BOUVERIE STREET, E. C.

1919

PRESS OF
THE NEW ERA PRINTING COMPANY
LANCASTER, PA.

PREFACE TO FIRST EDITION.

The aim in writing this book has been to present a systematic analysis of the stresses due to granular materials together with a discussion of the principles of design and the details of structures which contain the granular materials. Since a thorough knowledge of the theory of the retaining wall is essential to a correct understanding of the theory of pressures in bins, the design of retaining walls is taken up first. The design of bins for coal, ore, etc., is then taken up in detail, and is followed by the design of grain bins and elevators. The sequence of the different subjects is the same as the order in which the work was developed by the author, and it is thought to be logical and consistent. While algebraic methods for calculating stresses have been given due consideration, attention is called to the graphic methods for calculating the pressures on retaining walls, and in hopper bins.

Reinforced concrete is now very extensively used in the construction of retaining walls, bins, and grain elevators, and it has therefore appeared advisable to give a discussion of the theory of reinforced concrete and to develop the formulas necessary for use in design.

Experiments on the pressure of grains in bins have given pressures that agree closely with the values obtained by calculation for grain at rest, and that show the influence of grain in motion. Very few experiments have been made, however, on granular materials other than grain with sufficient care to give anything like a reliable check on calculated pressures. All experiments on the pressure of granular materials available to the author have been included in the discussion. The subject of costs has been given considerable attention and numerous examples of actual structures are described in detail.

In the author's practice and teaching he has felt the need of a systematic treatise on bin design, and this book has been written as a first contribution to the subject.

iii

The author is under obligations to many sources to which proper credit has been given in the text of the book. To obtain the latest practice in bin and grain elevator design the author has had to depend very largely upon engineers that make a specialty of this line of work. The author is under obligations to many engineers for data and plans; he especially wishes to thank Mr. H. A. Fitch, Chief Engineer the Minneapolis Steel & Machinery Co.; Mr. John S. Metcalf, President, The John S. Metcalf Co.; Mr. James MacDonald, President, The Mac-Donald Engineering Co.; and Mr. A. F. Robinson, Bridge Engineer Santa Fe Ry. Credit is due Mr. Howard C. Ford, Instructor in Civil Engineering in the University of Colorado, for assistance in preparing the drawings and in reading proof.   M. S. K.

January 26, 1907,
    University of Colorado,
      Boulder, Colo.

PREFACE TO THE SECOND EDITION.

In this enlarged and revised edition more than one hundred and fifty pages of new material, including many cuts, have been added. Chapter IV "Reinforced Concrete Retaining Walls" and Chapter VII "Methods of Construction and Cost of Retaining Walls" have been entirely rewritten. The additions include Chapter IA "Rankine's Theory Modified"; Chapter IVA "Effect of Cohesion.—Stresses in Bracing of Trenches.—Stresses in Tunnels"; additional examples of retaining walls; formulas for the length of the curve of suspension bunkers; additional experiments on the pressure of grain in bins; formulas and details for the design of rectangular bins; methods and forms for constructing grain bins; descriptions of three additional reinforced concrete grain elevators; and an appendix giving a brief résumé of concrete, plain and reinforced.

Credit is due Mr. W. C. Huntington, Instructor in Civil Engineering in the University of Colorado, for assistance in the calculations and in preparing the drawings.   M. S. K.

    Boulder, Colorado,
      August 23, 1911.

PREFACE TO THE THIRD EDITION.

The new material in this edition includes data on economic design of reinforced concrete retaining walls; formulas for wedge-shaped reinforced concrete beams; formulas for calculating the load on bin walls; formulas for calculating the unit pressures on bin walls by Airy's solution; the calculation of the pressures in sand boxes; fully worked out problems in the design of retaining walls and bins, and the report on the design of retaining walls adopted by the American Railway Engineering Association in March, 1917. Many minor additions have been made and all known errors have been corrected.

The adoption of the report on the design of retaining walls by the American Railway Engineering Association has for the first time defined a standard practice for the design of retaining walls and abutments.

Credit is due Mr. W. C. Huntington, Professor of Structural Engineering in the University of Colorado for assistance in making the calculations and in preparing the cuts, and to the American Railway Engineering Association for permission to reprint the report on the design of retaining walls.

While the material given in this edition has been under preparation for some time, the actual writing has been done while the author was engaged as Assistant Director in charge of construction of U. S. Government Explosives Plant C, Nitro, West Virginia.

M. S. K.

U. S. Government Explosives Plant C,
   Nitro, West Virginia,
      December 1, 1918.

v

TABLE OF CONTENTS.

Completed

Completed

PART I. THE DESIGN OF RETAINING WALLS.

Completed

CHAPTER I. RANKINE'S THEORY.

Completed

CHAPTER IA. RANKINE'S THEORY MODIFIED.

Completed

CHAPTER II.   COULOMB'S THEORY.

Completed

CHAPTER III.   DESIGN OF MASONRY RETAINING WALLS.

Specs.

Completed

CHAPTER IV.   REINFORCED CONCRETE RETAINING WALLS.

Completed

CHAPTER IVA. EFFECT OF COHESION. — STRESSES IN BRACING OF TRENCHES. — STRESSES IN TUNNELS.

Completed

CHAPTER V. EXPERIMENTS ON RETAINING WALLS.

Completed

CHAPTER VI. EXAMPLES OF RETAINING WALLS.

Completed

CHAPTER VII. METHODS OF CONSTRUCTION AND COST OF RETAINING WALLS.

Completed

CHAPTER VIIA. NOTES ON DESIGN OF RETAINING WALLS AND PRESSURES IN SAND BOXES.

PART II. THE DESIGN OF COAL BINS, ORE BINS, ETC.

CHAPTER VIII. TYPES OF COAL BINS, ORE BINS, ETC.

CHAPTER XIII. COST OF BINS.

CHAPTER XIV. METHODS OF HANDLING MATERIALS.

CHAPTER XVIII. THE DESIGN OF GRAIN BINS AND ELEVATORS.

Chapter XIX. Examples of Grain Elevators.

CHAPTER XX. COST OF GRAIN BINS AND ELEVATORS.

APPENDIX I.

CONCRETE, PLAIN AND REINFORCED.

CHAPTER I.

APPENDIX II.

APPENDIX ~~III.~~ IV.

THE DESIGN OF WALLS, BINS AND GRAIN ELEVATORS.

INTRODUCTION.

Probably no subject with which the civil engineer has had to deal has evoked so much discussion as the design of retaining walls. One class of writers has evolved elaborate mathematical theories, on the one hand, while another class has ridiculed all mathematical treatment, and has used " rule of thumb " methods for design. Many of the mathematical enthusiasts have failed to appreciate actual conditions of the wall and the filling; while most of the " rule of thumb " writers show an entire lack of knowledge of the fundamental theories underlying a theoretical discussion of the pressure on retaining walls.

While an exact determination of the pressure on retaining walls is difficult if not impossible on account of the lack of definite data on the condition of the filling and the foundation, it does not follow that a mathematical solution is useless. Experiments on homogeneous granular materials like wheat, sand, etc., have shown that the pressure follows laws which are definite and exact.

An argument against retaining wall formulas has been that many walls which theory shows are on the point of failure, have not failed, but would seem to have an ample factor of safety. This argument is threadbare, for what bridge engineer has not cudgeled his brain to find why certain bridges have not fallen down; and who is there that would presume to say that the application of theoretical analysis to bridge design is of no value. The answer to both examples is the same, the fault is more in the data than in the theory—we have failed to use brains in the analysis.

Rankine's theory

While the theory of Rankine as given in the following discussion is by no means perfect, it is the author's opinion that its intelligent use will put the design of retaining walls on as scientific a basis as the design of most engineering structures. Bridges are designed for the heaviest load that they are expected to carry, and not for the lightest load. Retaining wall formulas give maximum pressures for the conditions, which are certainly the ones upon which to base the design.

When retaining walls were built of cheap masonry, "rule of thumb" methods might do; but with the introduction of reinforced concrete retaining walls, and the storage of granular materials in bins, a mathematical treatment is certainly necessary. With improved methods of handling grain and other granular materials it has become necessary to design bins on economical lines. While the problem of bin design differs from the design of retaining walls in many ways, a thorough knowledge of the theory of the retaining wall is necessary to a correct understanding of the problem.

In the following treatise the author has endeavored to place the design of walls and bins on a scientific basis. The discussion will be given in three parts: Part I, The Design of Retaining Walls; Part II, The Design of Coal Bins, Ore Bins, etc.; Part III, The Design of Grain Bins and Elevators.

PART I.

THE DESIGN OF RETAINING WALLS.

Introduction.

SEMI-FLUIDS.—The laws of perfect fluids and of solids have been studied experimentally and theoretically and are well known. Many fluids are perfect fluids only above certain temperatures, and as the temperature falls become "viscous fluids" and after passing the chill point become solids. Other materials such as dry sand and shot occupy an intermediate position between fluids and solids and are called "semi-fluids"; approaching fluids when water is added, and solids when a cementing material between the grains causes cohesion in the mass. Dry sand, shot, wheat, and similar materials are almost perfect semi-fluids, the mass being without cohesion, the particles being held in place by friction on each other. The angle of internal friction is the angle whose tangent is the coefficient of internal friction of the particles upon one another, and is nearly always larger than the angle at which the material will stand if poured in a pile on a level floor. The angle of internal friction is commonly referred to as the angle of repose. If water be added to dry sand the angle of internal friction decreases and approaches zero, while if a cementing material such as clay be added, the angle of internal friction increases and approaches 90 degrees as a limit.

The laws of perfect semi-fluids such as sand and wheat have been studied experimentally and theoretically and are well known. Experiments made upon wheat in bins by the author and others and recorded in Chapter XVII prove the following: (1) the horizontal pressures vary as the depth in very shallow bins; (2) in deep bins the horizontal pressure is less than the vertical pressure (0.3 to 0.6 of the vertical pressure, depending on the grain and many other conditions), and increases very

3

little after a depth of $2\frac{1}{2}$ to 3 times the width or diameter of the bin is reached; (3) there is no active upward component in a granular mass; (4) the flow from an orifice in the side of a deep bin varies approximately as the cube of the orifice and is independent of the head, as long as the orifice is well covered.

RETAINING WALLS.—A retaining wall is a structure which sustains the lateral pressure of earth or some other granular mass which possesses some frictional stability. The pressure of the material supported will depend upon the material, the manner of depositing in place, and upon the amount of moisture, and will vary from zero to the full hydraulic pressure. If dry clay is loosely deposited behind the wall it will exert full pressure, due to this condition. In time the earth may become consolidated and cohesion and moisture make a solid clay, which may cause the bank to shrink away from the wall and there will be no pressure exerted. On the other hand all cohesion may be destroyed by the vibration of moving loads or by saturation, and the maximum theoretical pressures may occur. The pressures due to a dry granular mass, a semi-fluid, without cohesion, of indefinite extent, the particles held in place by friction on each other, will first be considered; after which the effect of cohesion and of limiting the extent of the mass will be considered.

Calculation of the Pressure on Retaining Walls.—To fully determine the pressure of the filling on a retaining wall it is necessary that the resultant of the pressure be known (*a*) in amount, (*b*) in line of action, and (*c*) in point of application. Many theories have been proposed for finding the pressure, each differing somewhat as to the assumptions and results. All theories for the design of retaining walls that have any theoretical basis come in two classes: (1) the Theory of Conjugate Pressures, due to Rankine, and commonly known as Rankine's Theory, and (2) the Theory of the Maximum Wedge, probably first proposed by Coulomb, and commonly known as Coulomb's Theory. Rankine's Theory determines the thrust in amount, in line of action, and in point of application. In Coulomb's Theory, with the exception of Weyrauch's solution, the line of action and point of application must be assumed, thus leading to numerous solutions of more or less merit. All solutions based on the theory of the wedge assume that the resultant thrust is applied at one third the height for a wall with a level or inclined surcharge, as is given by Rankine; but the resultant is assumed as making angles with a normal to the back of the wall varying from zero to the angle of repose of the filling. In Rankine's solution the resultant is parallel to the plane of the surcharge for a vertical wall.

(1) **RANKINE'S THEORY.**—In this theory the filling is assumed to consist of an incompressible, homogeneous, granular mass, without cohesion, the particles are held in position by friction on each other; the mass being of indefinite extent, having a plane top surface, resting on a homogeneous foundation, and being subjected to its own weight. The principal and conjugate stresses in the mass are calculated, thus leading to the ellipse of stress. In the analysis it is proved (a) that the maximum angle between the pressure on any plane and the normal to the plane is equal to the angle of internal friction, and (b) that there is no active upward component of stress in a granular mass. Both of these laws have been verified by experiments on semi-fluids. Rankine deduced algebraic formulas for calculating the resultant pressure on a vertical wall with a horizontal surcharge, and on a vertical wall with a surcharge equal to δ, an angle equal to or less than the angle of repose. The general case is best solved by constructing the ellipse of stress by graphics, or Weyrauch's algebraic solution may be used. The author has extended Rankine's solution so that it is perfectly general.

(2) **COULOMB'S THEORY.**—In this theory it is assumed that there is a wedge having the wall as one side and a plane called the plane of rupture as the other side, which exerts a maximum thrust on the wall. The plane of rupture lies between the plane of repose and the back of the wall. It may coincide with the plane of repose. For a vertical wall without surcharge (horizontal surface back of the wall), the plane of rupture bisects the angle between the plane of repose and the back of the wall, if the resultant thrust is assumed as normal to the

back of the wall.   Weyrauch makes the same assumptions as Rankine and by means of the maximum wedge obtains the same results as Rankine. All other solutions based on Coulomb's Theory arbitrarily assume the direction of the thrust.

(a) **Weyrauch's Solution.**—Weyrauch makes the same assumptions as Rankine.   He then assumes a wedge of maximum thrust, and determines the amount of and the line of action of the resultant pressure, using the principal which follows directly from Rankine's Theory. "that the forces upon any imaginary plane-section through the mass of earth have the same direction."   These assumptions, after much calculation, lead to two formulas, one giving the amount of the thrust, and the other the line of action, the angle the resultant thrust makes with a normal to the back of the wall.   Weyrauch's solution gives algebraic formulas which give the same results as the ellipse of stress, which can be constructed graphically with very much less work.   Rankine's and Weyrauch's solutions give identical results.

(b) **Cain's Solution.**—Professor William Cain assumes that the resultant thrust makes an angle with a normal to the back of the wall equal to ϕ', the angle of friction of the filling on the back of the wall, or equal to ϕ, the angle of repose of the filling if ϕ' is greater than ϕ.

(c) **Rebhann's Solution.**—Professor Rebhann makes the same assumptions as Professor Cain, and uses the graphic solution given in Chapter II.

(d) **Trautwine's Solution.**—In Trautwine's Civil Engineer's Pocket Book it is assumed, for a wall nearly vertical, that the plane of rupture in all cases bisects the angle between the plane of repose and the back of the wall.   This solution gives correct results for a vertical wall with horizontal surface back of the wall, but is in error for all other cases.

Other authorities assume that the resultant thrust is normal to the back of the wall, etc.   For a smooth vertical wall without surcharge all the above solutions lead to the same results, for the amount, direction, and point of application of the resultant thrust.

In the following discussion the formulas for the thrust of the filling on retaining walls will be deduced (a) according to Rankine's Theory, and (b) a general formula will be derived based on Coulomb's Theory of a Maximum Wedge.

Nomenclature.—The following nomenclature will be used:

ϕ = the angle of repose of the filling, *or angle of internal friction.*

ϕ' = the angle of friction of the filling on the back of the wall.

θ = the angle between the back of the wall and a horizontal line passing through the heel of the wall and extending from the back into the fill.

δ = angle of surcharge, the angle between the surface of the filling and the horizontal; δ is positive when measured above and negative when measured below the horizontal.

z = the angle which the resultant earth-pressure makes with a normal to the back of the wall.

λ = the angle between the resultant thrust, P, and a horizontal line.

h = the vertical height of the wall in feet.

d = the width of the base of the wall in feet.

b = the distance from the center of the base to the point where the resultant pressure, E, cuts the base.

P = the resultant earth-pressure per foot of length of wall.

E = the resultant of the earth-pressure and the weight of the wall.

w = the weight of the filling per cubic foot.

W = the total weight of the wall per foot of length of wall.

p_1 = the pressure on the foundation due to direct pressure.

p_2 = the pressure on the foundation due to bending moments.

p = the resultant pressure on the foundation due to direct and bending forces.

y = the depth of foundation below the earth surface.

μ = coefficient of friction = $\tan \phi$

μ' = coefficient of friction = $\tan \phi'$

CHAPTER I.

RANKINE'S THEORY.

Introduction.—In this theory the filling is assumed to consist of an incompressible, homogeneous, granular mass, without cohesion, the particles are held in position by friction on each other; the mass being of indefinite extent, having a plane top surface, and resting on a homogeneous foundation, and being subjected to its own weight. These assumptions lead to the ellipse of stress and make the resultant pressure on a vertical wall parallel to the top surface. The pressure on other than vertical walls can be determined by the ellipse of stress.*

ELLIPSE OF STRESS.—It will now be necessary to investigate the relations between the stresses in an unconfined, incompressible, granular mass, which is held together by friction of the particles on each other, and which has no cohesion.

Stress.—If a body be conceived to be divided into two parts by a plane traversing it in any direction, the force exerted between these two parts at the plane of division is *an internal stress*. Stress is force distributed over an area in such a way as to be in equilibrium. A state of internal stress is or may be exerted upon every plane passing through a point at which such a state exists.

Plane Stress.—A plane stress is a stress that is parallel to a given plane; for example, let the plane of the paper be this plane and let the stress acting on every plane which is at right angles to the plane of the paper be parallel to the plane of the paper, then such a stress is a plane stress. Plane stress only will be considered in this discussion. The obliquity of a stress is the angle between the direction of the stress and a normal to the plane on which the stress acts.

State of Stress.—The state of plane stress at any point in a body is completely defined when the intensity and obliquity of the stress on any

---

* The ellipse of stress gives indeterminate values for some walls leaning toward the filling. The author has extended Rankine's Theory in Chapter Ia to make it general.

8

two given planes passing through that point are known. Stress can be resolved into components the same as force. An oblique stress can be resolved into a normal component (tension or compression) and a component along the plane called the tangential component, or shear.

*Conjugate Stresses.**—If any state of stress exists at a point in a body the stress acting on a plane through the point will be parallel to a second plane through the point, and the stress acting on the second plane will be parallel to the first plane. Stresses so related are called *conjugate stresses.*

In Fig. 1 let the elementary prism be in equilibrium when acted upon by the stress *p* parallel to *A-C,* and stress *q* direction unknown. It is required to find the direction of stress *q*. Now the stress *p* acting

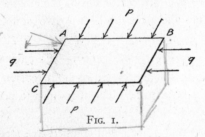

Fig. 1.

on the faces *A-B* and *C-D* must be a pair of forces in equlibrium; then to have equilibrium stress *q* acting on the faces *A-C* and *B-D*. must be a pair of forces in equilibrium, which can only occur when stress *q* is parallel to *A-B* and *C-D*. Conjugate stresses may be like (both tension or both compression) or unlike (one tension and the other compression).

*Principal Stresses.**—In any state of stress there is one pair of conjugate stresses at right angles to each other; *i. e.,* there are two planes at right angles to each other on which the stress is normal only. Stresses so related are *principal stresses.* For consider a plane at the point to rotate, and there will be some position where the stress on the plane is normal. The plane at right angles will have a conjugate stress which is also normal. It will be shown that one of the principal stresses is the greatest stress and the other principal stress is the least stress at the point. Any possible state of stress can be completely defined by principal stresses.

* Unit stress is meant where the term stress is used.

Tangential Components.—In Fig. 2 let p and q be tangential components acting on the right prism *A-B-C-D* and producing equilibrium. Then for equilibrium p must equal q. For the stress on *A-B*

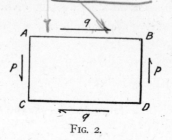

FIG. 2.

$= AB.q$, and the moment of the couple $AB.q$ is $AB.q.AC$. Also the stress on $A\text{-}C = AC.p$, and the moment of the couple $AC.p$ is $AC.p.AB$. But for equilibrium the moment of the two couples must be equal, which can only be if $p = q$.

Case I.—Equal-like Principal Stresses.—If a pair of principal stresses at a point be like (both compression or both tension), and be equal in intensity, the stress on a third plane through the point is of the same intensity and is normal to the plane.

In (a) Fig. 3, p and q are equal compressive stresses acting on the principal planes *A-A* and *B-B*, respectively, through the point *O*. It

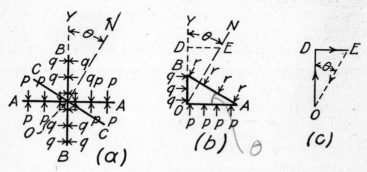

FIG. 3.

is required to find the intensity and direction of the stress, r, acting on the plane *C-C* through the point *O*.

Let *AOB* in (b), Fig. 3, be a differential triangular prism at *O*, having its faces in the planes. The prism is then in equilibrium under the action of the forces p, q, and r, acting on the faces OA, OB, and AB, respectively. In (c) lay off OD = total stress on AO = $p.OA$, and lay off DE = total stress on OB = $q.OB$. Now complete the force triangle ODE, and OE = the equilibrant = $AB.r$, in amount and direction.

Now tan $DOE = \dfrac{q.OB}{p.OA} = \dfrac{OB}{OA}$, since $p = q$.

Therefore, angle DOE = angle $OAB = \theta$, and OE is perpendicular to AB.

Also $OE^2 = DO^2 + DE^2$,
$$= p.^2OA^2 + q.^2OB^2,$$
$$= p^2(OA^2 + OB^2),\quad (A)$$
$$= p.^2AB^2,$$

and $OE = p.AB$

But $OE = r.AB$, and therefore $r = p = q$, which proves the theorem. The stresses in Case 1 are *fluid stresses*.

Case 2.—Equal-unlike Principal Stresses.—If a pair of principal stresses at a point be unlike (one compression and the other tension), and be of equal intensity, the resultant on any plane through the point is of the same intensity, and is inclined to the normal to the plane of principal stress at an angle θ, but on the opposite side from the resultant in Case 1.

In Fig. 4, (a) shows the planes and forces acting through the point O. Let OAB in (b) be a differential triangular prism at O with its faces in the given planes. The prism is in equilibrium under the action of the forces p, q, and r, acting on the faces OA, OB, and AB, respectively. In (c) lay off $OD = AO.p$, and $ED = OB.q$, and OE will be the equilibrant acting on the face $AB = AB.r$.

Now tan $EOD = \dfrac{ED}{OD} = \dfrac{q.OB}{p.OA} = \dfrac{OB}{OA}$, since $p = q$.

Therefore, angle $EOD = \theta$, and EO makes an angle with the normal to OA equal to θ, but on the opposite side from Case 1.

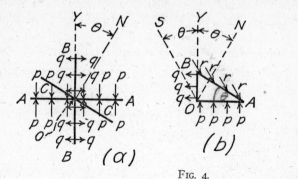

FIG. 4.

Now $OE^2 = DO^2 + DE^2$,   Same as in (A) P. 11,

$\qquad = p.^2AB^2$, and $OE = p.AB$, as in Case 1,

but $OE = AB.r$,

and $r = p = q$

The stresses in Case 2 are *right shearing stresses*.

Case 3.—*Given the principal stresses of the same kind but having unequal intensities to determine the intensity and direction of the stress on a third plane.* If p and q represent the intensities of the forces on the planes A-A and B-B, respectively, acting through the point O, in (a), Fig. 5, p being the greater, we have by algebra

$$p = \frac{p+q}{2} + \frac{p-q}{2} \text{ an identity,}$$

$$\text{and } q = \frac{p+q}{2} - \frac{p-q}{2} \text{ an identity.}$$

Now we may look on the plane A-A as having two separate stresses equal to $\frac{p+q}{2}$ and $\frac{p-q}{2}$ of the same kind, while upon the plane B-B we will have two stresses $\frac{p+q}{2}$ and $-\frac{p-q}{2}$ of opposite kinds.

We may now group the stresses separately; thus the equal-like stresses $\frac{p+q}{2}$ and $\frac{p+q}{2}$ acting on the planes A-A and B-B, and the equal-unlike stresses $\frac{p-q}{2}$ and $-\frac{p-q}{2}$ acting on the same planes A-A and B-B, respectively.

as in (a) figs 3 & 4.

as in Case I.

On tension or compression

Now the stress on the plane C-C for the equal-like stresses $\frac{p+q}{2}$ and $\frac{p+q}{2}$ is the force $r_1 = \frac{p+q}{2}$ acting normal to plane C-C. The stress on the plane C-C for the equal-unlike stresses $\frac{p-q}{2}$ and $-\frac{p-q}{2}$ will be a stress $r_2 = \frac{p-q}{2}$, and inclined at an angle θ to the line of prin-

as in Case II

Equal as in fig. b

Equal as in (b) & (c) fig. 4

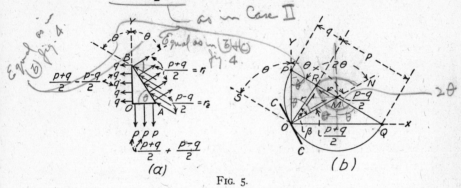

FIG. 5.

cipal stress. In (a), Fig. 5 we have the stresses acting as above and it is required to find the resultant of the stresses on the plane C-C.

In (b) lay off $OM = \frac{p+q}{2} = r_1$, normal to C-C, and from M lay off $MR = \frac{p-q}{2} = r_2$, and parallel to $\frac{p-q}{2}$ in (a). Now $OR = r$ will be the resultant force in direction and intensity. From the construction it will be seen that in (b) $MP = MQ = OM = \frac{p+q}{2}$.

Also $QR = MQ + MR$,

$$= \frac{p+q}{2} + \frac{p-q}{2},$$

$$= p$$

$$PR = MP - MR,$$

$$= \frac{p+q}{2} - \frac{p-q}{2},$$

$$= q$$

Resultant.

Class Prize.

$$\angle\, RMN = 2\theta$$

$$\angle\, ROM = \beta = \text{obliquity of } r.$$

The tangential component of r in Fig. 6 is

$$RT = MR \cdot \sin RMT,$$

$$= \frac{p-q}{2}\sin 2\theta,$$

$$r_t = (p-q)\sin\theta\cdot\cos\theta \qquad\qquad (1)$$

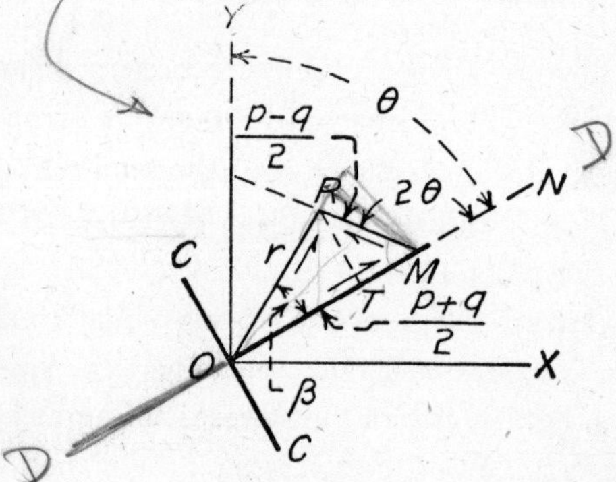

FIG. 6.

The normal component of r is

$$OT = OM - MT,$$

$$= OM + MR \cdot \cos 2\theta,$$

$$= \frac{p+q}{2} + \frac{p-q}{2}(\cos^2\theta - \sin^2\theta),$$

$$= \frac{p+q}{2}(\sin^2\theta + \cos^2\theta) + \frac{p-q}{2}(\cos^2\theta - \sin^2\theta),$$

$$r_n = p\cdot\cos^2\theta + q\cdot\sin^2\theta, \qquad\qquad (2)$$

Note.—If t_n is the normal component of the stress on a plane D-D, a plane normal to C-C,

$$t_n = p\cdot\cos^2(\theta + 90°) + q\cdot\sin^2(\theta + 90°),$$

$$= p\cdot\sin^2\theta + q\cdot\cos^2\theta$$

Now adding r_n and t_n

$$t_n + r_n = p(\sin^2 \theta + \cos^2 \theta) + q(\sin^2 \theta + \cos^2 \theta) = p + q \qquad (3)$$

which proves that the sum of the normal stresses on any two rectangular planes is a constant, and is equal to the sum of the principal stresses.

Now as the plane C-C in (b), Fig. 5, moves through all angles the point M will describe a circle around O, with a radius $= \dfrac{p+q}{2}$, and R will describe a circle about M, with a radius $= \dfrac{p-q}{2}$, OM and RM keeping equally inclined to the vertical (direction of principal stress) on opposite sides of it. The locus of the point R is an ellipse, the semi-major axis being $OM + MR = p$, and the semi-minor axis being $OM - MR = q$. This is called the ellipse of stress for the point O within the body at the point O. Its principal axes are normal to the planes of principal stress, the semi-axes being equal to the principal stresses. The radii vectores OR, OR_1, etc., are the stresses on the planes at O, to which OM, OM_1, etc., are normals.

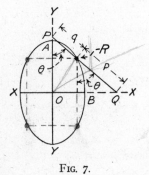

FIG. 7.

Equation of Ellipse of Stress.—The ordinary ellipsograph consists of a piece like PRQ, Fig. 7, whose extremities P and Q slide in two grooves YOY and XOX, respectively, at right angles to each other, while the point R traces an ellipse whose semi-axes are $PR = q$, and $RQ = p$.

Take coördinates of R as x and y,

$$\text{and } x = PR . \sin \theta = q . \sin \theta,$$

$$\frac{x}{q} = \sin \theta$$

$$y = RQ . \cos \theta = p . \cos \theta,$$

$$\frac{y}{p} = \cos \theta$$

Squaring and adding,

$$\frac{x^2}{q^2} + \frac{y^2}{p^2} = \sin^2 \theta + \cos^2 \theta = 1 \qquad (4)$$

Maximum value of $\beta = \phi$ the angle of obliquity of stress on plane C-C. It can be seen in Fig. 6 that β will be a maximum when MR is perpendicular to RO. For suppose triangle MOR constructed with angle ORM not a right angle, drop a perpendicular from M to OR at R', then $\sin \beta' = \dfrac{MR'}{OM}$. But MR' is less than MR and β' will be less than β.

In this case since angle $ORM = 90°$,

$$OR^2 = OM^2 - RM^2,$$

$$r^2 = \left(\frac{p+q}{2}\right)^2 - \left(\frac{p-q}{2}\right)^2,$$

$$= p.q,$$

$$\text{and } r = \sqrt{p.q},$$

$$\text{also } \sin \phi = \sin \beta = \frac{p-q}{p+q},$$

$$\text{and transposing } \frac{q}{p} = \frac{1-\sin\phi}{1+\sin\phi} \qquad (5)$$

$$\text{now } 2\theta = \text{angle } RMN, \text{ and}$$

$$\cos 2\theta = \cos RMN,$$

$$= -\sin ROM,$$

$$= -\frac{MR}{OM},$$

$$= -\frac{p-q}{p+q}$$

Now in a granular mass the particles will tend to slide on each other, the angle ϕ being the angle of internal friction in which the coefficient of friction is $\mu = \tan \phi$.

From equation (5) if p represents the vertical stress at any point in an unlimited, homogeneous, granular mass with a horizontal surface, the ratio of the horizontal component q to the vertical stress p will be

$$\frac{q}{p} = \frac{1 - \sin \phi}{1 + \sin \phi}$$

[handwritten: φ here is max value of B in (E) fig. 5 + fig. 6.]

[handwritten left margin: In perfect fluid, pressure intensity same intensity in all directions see for Hydraulics]

For a perfect fluid $\phi = 0$, and $p = q$, which we already know.

Angle of Repose.*—Loose earth will remain in equilibrium with its face at slopes whose inclinations to the horizontal are less than an angle ϕ, which is called the angle of repose. If piled at a greater

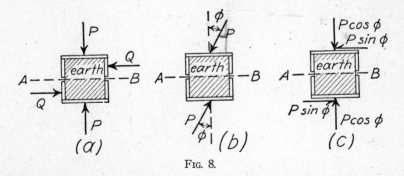

Fig. 8.

slope, cohesion will hold the face at a greater slope than ϕ for a time, but the earth will soon crumble down, until the slopes do not exceed ϕ. In (a) Fig. 8, two troughs filled with earth are acted upon by the two forces P and Q. The forces P tend to press the earth together, while the forces Q tend to cause slipping. If Q is just sufficient to cause slipping, then the coefficient of friction will be $\mu = \dfrac{Q}{P}$. Now if the forces Q are omitted and the forces P are inclined at an angle θ, when the earth is just on the point of slipping angle θ will be equal to ϕ, the angle of repose and the coefficient of friction will be $\mu = \dfrac{P . \sin \phi}{P . \cos \phi} =$

* This is more properly called the angle of internal friction, see Table IX.

2

[handwritten bottom: p. 126]
[handwritten: or, μ P cos φ = P sin φ, from (C) above.]
[handwritten: see P. 3]

tan ϕ which gives the relation between the coefficient of friction μ, and the angle of repose ϕ.

Now in a homogeneous, unlimited, granular mass with a level surface, if p is the vertical and q is the horizontal stress at any point, then $\dfrac{q}{p} = \dfrac{1 - \sin \beta}{1 + \sin \beta}$, where β is the angle of obliquity of the resultant stress r. Now if there is to be equilibrium the obliquity, β, cannot be greater than ϕ, the angle of repose, and the greatest ratio between q and p will be $\dfrac{q}{p} = \dfrac{1 - \sin \phi}{1 + \sin \phi}$

Vertical Retaining Wall Without Surcharge.—In Fig. 9, a vertical wall supports a filling with a horizontal slope ($\delta = 0$). Then from

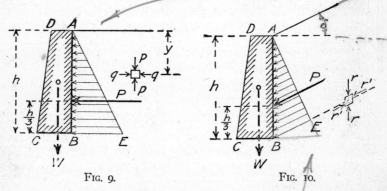

FIG. 9. FIG. 10.

the preceding discussion the horizontal pressure at any point will be $q = w.y.\dfrac{1 - \sin \phi}{1 + \sin \phi}$, where y is the depth and w is the weight of a cubic foot of earth, and the total pressure will be

$$P = \tfrac{1}{2} w.h.^2 \frac{1 - \sin \phi}{1 + \sin \phi} = \quad (6)$$

The stress q varies directly with the depth y, and the total stress P may be represented by the area of the triangle ABE, with the point of application of P at a point $\frac{1}{3}h$ above the base. The resultant stress P will be horizontal.

Vertical Retaining Wall With Surcharge.—In Fig. 10, the parallelopipedon is held in equilibrium by three forces: r vertical, s normal, and r' direction not yet determined. Now the stresses on every part of any imaginary plane in a granular mass will be parallel. The stresses on a vertical plane will be parallel to the plane of surcharge where the surcharge is positive, as will now be shown. The pressure, r, is equal to w.h.cos δ pounds per square foot, acting on the inclined surface and in a vertical direction. Now since r and r' are conjugate stresses, the stress on the vertical face of the parallelopipedon will be parallel to the inclined face of the parallelopipedon, and will be parallel to the plane of surcharge. The resultant pressure on a wall not vertical will not be parallel to the top of the surface, as will be shown by the ellipse of stress. (Several authors have erroneously assumed that in Rankine's solution the resultant pressure is always parallel to the top surface of the filling and have failed to grasp the underlying principles of the solution.)

To find the ratio of the intensity of the conjugate stresses r and r' whose obliquity is δ, proceed as follows:

In Fig. 11, draw any line ON, draw OR making an angle δ with

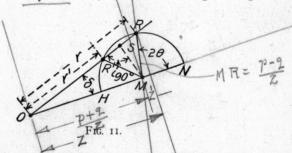

FIG. 11.

ON, lay off $OR = r$, and $OR' = r'$, and from S, the middle-point of RR' erect the perpendicular SM. Draw MR, MR', and arc $HR'RN$.

Now $OM = \dfrac{p+q}{2}$ and $MR = \dfrac{p-q}{2}$ as can be seen in Fig. 6.

$$\frac{OS}{OM} = \cos MOS, \text{ and solving}$$

$$OM = \frac{\frac{1}{2}(OR + OR')}{\cos \delta} = \frac{r + r'}{2 \cos \delta}$$

But $OM = \dfrac{p+q}{2}$, and

$$\dfrac{p+q}{2} = \dfrac{r+r'}{2\cos\delta} \tag{a}$$

Also $MR^2 = MS^2 + RS^2$,

$$= (OM^2 - OS^2) + RS^2,$$

$$= \left(\dfrac{p+q}{2}\right)^2 - \left(\dfrac{r+r'}{2}\right)^2 + \left(\dfrac{r-r'}{2}\right)^2,$$

$$= \left(\dfrac{p+q}{2}\right)^2 - r.r', \qquad \text{— } Class\ prove.$$

$$= \left(\dfrac{r+r'}{2\cos\delta}\right)^2 - r.r' \tag{b}$$

Therefore, $\dfrac{p-q}{2} = \sqrt{\left(\dfrac{r+r'}{2\cos\delta}\right)^2 - r.r'} \tag{c}$

From Fig. 11, $\cos 2\theta = \dfrac{2r.\cos\delta - p - q}{p - q} \tag{d}$

Now squaring (a) and (c), and dividing (c) squared by (a) squared, we have $\left(\dfrac{p-q}{p+q}\right)^2 = 1 - \dfrac{4r.r'.\cos^2\delta}{(r+r')^2}$

But when the earth is just in equilibrium

$$\dfrac{p}{q} = \dfrac{1 + \sin\phi}{1 - \sin\phi}, \text{ or } \sin\phi = \dfrac{p-q}{p+q}$$

Therefore, $\sin^2\phi = 1 - \dfrac{4r.r'.\cos^2\delta}{(r+r')^2}$, and

$$1 - \sin^2\phi = \cos^2\phi = \dfrac{4r.r'.\cos^2\delta}{(r+r')^2}, \tag{e}$$

$$\dfrac{\cos^2\phi}{\cos^2\delta} = \dfrac{4r.r'}{(r+r')^2},$$

$$(r+r')^2 = 4r.r'\dfrac{\cos^2\delta}{\cos^2\phi}$$

Fw (5) P.16 and (6) P.18.

Now subtract $4r.r'$ from both sides and

$$(r-r')^2 = 4r.r'\left(\frac{\cos^2\delta}{\cos^2\phi}-1\right),$$

$$(r-r')^2 = 4r.r'\frac{\cos^2\delta - \cos^2\phi}{\cos^2\phi} \tag{f}$$

Divide (f) by (e) and

$$\left(\frac{r-r'}{r+r'}\right)^2 = \frac{\cos^2\delta - \cos^2\phi}{\cos^2\phi}\cdot\frac{\cos^2\phi}{\cos^2\delta},$$

$$= \frac{\cos^2\delta - \cos^2\phi}{\cos^2\delta},$$

$$\text{and}\quad \frac{r-r'}{r+r'} = \pm\sqrt{\frac{\cos^2\delta - \cos^2\phi}{\cos^2\delta}} \tag{g}$$

Now by composition and division

$$\frac{r}{r'} = \frac{\cos\delta \pm \sqrt{\cos^2\delta - \cos^2\phi}}{\cos\delta \mp \sqrt{\cos^2\delta - \cos^2\phi}} \qquad\text{Notes.} \tag{h}$$

Now formula (h) represents both the active and the passive thrust at the point, the two stresses being equal in amount but opposite in direction. And since r' is less than r for the active forces, equilibrium of the wall will take place with the upper signs, and, reversing the fractions

$$\frac{r'}{r} = \frac{\cos\delta - \sqrt{\cos^2\delta - \cos^2\phi}}{\cos\delta + \sqrt{\cos^2\delta - \cos^2\phi}} \tag{i}$$

Now r is equal to $w.y.\cos\delta$, for the reason that the stress p is distributed over the area $a.\sec\delta$, and

$$r' = w.y.\cos\delta\,\frac{\cos\delta - \sqrt{\cos^2\delta - \cos^2\phi}}{\cos\delta + \sqrt{\cos^2\delta - \cos^2\phi}} \tag{j}$$

Now the maximum value of r' will be when $y = h$

$$r' = w.h.\cos\delta\,\frac{\cos\delta - \sqrt{\cos^2\delta - \cos^2\phi}}{\cos\delta + \sqrt{\cos^2\delta - \cos^2\phi}} \tag{7}$$

pressure parallel to surface, active.

Bay geometry (Head & Feldman)
Proposition 7. P. 166.

$\frac{1}{2}wh^2K.$

and
$$P = \tfrac{1}{2}w.h^2. \cos\delta \frac{\cos\delta - \sqrt{\cos^2\delta - \cos^2\phi}}{\cos\delta + \sqrt{\cos^2\delta - \cos^2\phi}} \quad (8)$$

If $\delta = \phi$, $P = \tfrac{1}{2}w.h^2 \cos\phi$ (8a)

Equations (6) and (8) are commonly called Rankine's Method. As such the method is very unsatisfactory; the two cases above being only special cases of the general method which follows.

Inclined Retaining Wall.—The ellipse of stress can be used to determine the resultant pressure on an inclined retaining wall.* This solution determines the amount and direction of the resultant and leads to the same equations as deduced by Weyrauch by a much longer process.

In Fig. 12 a retaining wall inclined at the angle θ with the horizontal sustains the pressure of a filling with a surcharge δ. The angle of repose of the filling is ϕ.

Ellipse of Stress at Point A.—Through A draw AO parallel to the top surface, and at any convenient point O, in AO, draw OD normal to AO. With point O as a center and a radius OD describe an arc intersecting a vertical line OM at the point M. Draw OC making an angle ϕ with OD. At any point E in OD describe an arc which shall be tangent to OC and cuts the vertical OM at F. Draw EF, and through M draw MG parallel to EF. Bisect the angle DGM, and draw $R'G$. Through O draw OR parallel to $R'G$. Now $OM.w$ is the stress, r, on the plane A-O, $OG = \dfrac{p+q}{2}$ and $GM = \dfrac{p-q}{2}$; OG and GM make equal angles with the principal axis OR'. If OG revolves around O, and GM around G, OG and GM always making equal angles with the principal axis OR', the ellipse of stress will be described as shown. To determine the pressure at the point A on the plane A-B, draw $OG' = OG$ at right angles to A-B. With G' as a center and a radius $OG' = OG$ describe an arc cutting the principal axis OR' at T. Draw TG'. With G' as a center and a radius $G'M' = GM$ describe an arc intersecting TG' at M'. Draw OM'. Then the pressure at A is $w.OM'$ acting in the direction $M'O$.

* For an application of this method to a problem see Fig. 27.

P.61.

The construction may be made at the point A. The line of principal stress acts through A. Draw AK normal to A-B and $= OG$; $QK = OG$; and $NK = GM$. Then $\underline{NA = OM'}$, is in line of pressure

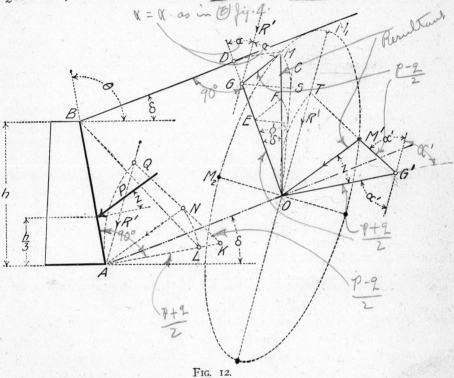

FIG. 12.

and the pressure at $A = w.AN$. With A as a center and a radius AN describe an arc and $AL = AN$. Then the resultant stress is $P =$ area triangle $ABL.w$.

Proof.—The pressure on a unit of the plane A-O due to the earth filling above the plane will be $OD.w$, and the obliquity of stress will be δ, so that the stress will be $OM.w$, acting vertically at the point O, and M is a point on the ellipse of stress. Now no active pressure in a granular mass can have an upward component; and since the maximum obliquity of the stress on the plane A-O is $\beta = \phi$, DO and CO are the limits for the direction of all active stress on the plane A-O. Now if point G were known the angle GSO will be $90°$, as shown in Fig. 6,

£A P.16

and in the discussion for maximum obliquity of stress. To determine the direction of MG, take any point E in OD, and describe an arc tangent to OC, and cutting OM at F. Then GM will be parallel to EF, and $OG = \frac{1}{2}(p+q)$, and $GM = \frac{1}{2}(p-q)$. The maximum principal stress will be $\frac{1}{2}(p+q) + \frac{1}{2}(p-q) = p = OM_1$, and the minimum principal stress will be $\frac{1}{2}(p+q) - \frac{1}{2}(p-q) = q = OM_2$.

The same results may be obtained directly from the discussion of the pressure on vertical walls as follows:

P. 22

In Fig. 13 let $P_1 = $ pressure on a vertical wall EB as given by formula (8). P_1 acts parallel to the top slope and at a point $\frac{1}{3}BE$ above B. Let the weight of the triangle DBE be G, which acts through the center of gravity of the triangle and intersects P_1 at point O. Then P_2 the resultant of P_1 and G will be the resultant pressure at O; makes the

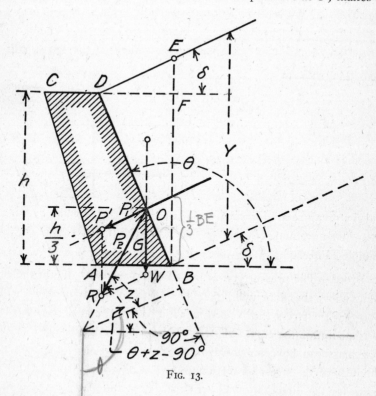

FIG. 13.

Class pure

angle z with a normal to the back of the wall, and an angle $z + \theta - 90°$ with the horizontal.*

The algebraic equations for the values of P_2 and z are complicated and will not be given.†

See fig. 10 P. 18.

Conclusion.—It will be seen that the direction of the resultant thrust on a vertical wall is parallel to the top plane surface, and that the pressure on an inclined plane may be calculated by the ellipse of stress. It can be easily proved that z, the angle between the direction of the resultant thrust and a normal to the plane, is never greater than ϕ, the angle of repose of the filling.

With a negative surcharge the maximum value of the resultant thrust consistent with stability occurs when the line of thrust is horizontal. This can be shown as follows: In Fig. 14 the passive resistance P is equal to the active resultant P on the vertical plane A-B, and both are parallel to the slope of the filling. Now if the surcharge on the right is negative as in Fig. 15, the passive resistance on the left is still P

(as in fig. 10 p. 18.)

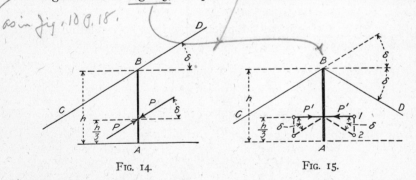

FIG. 14. FIG. 15.

and is equal to the passive resistance P on the right. Now if the active resultants on both sides of the plane have an upward component, the plane under certain conditions would be forced out of the fill. The maximum value of the active resultant pressure must therefore occur when the line of action of P is horizontal and will be equal to P'.

* For practical applications of this method see Fig. 32 and Fig. 34.
† For algebraic equations see Howe's Retaining Walls.

P. 91.

Foundations in Earth.—*Case I.*   Pressure uniform over the base of foundation as in Fig. 16, and equal p_0.   When the superstructure has just stopped subsiding, and the earth on each side is just on the point of heaving up, p_0 will be a maximum and we will have

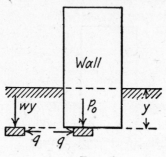

FIG. 16.

$$\frac{p_0}{q} = \frac{1 + \sin \phi}{1 - \sin \phi} \text{ or } q = p_0 \frac{1 - \sin \phi}{1 + \sin \phi}$$

At the same level outside of the foundation the horizontal pressure must be a maximum to be on the point of heaving, and

$$\frac{q}{w.y} = \frac{1 + \sin \phi}{1 - \sin \phi},$$

q being the active force and $w.y$ being the passive force.
Now eliminating q, we have

$$p_0 \lesseqgtr w.y \left(\frac{1 + \sin \phi}{1 - \sin \phi}\right)^2 \tag{9}$$

If h is the height of the wall and w' is the weight per cu. ft., then

$$w'h \lesseqgtr w.y \left(\frac{1 + \sin \phi}{1 - \sin \phi}\right)^2 \tag{10}$$

Case II.—Pressure varying uniformly from a maximum p_1 to a minimum p_2, as in Fig. 17.
By Case I

$$p_1 \lesseqgtr w.y \left(\frac{1 + \sin \phi}{1 - \sin \phi}\right)^2 \tag{11}$$

At the same level in the ground outside the foundation the minimum horizontal intensity is

$$q = w.y \, \frac{1 - \sin \phi}{1 + \sin \phi}$$

Now for equilibrium the pressure p_2 must produce a horizontal pres-

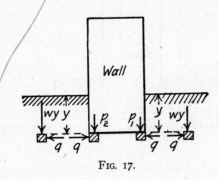

FIG. 17.

sure not less than q. Therefore p_1 must not exceed the value given in (9) and p_2 must not be less than $w.y$.

From the above discussion

$$\frac{p_1}{p_2} \leqq \left(\frac{1 + \sin \phi}{1 - \sin \phi} \right)^2 \tag{12}$$

CHAPTER Iᴀ.

Rankine's Theory Modified.

Introduction.—Professor Rankine proposed the solution given in Chapter I, and developed formulas for the two special cases of a vertical wall with a horizontal surcharge, and a vertical wall with a surcharge sloping up from the top of the wall. In both of these special cases the resultant thrust on the wall is parallel to the top surface of the filling, and most writers have erroneously assumed that in general in Rankine's solution the resultant thrust is always parallel to the top surface. For equilibrium in the mass it is necessary that there be both active stresses and passive resistances. For example if a horizontal plane be introduced in the filling the active stresses on the top of the plane will be resisted by passive resistances from below. The passive resistances in a granular mass are greater than the active stresses and are often confused with them. If a wall lean toward the filling so that the angle between the wall and the horizontal be equal to the angle of repose, there will be no active stresses acting on the wall, while the passive resistance of the filling will be large, unless the angle of repose is small. In calculating the pressure on a retaining wall by means of the ellipse of stress both active stresses and passive resistances will be obtained, and care must be used to choose the proper values, it being remembered (1) that there can be no active upward stress, and (2) that the maximum obliquity of active stresses is equal to the angle of repose.

Rankine's Solution Modified.—The resultant pressure on a wall due to a filling with a surcharge δ has been calculated in Fig. 17a for a wall AB'' nearly vertical, for a wall AB' leaning away from the filling, and for a wall AB''' leaning toward the filling. The resultant pressures on the wall leaning away from the filling and on the wall nearly ver-

28

tical have a downward component; while the resultant pressure on the
wall leaning toward the filling as given by the ellipse of stress has an
upward component. Now since active stresses in a granular mass can
have no upward components, the active pressure on the wall AB''' cannot be greater than the horizontal component of the upward inclined
stress given by the ellipse of stress (the active stresses may be much
less than the horizontal component as will be shown presently).

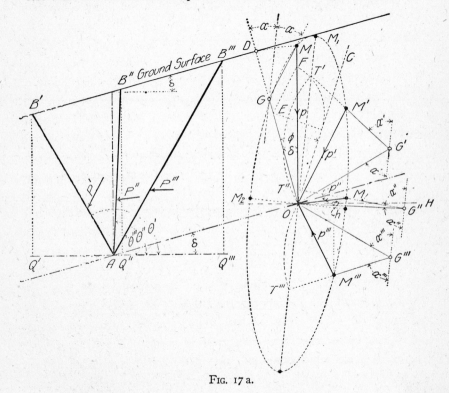

FIG. 17 a.

In Fig. 17b the resultant pressures on a wall leaning away from the
filling, a wall nearly vertical, and a wall leaning toward the filling have
been calculated for the condition when $\delta = \phi$. It will be seen that the
resultant stress on a wall inclined toward the filling so that $\theta = \phi$ will
be vertical and there will be no horizontal component, and no active
stress as the conditions require. It therefore appears that for the case

where $\delta = \phi$ the maximum active stresses may be assumed as the horizontal component of the upward inclined stresses given by the ellipse
of stress, for walls leaning toward the filling. For values of δ less
than ϕ the active stresses are less than the horizontal components of the
upward inclined stresses given by the ellipse of stress, and it is necessary to apply the fundamental laws of semi-fluids in order to obtain
correct results.

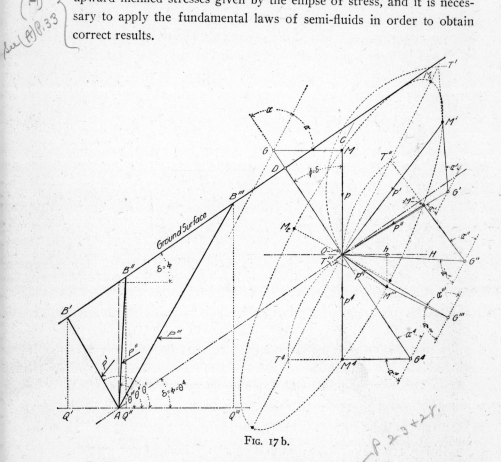

FIG. 17 b.

In Fig. 17c the wall AB slopes toward the filling at the angle of
repose. Since (1) there can be no active upward component of stress
in a granular mass, and (2) the maximum obliquity of active stresses
cannot be greater than the angle of repose, there will be no active
stresses acting on the wall AB. It will be seen that the wedge of filling

ABA' dissipates and destroys the pressure P, which acts on the plane A'-B.

In Fig. 17d the wall AB slopes toward the filling, making an angle θ greater than ϕ. It will be seen from Fig. 17c that the shaded prism $A5A'$ will dissipate the active stresses coming on the plane 5-A'. The prism $AB5$ will transmit the active stresses, the only effect of the prism being to change the direction of the stresses, the horizontal components of P' and P_1 being equal (this may be proved by the ellipse of stress).

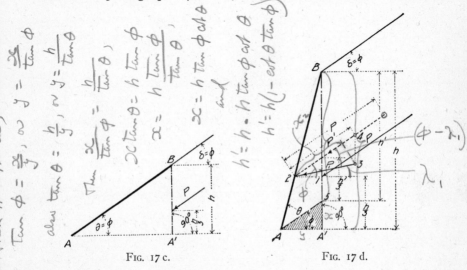

FIG. 17 c. FIG. 17 d.

In Fig. 17d, with $\delta = \phi$ and θ less than 90° the stress on the back of the wall $AB = P_1$, which is less than the stress P acting on the plane A'-B. This decrease in pressure is due to the triangular wedge $A5A'$ below the wall. The active stresses on the plane A'-B are parallel to the plane of repose, and the pressure on AB will be due to the stresses on the plane A'-B, transmitted through the wedge $AB5$, the only effect of the wedge being to change the direction of P_1.

Now in Fig. 17d if P is the pressure on the plane A'-B, and P' is the pressure on the plane 5-B, then

$$P : P' :: (h)^2 : (h')^2, \text{ but}$$

$$h' = h\,(1 - \cot\theta.\tan\phi), \text{ and}$$

$$P' = P(1 - \cot\theta.\tan\phi)^2 \qquad (12a)$$

Now in Fig. 17e the pressure on the wall AB will be

$$P_1 = P'\cos\lambda.\sec\lambda_1, \text{ and in Fig. } 17d$$

$$P_1 = P'\cos\phi.\sec\lambda_1$$

$$P_1 = P(1 - \cot\theta.\tan\phi)^2\cos\phi.\sec\lambda_1 \qquad (12b)$$

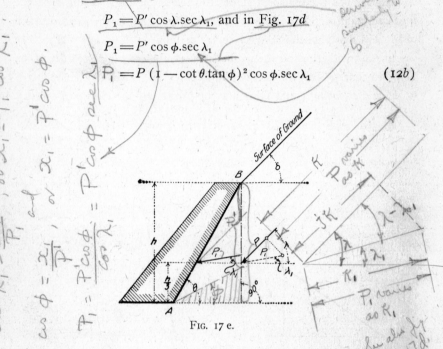

FIG. 17 e.

It will be seen that the wedge below the angle of repose causes a loss in P varying from o at $\theta = 90°$ to 100 per cent at $\theta = \phi$, when the percentage of loss is compared with P for $\theta = 90°$.

Now if j is the ratio of the projection of P_1 on P, divided by P, in Fig. 17d we will have

$$j = (1 - \cot\theta.\tan\phi)^2\cos\phi.\sec\lambda_1.\cos(\phi - \lambda_1) \qquad (12c)$$

Now if the angle that P_1 makes with the horizontal is known and the resultant P on a vertical plane A-B can be calculated, then if $P = \frac{1}{2}w.h^2.k$ and $P_1 = \frac{1}{2}w.h^2.k_1$, we will have $k_1 = j.k.\sec(\lambda - \lambda_1)$.

The values of j for $\delta = \phi = 33° 42'$ have been calculated by the author algebraically by equation (12c) and graphically by means of the ellipse of stress, and are given in Fig. 17h.

The values of j for $\delta=\phi=45°$ have been calculated by the author algebraically by equation $(12c)$ and graphically by means of the ellipse of stress, and are given in Fig. $17i$.

For other values of δ the value of j, for walls in which the ellipse of stress gives correct values, is

$$j = (1 - \cot \theta . \tan \phi)^2 \cos \delta . \sec \lambda_1 \cos (\delta - \lambda_1) \qquad (12d)$$

The values of j in Fig. $17h$ and Fig. $17i$ have been checked both graphically and algebraically for the values of δ less than ϕ, within the limits for which the ellipse of stress give true stresses, and show that with these limits j depends only upon θ and ϕ.

Several values of j will be calculated for different values of θ, ϕ and δ.

(1) Given $\theta=85°$, $\phi=33° 42'$; calculate j for $\delta=\phi$ and for $\delta=25°$.

Solution for $\delta=\phi=33° 42'$.—From Fig. $17j$, $\lambda_1=27°$, and from equation $(12c)$

$$j=(1-\cot 85° \tan 33° 42')^2 \cos 33° 42' \sec 27° \cos 6° 42'=0.82.$$

Solution for $\delta=25°$.—From Fig. $17j$, $\lambda_1=12°$, and from equation $(12d)$

$$j = (1 - \cot 85° \tan 33° 42')^2 \cos 25° \sec 12° \cos 13° =0.81.$$

Table $17h$ was calculated graphically, using the ellipse of stress and gives $j=0.8$, which is a satisfactory check.

(2) For $\theta=90°$ it will be seen by substituting in equation $(12c)$ and equation $(12d)$ that $j=1$ for all values of δ.

With our present knowledge of the laws of semi-fluids it is impossible to calculate the loss of the active stresses for walls with a surcharge δ less than ϕ, beyond the value of θ where the ellipse of stress gives correct active stresses. However, since the calculated values of j are independent of δ, but vary only with θ and with ϕ for all cases in which the ellipse of stress gives correct values of the active stresses, it is reasonable to assume that the ratio of loss is the same for all values of δ, ϕ and θ being constant.

For values of θ less than 71° 30', with $\phi = 33° 42'$, and for values *with $\delta = \phi$,* of θ less than 71° with $\phi = 45°$, j is equal to k_1. This can be proved

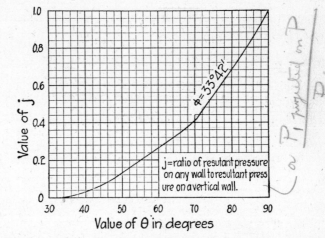

FIG. 17 h. RATIO j, WHERE $k_1 = j.k.$ SEC $(\delta - \lambda)$ [WHERE k FOR $\theta = 90°$, AND λ ARE TAKEN FROM FIG. 17 j.]

P.32

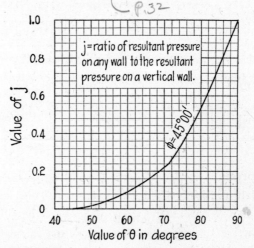

FIG. 17 i. RATIO j, WHERE $k_1 = j.k.$ SEC $(\delta - \lambda)$ [WHERE k FOR $\theta = 90°$, AND λ ARE TAKEN FROM FIG. 17 k.]

as follows. Now by definition $P.j = P_1.\cos\phi$ (since $\lambda_1 = 0$, and $\delta = \lambda = \phi$), and

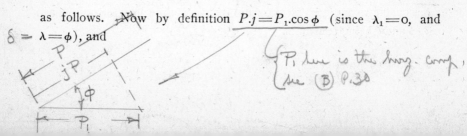

See my notes P.33

$$i = \frac{P_1.\cos\phi}{P} = \frac{k_1.\cos\phi}{k} \qquad (12d)$$

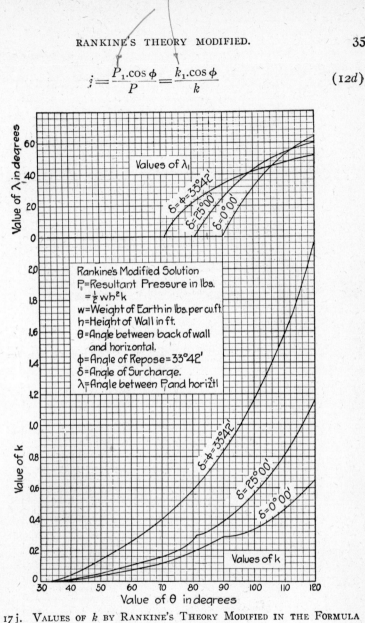

Values of λ_1

$\delta = \phi = 35°42'$
$\delta = 25°00'$
$\delta = 0°00'$

Rankine's Modified Solution
P = Resultant Pressure in lbs.
$= \frac{1}{2}wh^2 k$
w = Weight of Earth in lbs. per cu.ft.
h = Height of Wall in ft.
θ = Angle between back of wall
    and horizontal.
φ = Angle of Repose = 33°42'
δ = Angle of Surcharge.
λ_1 = Angle between P and horiz'tl

$\delta = \phi = 35°42'$
$\delta = 25°00'$
$\delta = 0°00'$

Values of k

Similar to 17·K. P. 36

FIG. 17j. VALUES OF k BY RANKINE'S THEORY MODIFIED IN THE FORMULA
$P = \frac{1}{2}w.h^2.k, \ \phi = 33° \ 42'$.

But

$$P = \frac{1}{2}w.h^2.\cos\phi \qquad P.22 \qquad (8a)$$

$$P = \frac{1}{2}w.h^2.k \quad \leftarrow \quad P.36 \qquad (12c)$$

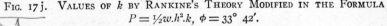

from these two equations,

$K = \cos\phi$

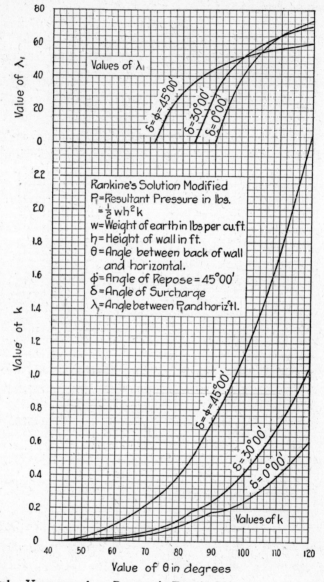

FIG. 17 k. VALUES OF k BY RANKINE'S THEORY MODIFIED IN THE FORMULA,
$$P = \tfrac{1}{2}w.h^2.k, \quad \phi = 45°.$$

from (8a) +(12e) P. 35

Equating (12d) and (12e) *Substituting*

$$k = \cos\phi, \text{ and } \quad \text{This in } (12d) P35$$

gives,

$$j = k_1$$

The values of k in the formula $P = \frac{1}{2}w.h^2.k$ are given in Fig. 17j, for $\phi = 33° \, 42'$, and for $\delta = \phi = 33° \, 42'$, $\delta = 25°$, and $\delta = 0°$. The values of k for $\delta = 0°$ were calculated by applying the ratio curve to the value of k for $\theta = 90°$ for values of θ less than $90°$, and by the ellipse of stress for values of θ from $90°$ to $120°$; while values of k for

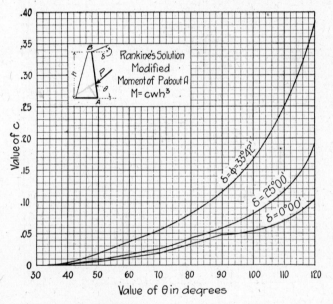

FIG. 17 l. MOMENT OF FILLING ABOUT INNER TOE OF WALL, BY RANKINE'S THEORY MODIFIED, $\phi = 33° \, 42'$.

$\delta = 25°$ were calculated directly by means of the ellipse of stress from $\theta = 120°$ to $\theta = 81°$, and from $\theta = 81°$ to $\theta = 33° \, 42'$ by applying the ratio curve to the values of k for $\theta = 90°$. Values of k for $\delta = \phi$ were calculated directly by means of the ellipse of stress as in Fig. 17b.

Values of k for $\phi = 45°$ were calculated in a similar manner, and are given in Fig. 17k.

The values of k in Fig. 17j may be calculated by using the values of j in Fig. 17h, the values of λ_1 in Fig. 17j, and the value of k for $\theta = 90°$ as follows:

Given $\theta = 80°$ and $\delta = 33° \, 42'$; calculate k.   From Fig. 17h for $\theta = 80°$, $j = 0.68$; and from Fig. 17j for $\theta = 80°$, $\lambda_1 = 22°$; and for $\theta = 90°$, $k = 0.83$.   Then for $\theta = 80°$

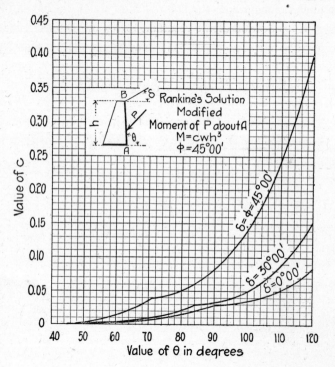

FIG. 17 m.   MOMENT OF FILLING ABOUT INNER TOE OF WALL, BY RANKINE'S
THEORY MODIFIED, $\phi = 45°$.

$$k_1 = j.\,k.\,\sec\,(33° \, 42' - 22°)$$
$$= 0.68 \times 0.83 \times \sec 11° \, 42'$$
$$= 0.58, \text{ which checks the value in Fig. 17} j.$$

Values of k for other values of θ and δ may be calculated in like manner.

The values of k as given by Cain's solution are given in Fig. 23a and Fig. 23b.

P. 50

P. 51.

(a) The values of c where $M = c.w.h^3 =$ the moment of the resultant thrust of the filling about the lower inner edge of a retaining wall with a straight back, are given for $\phi = 33° \; 42'$ in Fig. 17l, and for $\phi = 45°$ in Fig. 17m.

Values of c as calculated by Cain's solution are given in Fig. 23c and Fig. 23d. *P. 53* *P. 52*

The total moment about the point A is $M' = M +$ moment of wall. The point of application of the resultant thrust on the base of the wall is at a distance from A, $x = M' \div$ (weight of wall $+$ vertical component of resultant P).

Cain's solution and Rankine's Theory modified give results that agree very closely for values of θ in common use, while Cain's solution breaks down for values of θ near ϕ and greater than $90° + \phi$. Rankine's Theory modified is perfectly general and gives consistent results for all conditions.

CHAPTER II

COULOMB'S THEORY.

Introduction.—In this theory it is assumed that there is a wedge having the wall as one side and a plane called the plane of rupture as the other side, which exerts a maximum thrust on the wall. The plane of rupture lies between the angle of repose of the filling and the back of the wall. It may coincide with the plane of repose. For a wall without surcharge (horizontal surface back of the wall) and a vertical

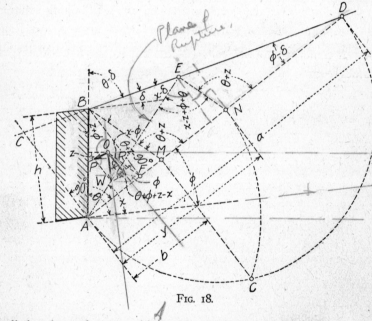

FIG. 18.

wall the plane of rupture bisects the angle between the plane of repose and the back of the wall. This theory does not determine the direction of the thrust, and leads to many other theories having assumed directions for the resultant pressure.

Algebraic Method.—In Fig. 18, the wall with a height h, slopes toward the earth, being inclined to the horizontal at an angle θ, and the earth has a surcharge with slope δ, which is not greater than ϕ, the angle of repose. It is required to find the pressure P against the retaining wall, it being assumed that the resultant pressure makes an angle z with a normal to the back of the wall.

It is assumed that the triangular prism of earth above some plane, the trace of which is the line AE, will produce the maximum pressure on the wall and on the earth below the plane, and that in turn the prism will be supported by the reactions of the wall and the earth. Let OW represent the weight of the prism ABE, the length of the prism being assumed equal to unity, let OP be the reaction of the wall, and OR be the reaction of the earth below.

Now the forces OW, OP, and OR will be concurrent and will be in equilibrium; OP and OR will therefore be components of OW. When the prism ABE is just on the point of moving, OP will make an angle with a normal to the back of the wall equal to z (different authorities assume values of z from zero to ϕ', the angle of friction of earth on masonry, or ϕ, the angle of repose of earth); while OR will make an angle with the normal to the plane of rupture AE equal to ϕ. Let P represent the pressure OP against the wall, W represent the weight of the prism of earth and w the weight per cubic foot.

In the triangle OWR angle $WOR = x - \phi$, and angle $ORW = \theta + \phi + z - x$. Through E draw EN, making the angle $AEN = \theta + \phi + z - x$ with AE. Then the triangle AEN is similar to triangle ORW, and

$$\frac{P}{W} = \frac{EN}{AN}, \text{ and}$$

$$P = W\frac{EN}{AN}$$

But W equals w. *area triangle* $ABE = \frac{1}{2}w.AB.BE.$ sin $(\theta - \delta)$, and

$$P = \tfrac{1}{2}w.\sin(\theta - \delta)\frac{AB.BE.EN}{AN} \tag{13}$$

Now P varies with the angle x, and will have a maximum value for some value of x, which may be found by differentiating (13) and placing the result equal to zero.

Now draw BM parallel to EN, and in the similar triangles BDM and EDN,

$$EN : BM :: ND : MD \text{, and}$$

$$EN = \frac{BM.ND}{MD}$$

$$BE : BD :: MN : MD \text{, and}$$

$$BE = \frac{BD.MN}{MD}$$

Substituting in (13)

$$P = \tfrac{1}{2}w . \sin(\theta - \delta)\frac{AB.BM.BD}{MD^2}\left(\frac{MN.ND}{AN}\right) \qquad (14)$$

Where all the variables are in parenthesis. It will be seen that EN moves parallel to its present position as x varies. Now let $AN = y$, $AD = a$, and $AM = b$, and then

$$\frac{MN.ND}{AN} = \left(\frac{(y - b)(a - y)}{y}\right) \qquad (15)$$

Differentiating (15) and placing the result equal to zero; we have a maximum when $y = \sqrt{ab}$*

Substituting in (14) we have

$$P = \tfrac{1}{2}w . \sin(\theta - \delta)\frac{AB.BM.BD}{MD^2}\frac{(a - \sqrt{ab})^2}{a} \qquad (16)$$

But $a = AD = AB\dfrac{\sin(\theta - \delta)}{\sin(\phi - \delta)}$,

$$MD = a - b,$$

$$BD = AB\frac{\sin(\theta - \phi)}{\sin(\phi - \delta)},$$

$$BM = AB\frac{\sin(\theta - \phi)}{\sin(\theta + z)}$$

Substituting in (16)

$$P = \tfrac{1}{2}w\frac{\sin^2(\theta - \phi)AB^2(a - \sqrt{ab})^2}{\sin(\theta + z)(a - b)^2},$$

$$P = \tfrac{1}{2}w\frac{\sin^2(\theta - \phi)AB^2}{\sin(\theta + z)}\left(\frac{1}{1 + \sqrt{\frac{b}{a}}}\right)^2$$

* It will be seen that y is a mean proportional between a and b, and is constructed as shown in Fig. 18 and in Fig. 19.

Now

$$\frac{AM}{AB} = \frac{\sin(z+\phi)}{\sin(\theta+z)},$$

$$\frac{AB}{AD} = \frac{\sin(\phi-\delta)}{\sin(\theta-\delta)}, \text{ and}$$

$$\sqrt{\frac{AM}{AB} \cdot \frac{AB}{AD}} = \sqrt{\frac{b}{a}}$$

$$= \sqrt{\frac{\sin(z+\phi) \cdot \sin(\phi-\delta)}{\sin(\theta+z) \cdot \sin(\theta-\delta)}}$$

also, $AB = \dfrac{h}{\sin\theta}$, and finally

$$P = \tfrac{1}{2}w.h^2 \frac{\sin^2(\theta-\phi)}{\sin^2\theta \cdot \sin(\theta+z)\left(1 + \sqrt{\dfrac{\sin(z+\phi) \cdot \sin(\phi-\delta)}{\sin(\theta+z) \cdot \sin(\theta-\delta)}}\right)^2} \quad (17)$$

$$= \tfrac{1}{2}w.h^2.K \quad (18)$$

which is the general formula for the pressure on a retaining wall.

Now if z in (17) is made equal to ϕ', the angle of repose of earth on the wall,

$$P = \tfrac{1}{2}w.h^2 \frac{\sin^2(\theta-\phi)}{\sin^2\theta \cdot \sin(\theta+\phi')\left(1 + \sqrt{\dfrac{\sin(\phi+\phi') \cdot \sin(\phi-\delta)}{\sin(\theta+\phi') \cdot \sin(\theta-\delta)}}\right)^2} \quad (19)$$

which is Cain's formula (43) in another form.

If z in (17) is made equal to δ, and θ made equal to 90°,

$$P = \tfrac{1}{2}w.h^2 \frac{\cos^2\phi}{\cos\delta\left(1 + \sqrt{\dfrac{\sin(\phi+\delta) \cdot \sin(\phi-\delta)}{\cos^2\delta}}\right)^2} \quad (20)$$

which is Rankine's formula (8) in another form.

If z in (17) is made equal to zero,

$$P = \tfrac{1}{2}w.h^2 \frac{\sin^2(\theta-\phi)}{\sin^3\theta\left(1 + \sqrt{\dfrac{\sin\phi \cdot \sin(\phi-\delta)}{\sin\theta \cdot \sin(\theta-\delta)}}\right)^2} \quad (21)$$

which gives the normal pressure on a wall.

If θ in $(21) = 90°$,

$$P = \tfrac{1}{2}w.h^2 \frac{\cos^2 \phi}{\left(1 + \sqrt{\dfrac{\sin \phi \cdot \sin (\phi - \delta)}{\cos \delta}}\right)^2}$$ (22)

If δ in $(22) = 0°$,

$$P = \tfrac{1}{2}w.h^2 \frac{\cos^2 \phi}{(1 + \sin \phi)^2},$$

$$= \tfrac{1}{2}w.h^2 \tan^2 (45° - \tfrac{1}{2}\phi)$$ (23)

$$= \tfrac{1}{2}w.h^2 \frac{1 - \sin \phi}{1 + \sin \phi}$$ (24)

which is Rankine's formula (6) for a vertical wall without surcharge.

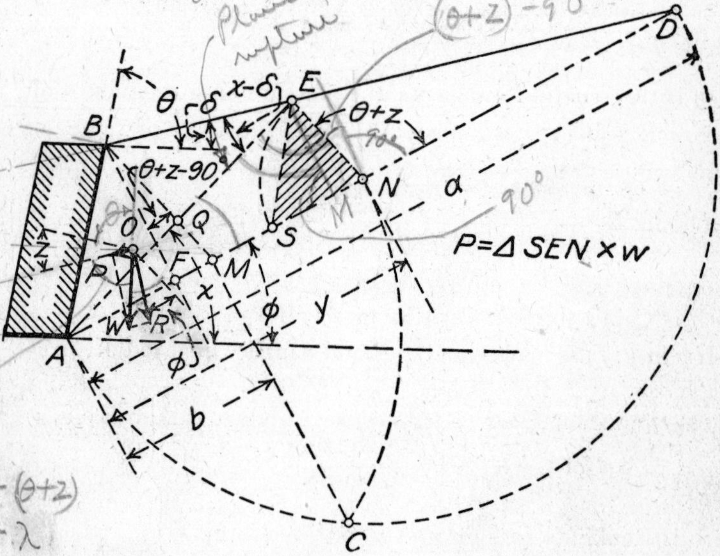

FIG. 19.

Graphic Method.*—In Fig. 19 the retaining wall AB sustains the pressure of the filling with a surcharge δ, and an angle of repose ϕ. It is required to calculate the resultant pressure P.

*If z is taken equal to ϕ', or ϕ if ϕ is less than ϕ', this solution becomes Rebhann's solution, or Cain's solution calculated by graphics.

y is mean proportional between a + b. See fig. 19.

The graphic solution is as follows: Through B in Fig. 19 draw BM making an angle with BF, the normal to AD, equal to $\lambda = \theta + z - 90°$, the angle that P makes with the horizontal. With diameter AD describe arc ACD. Draw MC normal to AD and with A as a center and a radius AC describe arc CN. Then $AN = y$, $AM = b$ and $y = \sqrt{a.b}$. Draw EN parallel to BM. With N as a center and radius EN describe arc ES. Then AE is the trace of the plane of rupture, and $P = $ area $SEN.w$. The proof is as follows:

In similar triangles BMD and END,

$$EN : BM :: ND : MD, \text{ and}$$

$$EN : BM :: (a - y) : (a - b),$$

$$EN = BM \frac{(a - y)}{(a - b)} \tag{25}$$

In similar triangles ENA and QMA,

$$EN : QM :: y : b,$$

$$EN = QM \frac{y}{b}$$

Equating the two values of EN,

$$BM \frac{(a - y)}{(a - b)} = QM \frac{y}{b}, \text{ and}$$

$$BM : QM :: \frac{y}{b} : \frac{a - y}{a - b}, \text{ and by}$$

subtraction

$$BM - QM : BM :: \frac{y}{b} - \frac{a - y}{a - b} : \frac{y}{b},$$

$$BQ = BM \frac{a(y - b)}{b(a - b)} \frac{b}{y} = BM \frac{ay - y^2}{(a - b)y}$$

since $y = \sqrt{a.b}$, and $BQ = BM \frac{(a - y)}{(a - b)} = EN \tag{25}$

$y^2 = ab$

Therefore triangle $ABE =$ triangle AEN.

Now $P = W \dfrac{\sin (x - \phi)}{\sin (\theta + \phi + z - x)}$, and $\quad$ (26)

$W = $ *area triangle ABE.w*,

$\quad = $ *area triangle AEN.w*. $\quad$ (27)

Now in triangle AEN,

$$\frac{EN}{AN} = \frac{\sin (x - \phi)}{\sin (\theta + \phi + z - x)},$$ $\quad$ (28)

and area triangle $AEN = \frac{1}{2}EN \cdot AN \cdot \sin (\theta + z)$

From equations (26), (27), and (28)

$$P = \text{\textit{area triangle } } AEN \frac{EN}{AN} w,$$

$$= \tfrac{1}{2}EN^2 \cdot \sin (\theta + z).w$$ $\quad$ (29)

Now in triangle SEN, $SN = EN$, and

area $SEN = \tfrac{1}{2}EN^2 \cdot \sin (\theta + z)$, and $\quad$ (30)

$$P = \text{\textit{area triangle } } SEN.w$$ $\quad$ (31)

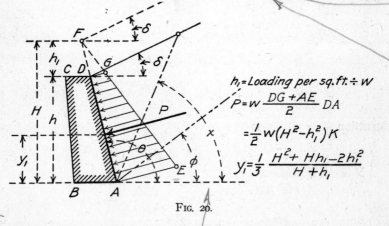

$h_1 = $ *Loading per sq.ft.* $\div w$

$P = w \dfrac{DG + AE}{2} DA$

$\quad = \dfrac{1}{2} w (H^2 - h_1^2) K$

$y_1 = \dfrac{1}{3} \dfrac{H^2 + H h_1 - 2 h_1^2}{H + h_1}$

Fig. 20.

Wall With Loaded Filling.—In Fig. 20, the filling is loaded with a uniformly distributed load. Calculate h_1 by dividing the loading per square foot by w. Let $h + h_1 = H$. Then the resultant pressure for a wall with height H will be

$$P_2 = \tfrac{1}{2}w.H^2.K$$ $\quad$ (32)

and the resultant pressure for a wall with height h_1, will be

$$P_1 = \tfrac{1}{2}w.h_1{}^2.K \tag{33}$$

The pressure on the wall AD will be

$$P = P_2 - P_1 = \tfrac{1}{2}w(H^2 - h_1{}^2)K \tag{34}$$

and the point of application is through the center of gravity of $ADGE$, which makes

$$y_1 = \tfrac{1}{3}\frac{H^2 + H.h_1 - 2h_1{}^2}{H + h_1} \tag{35}$$

See $H + 581 + 729$.
Ca. 154
H_2 12

Notes

Surcharge, δ, Equal to Angle of Repose, ϕ.—Where $\delta = \phi$ and P is parallel to the top surface, the plane of rupture will coincide with the plane of repose, for in this case in Fig. 21 $a = \infty$ and $y = \infty$. To calculate P proceed as in Fig. 21, then

See fig 19. + p. 45

$$P = \triangle SEN.w$$

Where the wall is vertical, $\theta = 90°$, and $\delta = \phi$, the normal component of P for all values of z is constant. To prove this, substitute $\delta = \phi$ in (8), multiply by $\cos \phi$ and compare with (41).

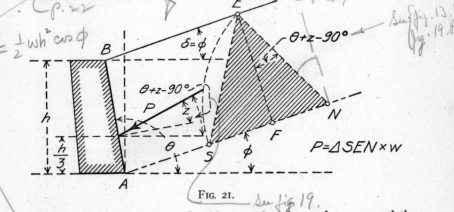

FIG. 21.

Surcharge, δ, Negative.—In this case the plane of repose and the plane of the surface of the filling meet at point D in Fig. 22. Draw BF and BM, making BF normal to AD and angle $FBM = \theta + z - 90°$. Then locate E graphically as in Fig. 19, and AE is the plane of rupture. Then the resultant stress is $P = \triangle SEN.w$.

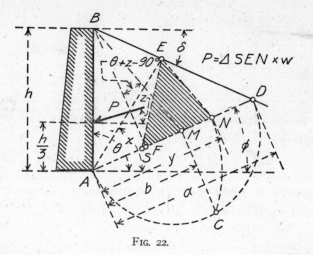

FIG. 22.

The maximum possible value of the active resultant pressure will occur when P is horizontal. The graphic solution for a vertical wall with P horizontal is given in Fig. 23.

Cain's Formulas.*—Professor William Cain assumes that the angle z is equal to ϕ', the angle of friction of the filling on the back of the wall. By substituting in (17) we have for a

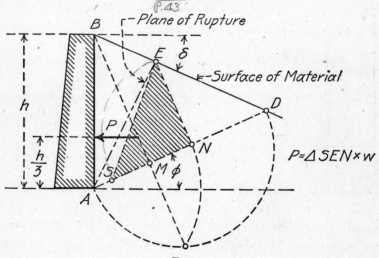

FIG. 23.

*Professor Rebhann makes the same assumptions and uses the graphic method of Fig. 19.

Vertical Wall With Level Surface, $\delta = 0.$

$$P = \tfrac{1}{2}w.h^2 \left(\frac{\cos\phi}{n+1}\right)^2 \frac{1}{\cos\phi'} \qquad (36)$$

where

$$n = \sqrt{\frac{\sin(\phi+\phi').\sin\phi}{\cos\phi'}}$$

If $\phi = \phi'$, then $n = \sqrt{2}\sin\phi$, and

$$P = \tfrac{1}{2}w.h^2 \frac{\cos\phi}{(1+\sin\phi\sqrt{2})^2} \qquad (37)$$

If $\phi' = 0$, then

$$P = \tfrac{1}{2}w.h^2.\tan^2\left(45° - \frac{\phi}{2}\right) \qquad (38)$$

Vertical Wall With Surcharge $= \delta.$

$$P = \tfrac{1}{2}w.h^2 \left(\frac{\cos\phi}{n+1}\right)^2 \frac{1}{\cos\phi'} \qquad (39)$$

where

$$n = \sqrt{\frac{\sin(\phi+\phi').\sin(\phi-\delta)}{\cos\phi'.\cos\delta}}$$

If $\delta = \phi$,

$$P = \tfrac{1}{2}w.h^2 \frac{\cos^2\phi}{\cos\phi'} \qquad (40)$$

If $\phi' = 0$, and $\delta = \phi$,

$$P = \tfrac{1}{2}w.h^2.\cos^2\phi \qquad (41),$$

Inclined Wall With Horizontal Surface.

$$P = \tfrac{1}{2}w.h^2 \left(\frac{\sin(\theta-\phi)}{(n+1)\sin\theta}\right)^2 \frac{1}{\sin(\phi'+\theta)} \qquad (42)$$

where

$$n = \sqrt{\frac{\sin(\phi+\phi').\sin\phi}{\sin(\phi'+\theta).\sin\theta}}$$

Inclined Wall With Surcharge $= \delta.$

$$P = \tfrac{1}{2}w.h^2 \left(\frac{\sin(\theta-\phi)}{(n+1).\sin\theta}\right)^2 \frac{1}{\sin(\phi'+\theta)} \qquad (43)$$

where

$$n = \sqrt{\frac{\sin(\phi+\phi').\sin(\phi-\delta)}{\sin(\phi'+\theta).\sin(\theta-\delta)}}$$

4

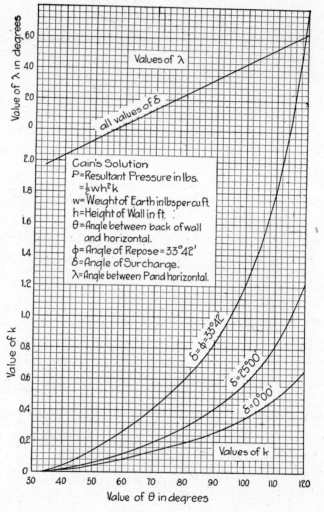

Value of λ in degrees

60
40   Values of λ
20
0   all values of δ

2.0   Cain's Solution
      P = Resultant Pressure in lbs.
1.8   = ½ wh²k
      w = Weight of Earth in lbs per cu.ft.
1.6   h = Height of Wall in ft.
      θ = Angle between back of wall
1.4   and horizontal.
      φ = Angle of Repose = 33°42'
1.2   δ = Angle of Surcharge.
      λ = Angle between P and horizontal.

Value of k

1.0
0.8   δ=φ=33°42'
0.6   δ=25°00'
0.4   δ=0°00'
0.2   Values of k
0
  30 40 50 60 70 80 90 100 110 120

Value of θ in degrees

FIG. 23 a.

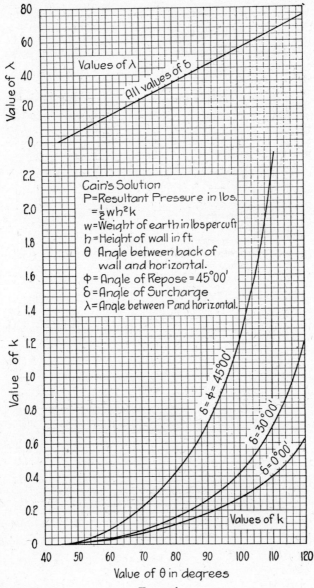

Cain's Solution
P = Resultant Pressure in lbs.
  = ½ wh²k
w = Weight of earth in lbs per cu ft
h = Height of wall in ft.
θ Angle between back of
   wall and horizontal.
φ = Angle of Repose = 45°00'
δ = Angle of Surcharge
λ = Angle between P and horizontal.

Values of λ
All values of δ

Values of k

δ = φ = 45°00'
δ = 30°00'
δ = 0°00'

Value of θ in degrees

FIG. 23 b.

Graphic Values for Cain's Solution.—The values of k in the formula $P = \frac{1}{2}w.h^2.k$, were calculated by means of formulas (36) to (43) and were checked by graphics, for different values of θ, δ and ϕ; λ is the angle between the resultant P and a horizontal line.

In Fig. 23a are given values of k and λ for $\phi = 33° 42'$, and for $\delta = \phi = 33° 42'$, $\delta = 25°$, and $\delta = 0°$.

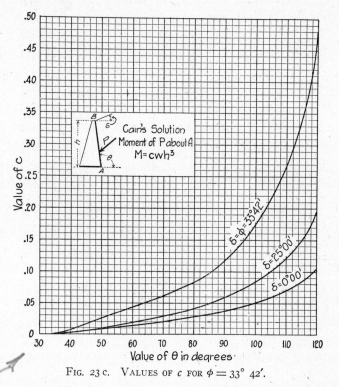

FIG. 23 c. VALUES OF c FOR $\phi = 33° 42'$.

In Fig. 23b are given values of k and λ for $\phi = 45°$, and for $\delta = \phi = 45°$, $\delta = 30°$, and $\delta = 0°$.

The values of c where $M = c.w.h^3$ have been calculated for $\phi = 33° 42'$ and for $\delta = \phi = 33° 42'$, $\delta = 25°$, and $\delta = 0°$, and are given in Fig. 23c.

The values of c where $M = c.w.h^3$ have been calculated for $\phi = 45°$ and for $\delta = \phi = 45°$, $\delta = 30°$, and $\delta = 0°$, and are given in Fig. 23d.

By comparing Fig. 23c and Fig. 23d with values of c for Rankine's Theory Modified in Fig. 15l and Fig. 15m, it will be seen that the over-turning moments as given by the two solutions are nearly identical for the walls commonly used.

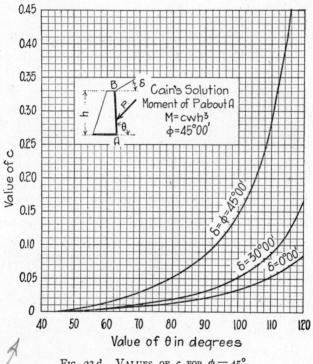

FIG. 23 d. VALUES OF c FOR $\phi = 45°$.

CHAPTER III.

Design of Masonry Retaining Walls.

Center of Pressure.—It will be seen that for all cases the resultant pressure on the back of the wall will be given by the formula [43]

$$P = \tfrac{1}{2}w.h^2.K \qquad (18)$$

Where K is the ratio of the horizontal to the vertical pressure, and is independent of the weight of the filling or the height of the wall, and depends upon the inclination of the back of the wall, θ, the angle of repose, ϕ, the angle of surcharge, δ, and the angle that the resultant thrust makes with a normal to the back of the wall, z. For any particular case, K will be a constant and the unit pressure at any point will vary as the height h. In Fig. 24, the resultant pressure, P, is rep-

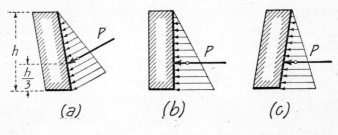

(a)   (b)   (c)

Fig. 24.

resented by the area of the shaded triangles, and the center of pressure will be at $\tfrac{1}{3}h$ from the base, the same as for fluid pressure.

Experiments made with models have shown that the center of pressure $= \tfrac{1}{3}h$ is sometimes exceeded. Goodrich recommends that for walls from 6 to 10 feet the center of pressure be taken at $0.4h$, and above 10 feet the center of pressure be taken at $\tfrac{1}{3}h$ above the base.* Scheffler assumed that the center of pressure is at $0.4h$.

* Trans. Am. Soc. C. E., Vol. LIII, p. 295; also see Chapter V.

It should be remembered that experiments have been made on small models and are liable to considerable error. It would appear reasonable with our present knowledge to always take the center of pressure at a point $\frac{1}{3}h$ above the base.

Stability of Retaining Walls.—A retaining wall must be stable (1) against overturning, (2) against sliding, and (3) against crushing the masonry or the foundation.

The factor of safety of a retaining wall is the ratio of the weight of a filling having the same angle of internal friction that will just cause failure to the actual weight of the filling. For a factor of safety of 2 the wall would just be on the point of failure with a filling weighing twice that for which the wall is built.

1. *Overturning.*—In Fig. 25, let P, represented by OP', be the resultant pressure of the earth, and W, represented by OW, be the weight of the wall acting through its center of gravity. Then E, represented by OR, will be the resultant pressure tending to overturn the wall.

Draw OS through the point A. For this condition the wall should be on the point of overturning, and the factor of safety against overturning would be unity. The factor of safety for $E = OR$ will be

$$f_0 = \frac{SW}{RW} \tag{44}$$

2. *Sliding.*—In Fig. 25 construct the angle H_1G equal to ϕ', the angle of friction of the masonry on the foundation. Now if E passes through 1, and takes the direction OQ, the wall will be on the point of sliding, and the factor of safety against sliding, f_s, will be unity. For $E = OR$, the factor of safety against sliding will be

$$f_s = \frac{QM'}{RM} \tag{45}$$

Retaining walls seldom fail by sliding.

The factor of safety against sliding is sometimes given as

$$f_s = \frac{F}{H} \tan \phi' \tag{46}$$

where H is the horizontal component of P. Equations (45) and (46) give the same values only where the resultant P is horizontal.

3. *Crushing.*—In Fig. 25 the load on the foundation will be due to a vertical force F, which produces a uniform stress $p_1 = \dfrac{F}{d}$ over the area of the base, and a bending moment $= F.b$, which produces compression, p_2, on the front and tension, p_2, on the back of the foundation.

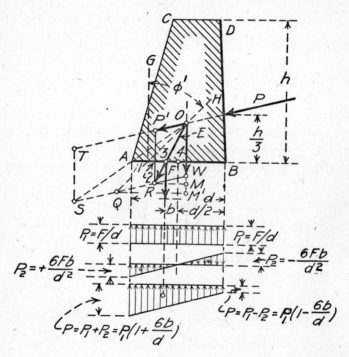

FIG. 25.

The sum of the tensile stresses due to bending must equal the sum of the compressive stresses, $= \frac{1}{4}p_2 d$. These stresses act as a couple through the centers of gravity of the stress triangles on each side, and the resisting moment is

$$M' = \tfrac{1}{4}p_2.d.\tfrac{2}{3}d = \tfrac{1}{6}p_2.d^2 \qquad (47)$$

But the resisting movement equals the overturning moment, and

$$\tfrac{1}{6}p_2.d^2 = F.b, \text{ and}$$

may also be obtained from $S = \dfrac{Mc}{I}$. See H_4 582.

STABILITY OF RETAINING WALLS.   57

$$p_2 = \pm \frac{6F.b}{d^2} \tag{48}$$

The total stress on the foundation then is

$$p = p_1 \pm p_2 = p_1 \left(1 \pm \frac{6b}{d} \right) \tag{49}$$

Now if $b = \frac{1}{6}d$, we will have

$$p = 2p_1, \text{ or } 0.$$

In order therefore that there be no tension, or that the compression never exceed twice the average stress the resultant should never strike outside the middle third of the base.

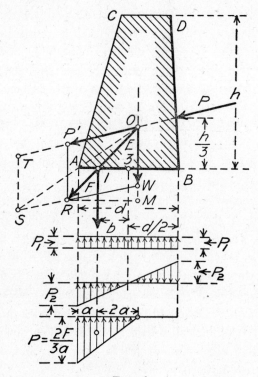

Fig. 26.

If the resultant strike outside of the middle third of a wall in which the masonry can take no tension, the load will all be taken by compression and can be calculated as follows:

In Fig. 26 the resultant F will pass through the center of gravity of the stress diagram, and will equal the area of the diagram.

$$F = \frac{3}{2}\, p.a, \text{ and}$$

$$p = \tfrac{2}{3}\, \frac{F}{a} \tag{50}$$

which gives a larger value of p than would be given if the masonry could take tension.

General Principles of Design.—The overturning moment of a masonry retaining wall of gravity section depends upon the weight of the filling, the angle of internal friction of the filling, the surcharge, and the height and shape of the wall. The resisting moment depends upon the weight of the masonry, the width of the foundation, and the cross-section of the wall. The most economical section for a masonry retaining wall is obtained when the back slopes toward the filling. In cold localities, however, this form of section may be displaced by heaving due to the action of frost, and it is usual to build retaining walls with a slight batter forwards. The front of the wall is usually built with a batter of from $\frac{1}{2}$ in. to 1 in. in 12 in. In order to keep the center of gravity of the wall back of the center of the base it is necessary to increase the width of the wall at the base by adding a projection to the front side. Where the wall is built on the line of a right of way it is sometimes necessary to increase the width of the base by putting the projection on the rear side, making an L-shaped wall. The weight of the filling upon the base and back of the wall adds to the stability of the wall. Where the wall is built to support an embankment expensive to excavate it is often economical to make the wall L-shaped, with all the projection on the front side.

In calculating the thrust on retaining walls great care must be exercised in selecting the proper values of w and ϕ, and the conditions of surcharge. It will be seen from the preceding discussion that the value of the thrust increases very rapidly as ϕ decreases, and as the surcharge increases. Where the wall is to sustain an embankment carrying a railroad track, buildings, or other loads, a proper allowance must be made for the surcharge.

The filling back of the wall should be deposited and tamped in approximately horizontal layers, or with layers sloping back from the wall; and a layer of sand, gravel or other porous material should be deposited between the filling and the wall, to drain the filling downward. To insure drainage of the filling, drains should be provided back of the wall and on top of the footing, and "weep-holes" should be provided near the bottom of the wall at frequent intervals to allow the water to pass through the wall. With walls from 15 to 25 feet high, it is usual to use "weepers" 4 inches in diameter placed from 15 to 20 feet apart. The "weepers" should be connected with a longitudinal drain in front of the wall. The filling in front of the wall should also be carefully drained.

The permissible point at which the resultant thrust may strike the base of the foundation will depend upon the material upon which the retaining wall rests. When the foundation is solid rock or the wall is on piles driven to a good refusal, the resultant thrust may strike slightly outside the middle third with little danger to the stability of the wall. When the retaining wall, however, rests upon compressible material the resultant thrust should strike at or inside the center of the base. Where the resultant thrust strikes outside of the center of the base, any settlement of the wall will cause the top to tip forward, causing unsightly cracks and local failure in many cases, and total failure where the settlement is excessive. Where extended footings are used it may be necessary to use some reinforcing steel to prevent a crack in the footing in line with the face of the wall.

Plain masonry walls should be built in sections, the length depending upon the height of the wall, the foundation and other conditions. Under usual conditions the length of the sections should not exceed 40 ft., 30–ft. sections being preferable, and in no case should the length of the section exceed about 3 times the height. Separate sections should be held in line and in elevation, either by grooves in the masonry, or by means of short bars placed at intervals in the cross-section of the wall, fastened rigidly in one section and sliding freely in the other. The back of the expansion joints should be water-proofed with 3 or 4 layers of burlap and coal tar pitch. The burlap should be about 30 inches wide, and the pitch and the burlap should be applied as on tar and gravel roofs. The joints between the sections of a retaining wall on the front side should be from $\frac{1}{8}$ to $\frac{1}{4}$ of an inch in width, and should be formed by a V-shaped groove made of sheet steel and fastened to the forms while the concrete is being placed. Where there is danger of the water in the filling percolating through the wall or in an alkali country, the surface of the back of the wall should be coated with a water-proof coating. The most satisfactory water-proof coating known to the author is a coal tar paint made by mixing refined coal tar, Portland cement and kerosene in the proportions of 16 parts refined coal tar, 4 parts of Portland cement and 3 parts of kerosene oil. The Portland cement and kerosene should be mixed thoroughly and the coal tar then added. In cold weather the coal tar may be heated and additional kerosene added to take account of the evaporation. This paint not only covers the surface but combines with it, so that two or three coats are sometimes required. While the surface of the concrete should be dry, coal tar paint will adhere to moist or wet concrete. In building retaining walls in sections, the end of the finished section should be coated with coal tar paint to prevent the adhesion of the next section.

The design of masonry retaining walls will be illustrated by three examples.

Problem 1.—Design a masonry retaining wall of sandstone weighing 150 lbs. per cu. ft., having a height of 18 feet and a top width of 2 feet, to retain a bank of sand sloping upwards at an angle of 22° 30'. Sand weighs 100 lbs. per cu. ft., and has an angle of repose $\phi = 33° 42'$, $1\frac{1}{2}:1$.

Solution.—The back of the wall in Fig. 27 will be assumed to batter

1 inch to the foot, and the foundation will be assumed as 7 ft. 6 in., which is approximately $\frac{4}{10}$ the height. A section of the wall one foot long will be investigated.

To calculate the resultant pressure P, proceed as follows:* Draw AO parallel to the surcharge $A'M_1$, and at any convenient point O in

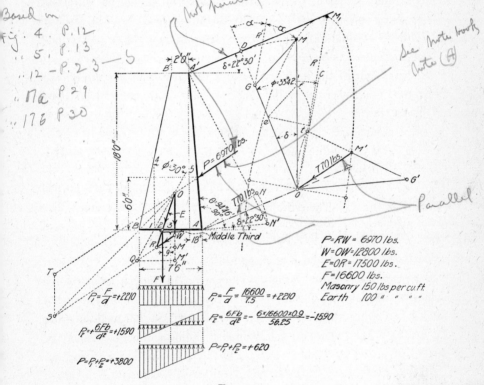

FIG. 27.

AO draw OD at right angles to AO. Draw OM vertical and locate M by striking the arc DM with O as a center. Draw OC making an angle ϕ with OD. At any point e in OD describe an arc tangent to OC and cutting OM at f. Through M draw MG parallel to ef. Bisect angle DGM, and through O draw OR parallel to GR'. Then OR is

* This problem is solved by means of the Ellipse of Stress, Fig. 12. The methods used in Fig. 32 and Fig. 34 will give the same results.

the principal axis of the ellipse of stress, and OM_1 is the maximum stress than can occur in the filling.   To calculate the maximum stress at A, draw OG' at right angles to the back of the wall $A\text{-}A'$, and make $OG' = OG$, with G' as the center and OG' as a radius describe an arc cutting the principal axis OR at t.   Draw $G't$, and with G' as a center and a radius equal to GM describe an arc cutting $G't$ at M'.   Then $M'O$ acting as shown is the intensity of the stress at A.   The resultant pressure P is equal to the area of the stress triangle $AA'N' \times w$, equals 6,970 lbs., and acts on $A\text{-}A'$ at $\frac{1}{3}$ the height of the wall.

The weight of the masonry is $W = 12,800$ lbs., acting through the center of gravity of the wall.   The resultant of W and R is $E = OR = 17,500$ lbs.

The resultant E cuts the foundation at a point, $b = 0.9$ ft. from the center, which is within the middle third.   The vertical component of E is $F = 16,600$ lbs.

1. *Stability Against Overturning.*—Through B draw OS and produce RW to S.   Then the factor of safety against overturning is $f_0 = \dfrac{SW}{RW} = 6$.   If E passed through B the wall would be on the point of overturning, and f_0 would equal unity.

2. *Stability Against Sliding.*—The coefficient of friction of the masonry on the footing will be taken as 0.57 and $\phi' = 30°$.   Through O draw $5Q$, cutting base of wall AB at 1, and making an angle $\phi' = 30°$ with 1–4.   Then factor of safety against sliding will be

$$f_s = \frac{QM'}{RM} = 2.0$$

This is ample, as the resistance of the filling in front of the toe will increase the factor of safety against sliding.   The factor of safety against sliding at any point above the base can be determined in a similar manner, but will be much greater on account of the greater value of ϕ' for masonry on masonry.

3. *Stability Against Crushing.*—In Fig. 27 the direct pressure will be $p_1 = \dfrac{F}{d} = 16,600 \div 7.5 = 2,210$ lbs. per sq. ft.

The pressure due to bending moment will be

$$p_2 = \pm \frac{6Fb}{d^2} = \pm \frac{6 \times 16,600 \times 0.9}{56.25}$$

$$= \pm 1,590 \text{ lbs. per sq. ft.}$$

and the maximum pressure will be $p = 2,210 + 1,590 = +3,800$ lbs., while the minimum pressure will be $p = 2,210 - 1,590 = +620$ lbs. per sq. ft. By comparing with the allowable pressures in Table III it will be seen that the pressure is a safe one for a good sand and gravel or clay foundation.

4. *Depth of Filling in Front of Wall.*—From formula (9) it will be seen that to prevent heaving we must have *P. 26*

$$p \leqq w.y \left(\frac{1 + \sin \phi}{1 - \sin \phi}\right)^2 \tag{9}$$

From which, when $w = 100$ lbs., $\phi = 33° 42'$ and $p = 3,800$ lbs. per sq. ft., $y \leqq 3.1$ ft. Which is less than the distance usually required to be safe from frost action.

The width of the top is about as small as is allowable where there is frost action. By spreading the footing the pressure can be decreased or the section may be slightly decreased.

The filling should be deposited and tamped in nearly horizontal layers, while a porous layer of gravel or similar material should be deposited just behind the wall to carry the moisture to the bottom of the wall, where a suitable drain should be provided with "weep-holes" leading through the wall at intervals of from 15 to 20 feet. The wall should be built in sections 30 to 40 ft. in length to prevent cracks due to contraction and expansion, and unequal settlement.

Problem 2. Design of Retaining Walls for West Alameda Avenue Subway, Denver, Colorado.—The height of the walls varied from 8′ to 29′ 3″, while the foundation soil varied from a compact gravel to a mushy clay. The design of the maximum section, which rests on a compact gravel, will be given. The concrete was mixed in the proportion of one part Portland cement, 3 parts sand and 5 parts screened gravel. Crocker and Ketchum, Denver, Colo., were the consulting engineers, the author being in charge of the design. The wall is shown in Fig. 50b.

The following assumptions were made: Weight of concrete, 150 lbs. per cu. ft.; weight of filling, $w = 100$ lbs. per cu. ft.; angle of repose of filling, $1\frac{1}{2}$: 1 ($\phi = 33° \, 40'$); surcharge 600 lbs. per sq. ft., equivalent to 6 feet of filling; maximum load on foundation, 6,000 lbs. per sq. ft.

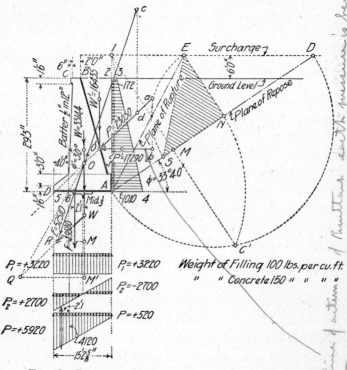

FIG. 28. RETAINING WALL, ALAMEDA AVENUE SUBWAY.

Solution.—After several trials the following dimensions were taken: Width of coping 2′ 6″, thickness of coping 1′ 6″, batter of face of wall $\frac{1}{2}$″ in 12″, batter of back of wall $3\frac{1}{2}$″ in 12″, width of base 15′ $2\frac{5}{8}$″ (ratio of base to height = 0.52), front projection of base 4′ 0″, other dimensions as shown in Fig. 28.

The property back of the wall will probably be used for the storage of coal, etc., and it was assumed that the surcharge came even with the back edge of the footing of the wall. The resultant pressure of the filling on the plane *A-2* was calculated by the graphic method of Fig. 19 and Fig. 20, and was found to be $P' = 17,290$ lbs. The weight of the filling in the wedge back of the wall is $W' = 16,435$ lbs., acting through the center of gravity of the filling. The resultant of P' and W' is $P = 23,850$ lbs. = the resultant pressure of the filling on the back of the wall. The weight of the masonry is $W = 33,144$ lbs., acting through the center of gravity of the wall, and the resultant of P and W is $E = 52,510$ lbs. = the resultant pressure of the wall and the filling upon the foundation. The vertical component of E is $F = 49,580$ lbs., and cuts the foundation, $b = 2.1$ feet from the middle.

1. *Stability Against Overturning.*—The line OD in this case is nearly parallel to the line QW which brings the point S in Fig. 28 at a great distance from the point W. The factor of safety against overturning was calculated on the original drawing and found to be $f_0 > 25$.

2. *Stability Against Sliding.*—The coefficient of friction of the masonry on the footing will be assumed to be $\tan \phi' = 0.57$ and $\phi' = 30°$. Through O, Fig. 28, draw OQ, cutting the base of wall $5A$ at 6, and making an angle $\phi' = 30°$ with a vertical line through 6. Then the factor of safety against sliding will be

$$f_s = \frac{QM'}{RM} = 2.5$$

This is ample as the resistance of the filling in front of the toe will increase the resistance against sliding.

3. *Stability Against Crushing.*—In Fig. 28 the direct pressure will be $p_1 = \frac{49,580}{15.21} = 3,220$ lbs. per sq. ft.

The pressure due to bending will be

$$p_2 = \pm \frac{6F.b}{d^2} = \pm \frac{6 \times 49,580 \times 2.1}{231.4}$$

$$= 2,700 \text{ lbs. per sq. ft.}$$

5

and the maximum pressure is

$$p = 3,220 + 2,700 = + 5,920 \text{ lbs. per sq. ft.}$$

and the minimum pressure is

$$p = 3,220 - 2,700 = + 520 \text{ lbs. per sq. ft.}$$

The allowable pressure was 6,000 lbs. per sq. ft., so that the pressure is safe for a compact gravel. Where the walls were supported on the mushy clay it was necessary to extend the projection of the footing on the front side and to bring the resultant F to the center of the wall.

4. *Upward Pressure on Front Projection of Foundation.*—Where projections are used on the foundations of retaining walls it may be necessary to reinforce the base to prevent the projection breaking off in line with the face of the wall. The bending moment of the upward pressure about the front face of the wall from Fig. 28 is

$$M = \tfrac{1}{2} (5,920 + 4,120) \, 4 \times 2.1 \times 12$$
$$= 506,000 \text{ in.-lbs.}$$

The tension on the concrete at the bottom of the footing will be

$$f = \frac{M.c}{I} = \frac{M.d/2}{I} = \frac{506,000 \times 27}{157,464}$$
$$= 88 \text{ lbs. per sq. in.}$$

Since the ultimate strength of the concrete in tension is approximately 200 lbs. per sq. in., no reinforcing is required. However, $\tfrac{3}{4}''$ □ bars were placed $18''$ centers and $3''$ from the bottom of the foundation.

5. **Overturning on Top of Footing.**—The footings were poured first, the forms were then built for the upper part of the wall, and the body of the wall was completed. It will therefore be necessary to investigate the stability of the body of the wall on top of the footing.

1. *Stability Against Crushing.*—In Fig. 28a, using the same method as in Fig. 28, the resultant pressure E strikes 3.4 feet from the center (outside the middle third) and $F = 37,040$ lbs. The compression on

the lower side, point D, is $p = 3,630 + 7,280 = 10,910$ lbs. per sq. ft., $= 76$ lbs. per sq. in., which is entirely safe. The tension on the upper side, point A, is $p = 3,630 - 7,280 = -3,650$ lbs. per sq. ft. $= 26$ lbs. tension per sq. in. While the adhesion of concrete on concrete will probably be larger than 26 lbs. per sq. in., a few vertical steel bars will be placed near the back face. The following approximate solution

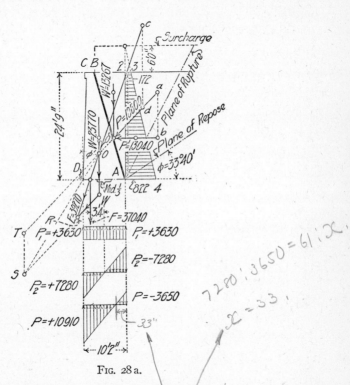

FIG. 28 a.

was used for calculating the size of bars. The total tension on the section per lineal inch of wall is $t = \frac{1}{2} \times 26 \times 33 = 429$ lbs. Bars $\frac{3}{4}'' \square$ were spaced 18'' centers. The approximate stress on each bar is then $T = 429 \times 18 = 7,722$ lbs. The allowable stress on a $\frac{3}{4}'' \square$ bar is $T = 16,000 \times 0.5625 = 9,000$ lbs. Deformed bars were used and should be imbedded a length $l = \dfrac{7,722}{120 \times 3} = 22''$. The bars were made $\frac{3}{4}'' \square \times 4$ ft. long and were placed about 9'' from back face of wall.

2. *Stability Against Overturning.*—The factor of safety against overturning from Fig. 28*a* is

$$f_0 = \frac{SW}{RW} = 3.4, \text{ which is ample.}$$

3. *Stability Against Sliding.*—The factor of safety against sliding for $\phi' = 30°$ was found on the original drawing as in Fig. 28 to be $f_s = 1.6$. The shear on the section is only 10 lbs. per sq. in. The section is safe against sliding.

Problem 3. Design of Concrete Abutment for West Alameda Avenue Subway, Denver, Colorado.—The height of the abutment is 21′ 6″ from the bottom of the footing to the top of the bridge seat, and 25′ 0⅜″ to the top of the back wall. The following assumptions were made: Weight of concrete, 150 lbs. per cu. ft.; weight of filling, $w = 100$ lbs. per cu. ft.; angle of repose of the filling, 1½ to 1 ($\phi = 33°$ 42′); surcharge 800 lbs. per sq. ft., equivalent to 8 feet of filling; maximum load on foundation 6,000 lbs. per sq. ft.

Solution.—After several trials the dimensions given in Fig. 29 were taken. The stability of the abutment was investigated for two conditions: (*a*) with a full live and dead load on bridge and on the filling, and (*b*) with no live load on the bridge and no surcharge coming on the filling above the wall, it being assumed that a locomotive is approaching the bridge from the right, and has reached the point 2 in (*b*) Fig. 29. The weight of the girders and the live load was assumed as uniformly distributed over a length of the abutment equal to the distance between track centers, and one lineal foot of wall was investigated.

Case (a).—The pressure of the filling on the plane *B*-2 was calculated as in Fig. 28, and is $P' = 14,700$ lbs., acting through the center of gravity of the trapezoid 2-3-4-*B*. The weight of the filling and surcharge is $W_2 + W_3 = 14,900$ lbs., which when combined with P' gives the resultant pressure of the filling on the wall $= P = 20,900$ lbs. The pressure P is then combined with the weight of the wall, $W_1 = 29,800$ lbs., and with the dead load and live load from the girder $= 12,820$ lbs., giving the resultant pressure on the foundation, $E = 59,400$ lbs., and acting, $b = 1.4$ feet from the center of the wall, and $F = 57,500$ lbs.

1. *Stability Against Overturning.*—The resultant E is nearly vertical and well within the middle third, so that the wall is amply safe against overturning.

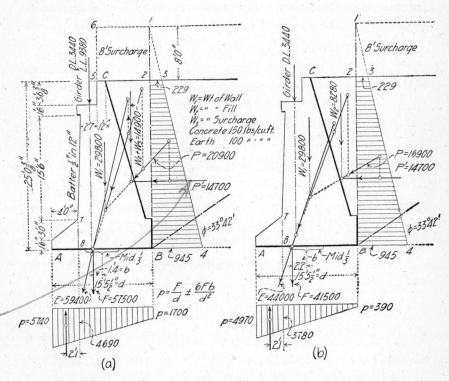

Fig. 29. Abutment for West Alameda Avenue Subway, Denver, Colo.

2. *Stability Against Sliding.*—Assuming that $\phi' = 30°$, then the coefficient of friction will be $\tan\phi' = 0.57$. Using the definition of factor of safety given in equation (46), the resistance of the wall against sliding will be $57,500 \times 0.57 = 32,765$ lbs. The sliding force is $P' = 14,700$ lbs., and the factor of safety is $32,765/14,700 = 2.23$, which is ample.

3. *Pressure on Foundation.*—The pressure on the foundation will

be $p = F/d \pm 6F.b/d^2 = +5,740$ and $+1,700$ lbs. per sq. ft., which is safe.

4. *Upward Pressure on Front Projection of Foundation.*—The base will be investigated on the plane 7-8 to see that the upward pressure will not break off the front projection of the foundation. The bending moment of the upward pressure about the front face of the wall in (*a*) Fig. 29 will be

$$M = \tfrac{1}{2}(5,740 + 4,690) 4 \times 2.1 \times 12$$
$$= 525,672 \text{ in.-lbs.}$$

The tension on the concrete at the bottom of the footing will be

$$f = \frac{M.c}{I} = \frac{M.d/2}{I} = \frac{525,672 \times 27}{157,464}$$
$$= 92 \text{ lbs. per sq. in.}$$

The footing is safe, but $\tfrac{3}{4}''$ □ rods were placed 18″ centers and 3″ from the bottom of the foundation, the same as in the retaining walls.

Case (b).—The solution is the same as for (a) except that the live load from the girder $= 9,980$ lbs., and the surcharge load 1-2-5-6 $= W_3$ $= 6,620$ lbs. were omitted. The wall is safe for overturning. The factor of safety against sliding is from (46) $f_s = 41,500 \times 0.57/14,700 = 1.6$, which is safe. The pressure on the foundation is safe.

The back wall was placed after the bridge seats were finished. To bond the back wall to the abutment, $\tfrac{1}{2}''$ □ rods 4 ft. long, spaced 18″ centers, were placed in two rows 3″ from the back and front face, one half of the length of the rod being imbedded in the main wall.

Empirical Methods.—Take a rectangular masonry retaining wall as in Fig. 30. The masonry weighs 150 lbs. per cubic foot, the filling weighs 100 lbs. per cubic foot, and the ratio of the lateral to the vertical pressure will be taken as four-tenths.*

Then the resultant pressure is

$$P = \tfrac{4}{10} \cdot \frac{100h^2}{2} = 20h^2$$

* See Table IX for angles of repose and ratios of lateral to vertical pressures.

Total weight of wall is

$$W = 150b.h.$$

Now in order that the maximum pressure be not greater than twice the average, and that there be no tension on the back side of the foundations, d must not be greater than $\frac{b}{6}$.

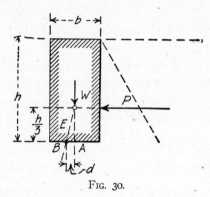

Fig. 30.

Taking moments about B we have

$$W.d - P\frac{h}{3} = 0$$

$$150b.h.\frac{b}{6} - 20h^2.\frac{h}{3} = 0$$

$$15b^2 = 4h^2$$

$$b = h\sqrt{\tfrac{4}{15}} = 0.52h = \frac{h}{2} \text{ (approx.)}$$

Trautwine's Rules.—Trautwine gives the following ratio of width of foundation b to height h, when the earth backing is loosely placed.

Wall of cut stone, or of first-class ranged rubble, in mortar $b = .35h$.

Wall of common scabbled mortar-rubble, or brick $b = .40h$.

Wall of well scabbled dry rubble $b = .50h$.

A mixture of sand or earth, with or without a large proportion of round bowlders, paving pebbles, etc., will weigh more and the thickness of the wall should be increased about one-eighth to one-sixth part.

Value of Empirical Rules.—The empirical rules by Trautwine and others are given without reference to the character of the foundation, the conditions of surcharge, and the cross-section of the wall, and are of little value. A theoretical investigation based on carefully selected constants leads to a proper distribution of the material in the wall, and an economical design.

The cross-sections of 27 retaining walls having gravity sections are shown in the folding insert, Fig. 50a. The ratio of width of base to height of wall is given in black type for each wall. The ratio of base to height varies from $R = 0.30$ for a special wall (27) for the East Boston Tunnel (apparently on solid rock) to $R = 0.69$ for a wall on water-bearing earth (24) for the Penn., N. Y. & L. I. R. R. A study of the walls in Fig. 50a will give many excellent ideas on design and shows that Trautwine's rules are not in accord with good practice. Fig. 50a was prepared from data furnished by Mr. Frank H. Carter, Associate Member Am. Soc. C. E., to whom thanks is due. Mr. Frank H. Carter gives the values for the angle of repose, ϕ, for the filling of retaining walls as in Table IIA.

TABLE IIA.*

ANGLES OF REPOSE OF MATERIALS.

Materials.	Degrees.	Materials.	Degrees.
Moist earth	45	Dry sand	35
Dry earth	40	Wet earth	30
Sharp gravel	40	Round gravel	30
Moist sand	40	Wet sand	30

The Illinois Central R. R. uses $\phi = 45°$ for the dry sand filling for track elevation in Chicago. Mr. Fred L. Thompson, bridge engineer, advises the author that the walls built on this assumption give satisfactory results.

In Volume 10, Part 2 of the Proceedings of Am. Ry. Eng. and M. of W. Assoc., p. 317, the Committee on Masonry submitted a report on the design of retaining walls. The committee recommends that ϕ be taken as $1\frac{1}{2}:1$ for average conditions, and that Rankine's solution be

* Also see Table IX and Table II.

used in design. Cross-sections of several walls that have failed are given, and the reasons for failure are pointed out. Much valuable data are given on the design of retaining walls.

Data.—The coefficients of friction of various materials are given in Table I. The conditions of surface and amount of moisture cause wide variations in the coefficients.

TABLE I.

COEFFICIENTS OF FRICTION.

Materials.	Coefficients.	Materials.	Coefficients.
Dry masonry on dry masonry...	0.6 to 0.7	Masonry on dry clay.............	0.5 to 0.6
Masonry on masonry with wet		Masonry on moist clay.	0.33
mortar.........	0.75	Earth on earth.	0.25 to 1.0
Timber on stone	0.4	Hard brick on hard brick.......	0.7
Iron on stone.	0.3 to 0.7	Concrete blocks on concrete	
Timber on timber	0.2 to 0.5	blocks............................	0.65

Approximate values of angle of repose, ϕ, are given in Table II.

TABLE II.

ANGLES OF REPOSE, ϕ, FOR MATERIALS.*

Materials.	ϕ	Materials.	ϕ
Earth, loam	30° to 45°	Clay............	25° to 45°
Sand, dry........	25° to 35°	Gravel.......	30° to 40°
Sand, moist...................	30° to 45°	Cinders	25° to 40°
Sand, wet.....................	15° to 30°	Coke......................	30° to 45°

Allowable pressures on foundations to be used in the absence of more definite data are given in Table III.

TABLE III.

ALLOWABLE PRESSURE ON FOUNDATIONS.

Material.	Pressure in Tons per Sq. Ft.
Soft clay.........	1 to 2
Ordinary clay and dry sand mixed with clay.........................	2 to 3
Dry sand and clay.....................	3 to 4
Hard clay and firm, coarse sand..	4 to 6
Firm, coarse sand and gravel.........	6 to 8
Bed rock...	15 and up.

* Also see Table IX and Table IIa.

The allowable pressures on masonry are given in Table IV.

TABLE IV.
ALLOWABLE PRESSURE ON MASONRY.

Materials.	Pressure in Tons per Sq. Ft.
Common brick, Portland cement mortar.............................	12
Paving brick, Portland cement mortar	15
Rubble masonry, Portland cement mortar............................	12
Sandstone, first class masonry...........................	20
Limestone, " " "	25
Granite, " " "	30
Portland cement concrete, 1–2–4.	25
" " " 1–3–6.................................	20

The weights, specific gravities and crushing strengths of masonry are given in Table V.

TABLE V.
WEIGHT, SPECIFIC GRAVITY AND CRUSHING STRENGTH OF MASONRY

Materials.	Weight in Pounds per Cubic Foot.	Specific Gravity.	Crushing Strength in Pounds per Square Inch
Sandstone........................	150	2.4	4,000 to 15,000
Limestone..	160	2.6	6,000 to 20,000
Trap...	180	2.9	19,000 to 33,000
Marble.......................................	165	2.7	8,000 to 20,000
Granite.......................................	165	2.7	8,000 to 20,000
Paving brick, Portland cement.........	150	2.4	2,000 to 6,000
Stone concrete, Portland cement......	140 to 150	2.2 to 2.4	2,500 to 4,000
Cinder concrete, Portland cement.....	112	1.8	1,000 to 2,500

The average weights of materials are given in Table VI.

TABLE VI.
WEIGHT OF DIFFERENT MATERIALS.

Materials.	Wt. per Cu. Ft. Lbs.	Materials.	Wt. per Cu. Ft. Lbs.
Loam, loose.	75 to 90	Sand, wet	110 to 120
Loam, rammed..	90 to 100	Gravel	120 to 135
Sand, dry......................	90 to 110	Soft flowing mud............	105 to 120

For definitions of terms used in masonry construction, and for specifications for stone masonry, see Appendix II and Appendix III.

SPECIFICATIONS FOR CONCRETE RETAINING WALLS.—The following extracts have been taken from the specifications prepared by Crocker and Ketchum, Consulting Engineers, for the concrete retaining walls for the West Alameda Avenue Subway, Denver, Colo.

16. **MATERIALS. Cement.**—The cement shall be furnished by the Companies on board cars or in store houses at the site of the work as required. The cement shall be Portland, and shall meet the requirements of the Standard Specifications of the American Society for Testing Materials.

17. **Concrete Aggregate.**—The fine aggregate shall pass a screen with ¼ in. mesh, while the coarse aggregate shall all be retained on a screen with ¼ in. mesh and all shall pass a screen with 3 in. mesh. The sand and gravel shall be obtained from the excavation of the open cut of the Subway. The Consulting Engineers reserve the right to change the proportions of sand and screened gravel (§34 and §35) from time to time, as may be necessary to secure a dense concrete of desired consistency. Payment to the Contractor for the screening will be made on the basis of unit price per cubic yard of gravel measured after screening.

18. **Water.**—The water used in mixing concrete shall be clean and reasonably clear, free from acids and injurious oils, alkalies or vegetable matter.

19. **Lumber.**—Lumber for forms shall have a nominal thickness of 2″ before surfacing, and shall be of a good quality of Douglas fir or Southern long leaf yellow pine. Lumber used for forms of face work shall be dressed on one side and both edges to a uniform thickness and width. Lumber for backing and other rough work may be unsurfaced and of an inferior grade of the kinds above specified.

20. **Reinforcing Steel.**—All reinforcing steel shall be plain bars, and shall comply with the specifications for structural steel as given in the Standard Specifications of the American Railway Engineering Association.

21. **EXCAVATION.**—The subway is being excavated by the Companies but the contractor shall make all necessary excavations for wall and pedestal footings, and shall furnish all necessary sheeting and supports and bracing to hold the forms in place during the construction of the work. The cost of the necessary sheeting and supports shall be included in the unit price for excavation. The Contractor shall provide all pumps and other equipment incidental to such excavation.

22. All excavation shall be measured in vertical prisms whose end areas are of sufficient size to include the footing courses, and the sheeting surrounding the same. "Wet excavation" shall include all excavation below the surface of standing water in open pits.

23. **CONCRETE. Machine Mixing.**—Machine mixers, preferably of the batch type, shall be used except where the volume of concrete to be mixed is not sufficient to warrant their use. The requirements are that the product delivered shall be of the specified proportions and consistency, and thoroughly mixed.

24. **Mixing by Hand.**—When it is necessary to mix by hand the mixing shall be done on water tight platforms of sufficient size to accommodate men and materials for the progressive and rapid mixing of at least two batches of concrete at the same time. Batches shall not exceed one-half yard. The mixing shall be done as follows: The fine aggregate shall be spread evenly upon the platform, then the cement upon the fine aggregate and these mixed thoroughly until of an even color. Then add the coarse aggregate which, if dry, shall first be thoroughly wet down. The mass shall then be turned with shovels until thoroughly

mixed and all the aggregate covered with mortar, the necessary amount of water being added as the mixing proceeds.

25. **Consistency.**—The material shall be mixed wet enough to produce a concrete of such consistency that it will flow into the forms and about the metal reinforcement, and which on the other hand can be conveyed from the place of mixing to the forms without the separation of the coarse aggregate from the mortar.

26. **Retempering.**—Retempering mortar or concrete, i. e., remixing with water after it has partially set will not be permitted.

27. **Placing of Concrete.**—Concrete after the addition of water to the mix, shall be handled rapidly from the place of mixing to the place of final deposit, and under no circumstances shall concrete be used that has partially set before final placing.

28. The concrete shall be deposited in such a manner as will prevent the separation of the ingredients and permit the most thorough compacting. It shall be compacted by working with a straight shovel or slicing tool kept moving up and down until all the ingredients have settled in their proper place, and the surplus water is forced to the surface. All concrete must be deposited in horizontal layers of uniform thickness throughout. Temporary planking shall be placed at ends of partial layers so that the concrete shall not run out to a thin edge. In placing concrete it shall not be dropped through a clear space of over 6 ft. vertical. For greater heights a trough or other suitable device must be used to deliver the concrete in place, and in depositing each batch this trough or other device must first be carefully filled with concrete and then as fast as concrete is removed at the bottom it shall be replenished at the top.

29. The work shall be carried up in alternate sections of approximately 32 feet in length as shown on the plans, and each section shall be completed without intermission. In no case shall work on a section stop within 18 in. of the top.

30. Before depositing concrete, the forms shall be thoroughly wetted, except in freezing weather, and the space to be occupied by the concrete cleared of debris.

31. **Expansion Joints.**—Expansion joints shall be provided (sections were approximately 32 ft. long) as shown on the plans. The wall shall be constructed in alternate sections, the ends of the sections being formed by vertical end forms, the section being completed as though it were the end of the structure. Before placing the remaining sections the end forms shall be removed and the surface of the concrete shall be painted with coal tar paint, composed of sixteen (16) parts coal tar, four (4) parts Portland cement and three (3) parts kerosene oil. The expansion joints shall be finished on the exposed side by the insertion in the forms of a metal mold that will give a groove ¼" wide, 1" deep and shall have a draft of 1". The wall sections shall be locked together by means of bars as shown on the plans.

32. **Forms.**—Forms shall be substantial and unyielding and built so that the concrete shall conform to the design, dimensions and contours, and so constructed as to prevent the leakage of mortar. Where corners of the masonry and other projections liable to injury occur, suitable moldings shall be placed in the angles of the forms to round or bevel them off. Material once used in forms shall be cleaned before being used again.

33. The forms must not be removed within 36 hours after all the concrete in that section has been placed; in freezing weather they must remain until the concrete has had sufficient time to become thoroughly set.

34. **Proportioning.**—In proportioning concrete, a barrel or 4 sacks of Portland cement shall be assumed to contain 3.8 cubic feet, while the sand and gravel shall be measured loose in a measuring vessel. The proportions required for concrete are as follows:

For footings, walls of retaining walls, abutments, and pedestals, one (1) part Portland cement, three (3) parts sand and five (5) parts gravel. For bridge seats and copings, one (1) part Portland cement, two (2) parts sand and four (4) parts gravel.

35. The tops of the bridge seats, pedestals, and copings, shall be finished with a smooth surface composed of one (1) part Portland cement and two (2) parts sand applied in a layer 1″ thick. This must be put in place with the last course of concrete.

36. **Water-Proofing.**—The expansion joints in the retaining walls and abutments shall be water-proofed as follows: After the forms have been removed and the concrete is thoroughly dried, the back of the wall for a distance of 18″ on each side of the expansion joints shall be mopped with hot refined coal tar pitch. A layer of burlap shall then be placed so as to cover the expansion joints, and the burlap shall be mopped with coal tar pitch. In the same manner two additional layers of burlap shall be applied, making a 3-ply water-proofing.

37. **Reinforcing Bars.**—Reinforcing bars, where used, shall be placed 3″ clear from the outside surface of the concrete, and shall be placed in the position shown on the plans. Care must be taken to insure the coating of the metal with mortar, and a thorough compacting of concrete around the bars. All reinforcing bars shall be clean and free from all dirt or grease.

38. **Freezing Weather.**—Concrete shall not be mixed or deposited at a freezing temperature, unless special precautions are taken to avoid the use of materials containing frost or covered with ice, and means are provided to prevent the concrete from freezing. Where the temperature of the air during the time of mixing and placing concrete is below 40° Fahr. the water used in mixing the concrete shall be of such a temperature, that the temperature of the concrete when delivered in the forms shall not be lower than 60° Fahr. Special precautions shall be taken not to scald the cement.

39. **Placing in Water.**—Concrete shall not be deposited under water except on the approval of the Consulting Engineers. Where water is encountered without current, but in such quantity that it cannot be lowered to the required depth and maintained there, or where such lowering would cause further difficulty, concrete may be deposited through troughs or other device in the manner designated above.

40. **Cleaning Up.**—Upon the completion of any section of the work the Contractor shall remove all debris caused by his operations and leave the work ready for backfilling.

CHAPTER IV.

REINFORCED CONCRETE RETAINING WALLS.

Introduction.—Concrete reinforced with steel or iron has been extensively used in retaining wall construction. Retaining walls of reinforced concrete may be built (1) with a spreading base and a thin vertical section, or (2) may be built with a thin vertical section strengthened by buttresses or counterforts. Reinforced concrete slab or T-walls are economical for heights up to 18 to 20 feet; for greater heights the counterfort wall is economical. The principal advantage of a reinforced concrete wall over a plain concrete wall is in the saving of material in substituting a thin reinforced wall for the gravity section, and in substituting earth filling on the back of the footing in place of the expensive concrete. The data and formulas required in the design of reinforced concrete retaining walls are given in Appendix I.

GENERAL PRINCIPLES OF DESIGN.—The same precautions should be observed in designing reinforced concrete retaining walls as in designing plain masonry walls—which see. Details of forms and methods of mixing and placing concrete are given in Chapter VII. The reinforcing steel should be placed in the correct position and securely wired in place. The concrete should be well mixed and should be deposited very wet in order to properly coat the reinforcing bars, and to make a uniformly dense concrete.

Proportions of Wall.—In a slab or T-wall the relative length of the toe and heel of the foundation slab will depend upon local conditions or special requirements. The heel should be long enough so that the weight of the wall and the prism of the filling above the heel, when multiplied by the coefficient of friction is greater than the horizontal thrust on the wall. This will be satisfied if the heel is from one third to four tenths of the length of the base. Where conditions permit make

78

the heel approximately four tenths the length of the base. Where retaining walls are built along a right of way it is often necessary to keep the entire wall on the property and the wall is all heel, as in Fig. 33*a* to Fig. 33*d*.

The economical spacing of counterforts will depend upon the height of the wall, and will vary from 8 feet for low walls to 12 feet for high walls, with 10 feet as a common spacing.

Materials.—The materials and workmanship should comply with the requirements in the " Specifications for Plain and Reinforced Concrete " in Appendix I. The concrete recommended for general use in reinforced concrete walls is a mixture of one (1) part Portland cement, two (2) parts fine aggregate, and four (4) parts coarse aggregate (1 : 2 : 4 concrete). A mixture of one part Portland cement, three (3) parts fine aggregate, and six (6) parts coarse aggregate (1 : 3 : 6 concrete) may be used in monolithic walls and foundations. In all cases sufficient cement is to be used with the fine aggregate to make a dense mortar, and sufficient mortar is to be used to more than fill the voids in the coarse aggregate and make a dense concrete.

Working Stresses.—For a good 1 : 2 : 4 Portland cement concrete and structural steel reinforcement, the following working stresses may be used:

Tensile stress in steel reinforcement, $f_s = 16,000$ lbs. per sq. in.
Bending compressive stress in concrete, $f_c = 650$ lbs. per sq. in.
Ratio of moduli of elasticity of steel and concrete, $n = 15$.
Shear in concrete not combined with tension or compression,
  120 lbs. per sq. in.
Shear as a measure of diagonal tension in a beam not reinforced to carry diagonal tension (where $v = V/b.j.d$), $v = 40$ lbs. per sq. in.
Shear as a measure of diagonal tension in a beam where part of the bars are bent-up, $v = 60$ lbs. per sq. in.
Shear as a measure of diagonal tension in a beam fully reinforced for diagonal tension, $v = 120$ lbs. per sq. in.
Bond stress on plain round and square bars, 80 lbs. per sq. in.

Bond stress on drawn wire,   40 lbs. per sq. in.

Bond stress on deformed bars, depending upon the form,

80 to 150 lbs. per sq. in.

Bond stress on plain round or square bars with hooked ends, bent 180° around a radius of 3 diameters,   100 lbs. per sq. in.

Spacing of Bars.—The lateral spacing of parallel bars should not be less than $2\frac{1}{2}$ diameters center to center, nor should the distance from the side of the beam to the center of the closest bar be less than two diameters. The clear spacing between two layers of bars should not be less than $\frac{1}{2}$ inch, nor $2\frac{1}{2}$ diameters center to center of bars.

Length of Bar to Imbed in Concrete.—The ultimate bond strength of concrete on plain steel may be taken at from 200 to 300 pounds per square inch. With a working stress of 80 pounds per square inch and a tensile unit stress of 16,000 pounds per square inch, a plain round or square bar should be imbedded a length of $16,000/(4 \times 80)$ or 50 diameters. A deformed bar with an allowable bond stress of 100 pounds per square inch should be imbedded 40 diameters. Where bars can not be imbedded for the required length they should be bent or anchored. Where the ends are hooked, the bends should be 180° with a short length of straight rod beyond the bend. Experiments by Bach with rods $\frac{3}{4}$ and 1 inch in diameter and a length of bend of about 3 diameters, and imbedded a length of 20 inches show that the initial slip was only slightly retarded, but that the ultimate bond strength was increased 50 per cent.

Expansion and Contraction.—The coefficient of expansion of concrete is practically the same as for steel, about 0.0000065. Concrete is sensitive to temperature changes and expansion joints should be provided in all retaining walls not reinforced to take temperature stresses, every 30 to 40 feet throughout the length of the structure. To provide against the structure being thrown out of line by unequal settlement each section of the wall should be joined by rods set rigidly in one section and free to move in the adjoining section, or be grooved into the adjoining section. Reinforced concrete retaining walls are commonly built without expansion and contraction joints. No amount of reinforcement can entirely prevent contraction cracks. The reinforcement will, however, distribute the cracks uniformly over the section, the greater the amount of reinforcement the smaller the cracks. The size and distribution of the cracks will also depend upon the bond strength of the rods.

In calculating the steel required to reinforce for expansion and contraction, the temperature stresses in the steel must be considered. If the drop in temperature in the steel be 50°, the temperature stress in the steel $= 50 \times 0.0000065 \times 30,000,000 = 9,750$ pounds per sq. in. If the tensile strength of the concrete be 200 pounds per sq. in. and the elastic limit of the steel be 40,000 pounds per sq. in., the available stress in the steel $= 40,000 - 9,750 = 30,250$ pounds per sq. in., and the required percentage of steel is $p = \dfrac{200}{30,250} = 0.0066$ (0.66 per cent). If the elastic limit be 60,000 pounds per sq. in. the steel ratio will be $p = 0.004$ (0.4 per cent). For temperature reinforcement bars made of high elastic limit steel are desirable, *as shown here;*

While the calculations show that the percentage of longitudinal steel reinforcement for expansion and contraction should be from 0.4 per cent to 0.66 per cent, yet experience shows that walls reinforced with from 0.1 per cent to 0.3 per cent of steel give very satisfactory results, where the foundations are stable. Where there is a tendency for the wall to be thrown out of line the full amount of reinforcement should be used. The reinforcing steel for temperature stresses should be placed as near the exposed faces as practicable, and the rods should preferably be of small size. *Class why ?*

The American Railway Engineering Association has adopted the following: "Reinforcement for shrinkage or temperature stresses shall be not less than 0.33 per cent, of a form of bar capable of developing a high bond resistance and shall be placed near the exposed surface of the concrete."

DESIGN OF REINFORCED CONCRETE RETAINING WALLS.—The design of reinforced concrete retaining walls will be illustrated by means of two examples.

6

Problem 1. Design of a Reinforced Concrete Cantilever Wall.—

Design a reinforced concrete retaining wall of the cantilever type to carry a sand filling which is 16 feet high, weighs 100 lbs. per cu. ft., has an angle of repose, $\phi = 33°$ 42′, and slopes back from the wall at the angle of repose, $\delta = \phi$. The following additional data are given: Weight of concrete, 150 lbs. per cu. ft.; allowable pressure on foundation, 6,000 lbs. per sq. ft.; $f_s = 16,000$ lbs. per sq. in.; $f_c = 650$ lbs. per

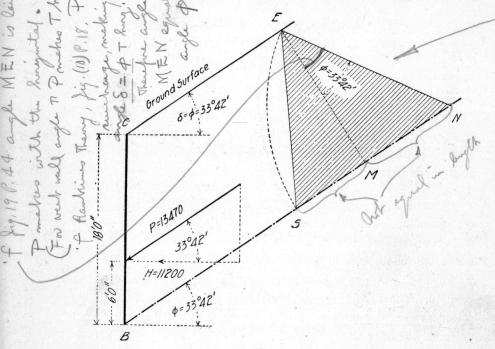

FIG. 31.

sq. in.; $v = 40$ lbs. per sq. in.; $u = 80$ lbs. per sq. in. for plain bars, and 100 lbs. per sq. in. for bars hooked at the ends; $n = 15$; angle of friction of material upon which wall rests is $\phi' = 30°$. Formulas for the design of reinforced concrete are given in Appendix I.

Solution. Vertical Beam.—The bottom of the foundation will need to be about 4 feet deep and we will assume the stem of the wall

Assuming vertical wall. See also note to fig. 28, P. 64.

See fig. 21, P. 47. + for (31) P. 46.

to be 18 feet high. The front of the slab will be vertical while the back will have a slight batter.

Horizontal Pressure on Vertical Beam. (*a*) *Graphic Solution.*—In Fig. 31 the resultant pressure is $P =$ area $\triangle SEN.w = 13,470$ lbs., and is parallel to the top surface. The horizontal component of P is $H = 11,200$ lbs. (*b*) *Algebraic Solution.*—From formula (8*a*), Chapter I,

$$P = \tfrac{1}{2}w.h^2.\cos\phi \qquad\qquad P.22 \qquad (8a)$$

and

$$H = \tfrac{1}{2}w.h^2.\cos^2\phi$$

For

$$h = 18 \text{ ft.,} \quad H = 11,200 \text{ lbs.;}$$
$$h = 12 \text{ ft.,} \quad H = 4,980 \text{ lbs.;}$$
$$h = 6 \text{ ft.,} \quad H = 1,245 \text{ lbs.}$$

Bending Moments in Vertical Beam.—The horizontal pressure acts at $h/3$ above the base and the bending moment about any horizontal section will be $M = H.h/3$.

For

$$h = 18 \text{ ft.,} \quad M = 806,000 \text{ in.-lbs.;} \quad Clear\ Pour$$
$$h = 12 \text{ ft.,} \quad M = 239,000 \text{ in.-lbs.;}$$
$$h = 6 \text{ ft.,} \quad M = 29,900 \text{ in.-lbs.}$$

Depth of Vertical Beam Required to Carry Moment.—From equation (6*b*), Appendix I, the depth from the front face to the center of the reinforcing steel is — *Steel in side next to filling*

$$d = \sqrt{\frac{M}{R.b}} \qquad\qquad (6b) \quad P.50.$$

With $f_s = 16,000$ and $f_c = 650$; from Fig. 2, Appendix I, $R = 107$, and $p = 0.0075$.

For

$$h = 18 \text{ ft.,} \quad d = 25.1 \text{ ins.;}$$
$$h = 12 \text{ ft.,} \quad d = 13.7 \text{ ins.;}$$
$$h = 6 \text{ ft.,} \quad d = 4.8 \text{ ins.}$$

Depth of Vertical Beam Required to Carry Shear.—From formula (68) the maximum shear is

$$v = \frac{V}{b.j.d} \tag{68}$$

From Fig. 2, $j = 0.875$; also $b = 12$ ins., and $V = H$, and allowable shear $= 40$ lbs. per sq. in.

Now solving (68) for d we have

$$d = \frac{V}{j.b.v} = \frac{H}{0.875 \times 12 \times 40}$$

For

$h = 18$ ft., $H = 11{,}200$ lbs., $d = 26.7$ ins.;

$h = 12$ ft., $H = 4{,}980$ lbs., $d = 11.9$ ins.;

$h = 6$ ft., $H = 1{,}245$ lbs., $d = 3.0$ ins.

Depth of Vertical Beam.—The beam will be taken as 30 inches deep at the base and 12 inches deep at the top, giving a value of $d = 30 - 3 = 27$ inches at the bottom, and $12 - 3 = 9$ inches at the top; also for $h = 12$ feet, $d = 21$ inches, and for $h = 6$ feet, $d = 15$ inches; the steel being placed with its center 3 inches from the back of the wall.

Steel Reinforcement.—The required value of R is given by formula (6a) and is

$$R = \frac{M}{b.d^2} = \frac{806{,}000}{12 \times 27^2} = 92.2$$

From Fig. 2, with $R = 92.2$, and $f_s = 16{,}000$, we find $f_c = 590$, $p = 0.0066$, and $j = 0.875$. The steel area per lineal foot at the base will be $A = p.b.d = 0.0066 \times 12 \times 27 = 2.14$ sq. in. The steel reinforcement at the base will be $\frac{7}{8}''\ \square$ bars spaced 4 ins. center to center, giving $A = 2.297$ sq. in. for $b = 12$ ins.

Bond Stress.—The bond stress at the base will be found from formula (67) and is

$$u = \frac{V}{j.d.\Sigma o} = \frac{11{,}200}{0.875 \times 27 \times 3 \times 3.5} = 45.2 \text{ lbs.}$$

per sq. in.   The allowable bond stress is 80 lbs. per sq. in.

For $h = 12$ feet the required value of R is

$$R = \frac{M}{b.d^2} = \frac{239,000}{12 \times 21^2} = 45.2$$

From Fig. 2 with $R = 45.2$, and $f_s = 16,000$, we find $p = 0.0032$. One half of the bars will be cut off at this point leaving $\frac{7}{8}''$ □ bars spaced 8 ins. center to center, which gives $p = 0.0046$. For $p = 0.0046$, and $R = 45.2$ in Fig. 2 we find that $f_s = 11,000$, $f_c = 325$, and $j = 0.90$. Bond stress from (67) is

$$u = \frac{V}{j.d.\Sigma o} = \frac{4,980}{0.90 \times 21 \times 5.25} = 50 \text{ lbs. per sq. in.}$$

Allowable bond stress $= 80$ lbs. per sq. in.

At $h = 6$ feet the $\frac{7}{8}''$ □ bars will be spaced 16 ins. center to center, giving $p = 0.0032$. From Fig. 2 with $p = 0.0032$ and $f_s = 16,000$, we find $R = 46$, and $j = 0.92$. The required value of R is

$$R = \frac{M}{b.d^2} = \frac{29,900}{12 \times 15^2} = 11.1$$

Bond stress from (67) is

$$u = \frac{V}{j.d.\Sigma o} = \frac{1,245}{0.92 \times 15 \times 2.62} = 36 \text{ lbs. per sq. in.}$$

The steel reinforcement in the vertical beam will be $\frac{7}{8}''$ □ bars spaced 4 ins. center to center at the base, 8 ins. center to center at 6 feet above the base and 16 ins. center to center at 12 feet above the base. The vertical bars will be hooked at the bottom as shown in Fig. 31b.

Design of Footing.—The base will be taken 12 feet long with the toe 4 feet from the face of the wall. The steel will be placed 3 inches from the bottom and the slab will be taken 24 inches deep.

Foundation Pressures.—The pressure on the vertical section A''-J is $P' = \frac{1}{2}w.h^2 \cos \phi = 25,300$ lbs., acting at $\frac{1}{3} A''$-J above J. The pressure P' was also calculated by the graphic method shown in Fig. 21, Chapter II. $P' = 25,300$ lbs. is combined with the weight of the filling $= 12,885$ lbs., and with the weight of the wall $= 8,325$ lbs., and gives a resultant pressure on the base $KJ = E = 41,070$ lbs. The vertical component of E is $F = 35,260$ lbs. The resultant E cuts the base, $b = 1.58$ ft. from the center of the wall.

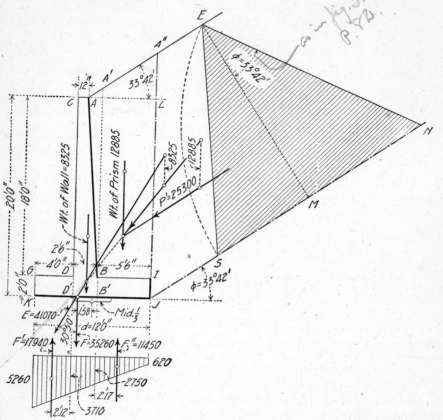

FIG. 31 a.

The pressure on the toe from (49), Chapter III, is

$$p = \frac{F}{d} + \frac{6F.b}{d^2} = \frac{35,260}{12} + \frac{6 \times 35,260 \times 1.58}{144}$$

$$= 2,940 + 2,320 = 5,260 \text{ lbs. per sq. ft.}$$

The pressure on the heel is

$$p = \frac{F}{d} - \frac{6F.b}{d^2} = 2,940 - 2,320 = 620 \text{ lbs. per sq. ft.}$$

The allowable pressure is 6,000 lbs. per sq. ft.

Shear at Section D-D'.—The pressure on the section of the footing K-D' is $F' = 17,940$ lbs., which is the shear on the section D-D'. Assuming $j = 0.875$ the maximum unit shear from (68) is

$$v = \frac{V}{b.j.d} = \frac{17,940}{12 \times 0.875 \times 21} = 81 \text{ lbs. per sq. in.}$$

The allowable maximum shear is 40 lbs. per sq. in., and a fillet will be used to reduce the shear to the required value. *See fig. 316. P.90.*

Solving formula (68) for d, we have

$$d = \frac{V}{b.j.v} = \frac{17,940}{12 \times 0.875 \times 40} = 42.5 \text{ inches.}$$

The fillet must extend above the slab a distance of $42.5 - 21 = 21.5$ inches. The fillet will be made 24 inches high and 24 inches long. The shear at the end of the fillet will be *class check.*

$$v = \frac{V}{b.j.d} = \frac{9,745}{12 \times 0.875 \times 21} = 45 \text{ lbs. per sq. in.,}$$

which is greater than the 40 lbs. per sq. in. allowable, but will be permitted as the average shear is only 35 lbs. per sq. in., and the stresses in the steel are low.

Bending Moment at D-D'.—The bending moment of the pressures about D-D' is

$$M = 17,940 \times 2.12 \times 12 = 456,500 \text{ in-lbs.} \quad P.503$$

With $f_s = 16,000$, $f_c = 650$, from Fig. 2, $p = 0.0078$, and $R = 107$. The required depth for bending moment from (6b) is

$$d = \sqrt{\frac{M}{R.b}} = \sqrt{\frac{456,500}{107 \times 12}} = 18.8 \text{ inches.}$$

Neglecting the fillet the effective depth is 21 inches and from (6a)

$$R = \frac{M}{b.d^2} = \frac{456,500}{12 \times 441} = 86.3$$

P.503 From Fig. 2 with $R = 86.3$, and $f_s = 16,000$, we find $p = 0.0060$, and $j = 0.885$. The steel required will then be $A = 21 \times 12 \times 0.0060 = 1.52$

sq. in.   The reinforcing will be $\frac{7}{8}''$ ☐ bars spaced 6 ins. center to center, giving $A = 1.53$ sq. in.   The bars were spaced 4 ins. centers to conform to the spacing of the vertical bars.

For bond stress it will be necessary to consider the fillet at D-D'. The value of p considering the fillet is $p = 0.0021$, and from Fig. 2, $j = 0.95$.   Then the bond stress from (67) is

$$u = \frac{V}{j.d.\Sigma o} = \frac{17,940}{0.95 \times 45 \times 5.25} = 80 \text{ lbs. per sq. in.,}$$

which is satisfactory.

The bond stress at the end of the fillet from (67) is

$$u = \frac{V}{j.d.\Sigma o} = \frac{9,745}{0.885 \times 21 \times 5.25} = 100 \text{ lbs. per sq. in.}$$

The horizontal rods will be hooked at the ends as shown in Fig. 31b, which will make the bond stress satisfactory.

Shear at Section B-B'.—The maximum shear at B-B' will occur when the wall is just on the point of overturning, and is equal to the weight of the filling above the heel slab, and is

$$V = \frac{22.67 + 19.0}{2} \times 5.5 \times 100 = 11,450 \text{ lbs.}$$

$$v = \frac{V}{b.j.d} = \frac{11,450}{12 \times 0.875 \times 21} = 52 \text{ lbs. per sq. in.,}$$

which is greater than the allowable shear of 40 lbs. per sq. in.   A fillet 2 ft. by 2 ft. reinforced with $\frac{7}{8}''$ ☐ bars spaced 8 ins. center to center, as shown in Fig. 31b, will be used and the shear will be low, but will be investigated presently.

Bending Moment at B-B'.—The maximum bending moment will occur when the wall is just on the point of overturning, and will be

$$M = 11,450 \times 2.8 \times 12 = 385,000 \text{ in.-lbs.}$$

From (6a) the required value of R is

$$R = \frac{M}{b.d^2} = \frac{385,000}{12 \times 441} = 73$$

From Fig. 2 with $f_s = 16,000$, and $R = 73$, we find $p = 0.0052$, and

P.503

$j = 0.89$. The steel required is $A = 12 \times 21 \times 0.0052 = 1.31$ sq. in. To make the spacing uniform $\frac{7}{8}''$ □ bars will be spaced 8 ins. center to center, and $\frac{7}{8}''$ □ inclined bars spaced 8 ins. center to center will be used in the fillet, as shown in Fig. 31*b*. The effective depth of the beam will then be approximately, $d = \frac{1}{2}(21 + 45) = 33$ ins., from which $p = 0.006$, and

$$R = \frac{M}{b.d^2} = \frac{385,000}{12 \times 1089} = 30$$

Then from Fig. 2, $f_s = 12,000$, and $f_c = 500$.

Shear at B-B'.—The maximum shear at B-B' is from (68) then approximately

$$v = \frac{V}{b.j.d} = \frac{11,450}{12 \times 0.88 \times 33} = 34 \text{ lbs. per sq. in.,}$$

which is safe.

Bond Stress at B-B'.—The bond stress is from (67) then approximately

$$u = \frac{V}{j.d.\Sigma o} = \frac{11,450}{0.88 \times 33 \times 10.5} = 38 \text{ lbs. per sq. in.,}$$

which is safe.

Bond Stress at End of Fillet.—The shear at the end of the fillet is

$$V = \frac{22.67 + 20.44}{2} \times 3.67 \times 100 = 7,710 \text{ lbs.}$$

From equation (67)

$$u = \frac{7,710}{j.d.\Sigma o} = \frac{7,710}{0.875 \times 21 \times 10.5} = 30 \text{ lbs. per sq. in.,}$$

which is safe.

Overturning.—The resultant strikes well within the middle third, and the wall is safe.

Sliding.—The angle between E and the vertical is 30° 50′, so that the factor of safety against sliding is greater than one. As an added factor of safety and to give sufficient anchorage for the vertical bars a cut-off wall will be put in as shown in Fig. 31*b*.

Temperature Reinforcement.—The vertical beam will be reinforced above the ground with $24 - \frac{1}{2}''$ □ bars placed as shown in Fig.
31b.   This gives an area of steel $= 6$ sq. in., and a value of $p = 6/3,510$

$$P = \frac{as}{bd}$$

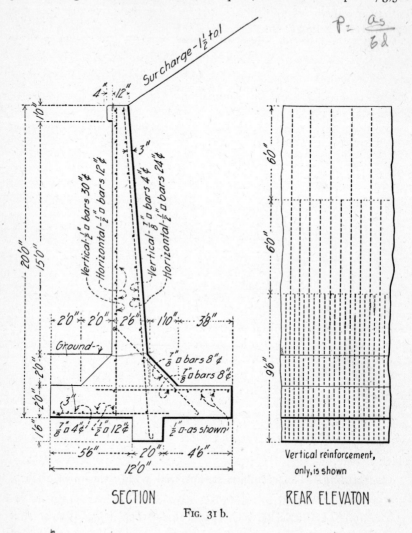

SECTION   REAR ELEVATON

FIG. 31 b.

$= 0.0014$ or 0.14 per cent.   The bars will be spaced 12 ins. center to
center on the front face and will be wired to vertical bars $\frac{1}{2}''$ □ spaced
30 ins. center to center.

The design of the wall is shown in Fig. 31*b*.

Problem 2.   Design of a Reinforced Concrete Counterfort Wall.

—Design a reinforced concrete counterfort retaining wall 20 feet high above the base, to carry a sand filling which weighs 100 lbs. per cu. ft. and has an angle of repose, $\phi = 37°$ 30′. The wall in addition is to carry a surcharge of 600 lbs. per sq. ft. The following additional data are given: Weight of concrete, 150 lbs. per cu. ft.; allowable pressure on foundation, $p = 4,000$ lbs. per sq. ft.;

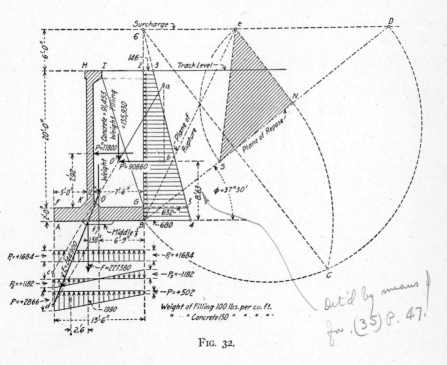

FIG. 32.

$f_s = 16,000$ lbs. per sq. in.; $f_c = 650$ lbs. per sq. in.; $v = 40$ lbs. per sq. in.; $u = 80$ lbs. per sq. in. for plain bars, and 100 lbs. per sq. in. for bars hooked at the ends; $n = 15$; angle of friction of material on which wall rests is $\phi' = 30°$. The vertical slabs between the counterforts are to be designed as simple beams with a clear span equal to the distance between the counterforts, and with a bending moment of $M = \frac{1}{8} p.l^2$.

Solution.—The following dimensions are tentatively assumed and the wall will be investigated. Depth of foundation slab, 2' 0"; width of base 13' 6" (ratio of width of base to height $=0.614$), spacing of counterforts, 10' 0" center to center; thickness of counterforts, 1' 6". A section of the wall 10 feet long will be considered.

Design of Vertical Slab. *Pressures on Vertical Slab.*—The pressures on the vertical slab which carries the filling will be calculated by algebraic and graphic methods.

Algebraic Solution.—The pressure per sq. ft. of the filling on the slab will be given by the formula $p=w.h.k$, where $w=$ weight of filling $=100$ lbs. per cu. ft.; $h=$ depth in feet below the top of the surcharge, and $k=(1-\sin\phi)/(1+\sin\phi)=0.243$.
For

$$h=28 \text{ ft.,} \quad p=680 \text{ lbs. per sq. ft.}$$
$$h=26 \text{ ft.,} \quad p=632 \text{ lbs. per sq. ft.}$$
$$h=21 \text{ ft.,} \quad p=510 \text{ lbs. per sq. ft.}$$
$$h=16 \text{ ft.,} \quad p=389 \text{ lbs. per sq. ft.}$$
$$h=11 \text{ ft.,} \quad p=268 \text{ lbs. per sq. ft.}$$

Graphic Solution.—The graphic solution was made for a section 10 ft. long, using the methods explained in Fig. 19 and Fig. 20, Chapter II. The total horizontal pressure of the filling on the plane B-2 is $P'=90,860$ lbs., or 9,086 lbs. per lineal foot of wall, and acts through the center of gravity of the trapezoid B-4-3-2, and is equal to the area of the trapezoid $\times w$. The unit pressures calculated by the graphic method are the same as those obtained by the algebraic method.

Bending Moment in Vertical Slab.—The slab will be assumed as a simple beam with a span equal to the clear distance between counterforts, and the bending moment will then be $M=\frac{1}{8}p.l^2$, where $p=$ pressure of the filling, and $l=8' 6"=102"$. A slab 12 inches wide (high) will be considered.
For

$$h=26 \text{ ft.,} \quad M=68,500 \text{ in.-lbs.}$$
$$h=21 \text{ ft.,} \quad M=55,200 \text{ in.-lbs.}$$

$$h = 16 \text{ ft.,} \quad M = 42{,}200 \text{ in.-lbs.}$$
$$h = 11 \text{ ft.,} \quad M = 29{,}000 \text{ in.-lbs.}$$

Thickness of Slab Required.—The slab will be made of a uniform thickness, so that the thickness required at the bottom will control. The depth, *d*, required by the bending moment is given by the formula

$$d = \sqrt{\frac{M}{R.b}} \qquad (6b)$$

With $f_s = 16{,}000$, and $f_c = 650$, from Fig. 2, $R = 107$, and $p = 0.0078$. Substituting in (6b) we have

$$d = \sqrt{\frac{68{,}500}{107 \times 12}} = 7.5 \text{ ins.}$$

The depth, *d*, required to carry the shear is given by the formula

$$v = \frac{V}{b.j.d} \qquad (68)$$

and

$$d = \frac{V}{v.b.j}$$

$V = \frac{1}{2}(632 \times 8.5) = \overset{2686}{2{,}936} \text{ lbs.}$; $v = 40$ lbs. per sq. in., and *j* is approximately 0.875. The depth required to carry shear is then, $d = 6.4$ ins.

It is difficult to place concrete in a form where the wall is thin, and a depth of 12 ins. will be arbitrarily adopted. The steel reinforcement will be placed with its centers 3″ from the front face, giving a depth, $d = 9$ ins.

Area of Steel Required.—Since the slab is thicker than required to carry the bending moment the compression in the concrete will be less than $f_c = 650$ lbs. per sq. in. if the stress in the steel is $f_s = 16{,}000$ lbs. per sq. in. The required value of *R* is given by the formula (6a), $R = M/b.d^2$, which for $b = 12$ ins., and $d = 9$ ins., gives $R = 70.5$, and from Fig. 2 for $R = 70.5$, and $f_s = 16{,}000$, gives $p = 0.005$, $f_c = 500$, and $j = 0.89$. The values of *R*, f_c and *p* for the different heights are For

$$h = 26 \text{ ft.,} \quad R = 70.5, \quad f_c = 500, \quad p = 0.005;$$
$$h = 21 \text{ ft.,} \quad R = 56.8, \quad f_c = 440, \quad p = 0.004;$$

$$h = 16 \text{ ft.,} \quad R = 43.3, \quad f_c = 370, \quad p = 0.003;$$
$$h = 11 \text{ ft.,} \quad R = 29.8, \quad f_c = 300, \quad p = 0.002.$$

The area of steel required per vertical linear inch is $A = d.p = 9.p$. If $\frac{1}{2}''$ ☐ bars with an area of 0.25 sq. in. are used, the spacing of the bars will be, $s = 0.25 \div 9.p$.

For

$$h = 26 \text{ ft.,} \quad p = 0.005, \quad s = 5.6 \text{ ins.;}$$
$$h = 21 \text{ ft.,} \quad p = 0.004, \quad s = 7.0 \text{ ins.;}$$
$$h = 16 \text{ ft.,} \quad p = 0.003, \quad s = 9.3 \text{ ins.;}$$
$$h = 11 \text{ ft.,} \quad p = 0.002, \quad s = 13.9 \text{ ins.}$$

The spacing required for a safe bond stress of $u = 80$ lbs. per sq. in. may be obtained from the equation

$$u = \frac{V}{j.d.\Sigma o} \tag{67}$$

If s is the spacing of the bars, then $\Sigma o = 12 \times o/s$, where o is the circumference of one bar. The spacing for bond is then $s = \dfrac{12.u.j.d.o}{V}$, where $u = 80$ lbs. per sq. in., $j = 0.875$ (approx.), $d = 9$ ins. and $o = 2.0$ sq. in.

For

$$h = 26 \text{ ft.,} \quad V = 2,685, \checkmark \quad s = 5.6 \text{ ins.;}$$
$$h = 21 \text{ ft.,} \quad V = 2,170, \checkmark \quad s = 7.0 \text{ ins.;}$$
$$h = 16 \text{ ft.,} \quad V = 1,650, \checkmark \quad s = 9.2 \text{ ins.;}$$
$$h = 11 \text{ ft.,} \quad V = 1,140, \quad s = 13.3 \text{ ins.}$$

The following spacing will be adopted for the $\frac{1}{2}''$ ☐ reinforcing bars in the vertical slab.

From

$$h = 26 \text{ to } 21 \text{ ft.,} \quad \tfrac{1}{2}'' \,\square, \quad 5 \text{ ins. center to center;}$$
$$h = 21 \text{ to } 16 \text{ ft.,} \quad \tfrac{1}{2}'' \,\square, \quad 7 \text{ ins. center to center;}$$
$$h = 16 \text{ to } 11 \text{ ft.,} \quad \tfrac{1}{2}'' \,\square, \quad 9 \text{ ins. center to center;}$$
$$h = 11 \text{ to } 6 \text{ ft.,} \quad \tfrac{1}{2}'' \,\square, \quad 12 \text{ ins. center to center.}$$

Design of Foundation Slab.—The foundation slab has been taken as 13 ft. 6 in. wide and 2 ft. thick. The foundation pressures were calculated by algebraic and graphic methods.

Foundation Pressures. Algebraic Method.—The pressure at 2 in the plane B-2 is $p_1 = w.h_1.k = 100 \times 6 \times 0.243 = 146$ lbs. per sq. ft., while the pressure at B is $p_2 = w.h.k = 100 \times 26 \times 0.243 = 680$ lbs. per sq. ft. The pressure on the plane B-2 will then be $P' = \frac{1}{2}(146 + 680)$ 26 = 90,860 lbs. From equation (35), Chapter II, the line of action of P' above the base is $y = 8.63$ ft. The moments of the forces are given in Table VIA.

TABLE VIA.

CALCULATION OF MOMENTS ABOUT THE HEEL, B, OF THE FOUNDATION FOR A 10-FT. SECTION OF WALL.

Section.	Dimensions, ft.	Weight, lbs.	Moment arm, ft.	Moment, ft.-lbs.
Filling	6.25 × 1.0 × 10.0	6,250	3.125	19,520
	19.0 × 7.5 × 8.5	121,100	3.75	454,000
	6.25 × 9.5 × 1.5	8,580	2.083	17,870
Retaining wall				
Coping	2.5 × 1.0 × 10	3,750	7.50	24,380
Vertical slab	19.0 × 1.0 × 10	28,500	8.00	228,000
Counterfort	6.25 × 9.5 × 1.5	13,360	4.17	55,650
	1.25 × 19.0 × 1.5	5,340	6.89	36,800
Foundation slab	13.5 × 2.0 × 10	40,500	6.75	273,500
	Total	227,380		1,109,720

Total weight of filling, 135,930 lbs.
Total weight of wall,   91,453 lbs.
Distance from heel to centroid of vertical loads is

$$x = \frac{1,109,720}{227,380} = 4.88 \text{ ft.}$$

The resultant of the horizontal pressures and the vertical loads is
$$E = \sqrt{90,860^2 + 227,380^2} = 244,900 \text{ lbs.}$$
and
$$F = 227,380 \text{ lbs.}$$

The resultant E will cut the base at a distance from the heel

$$x = \frac{90,860 \times 8.63 + 227,380 \times 4.88}{227,380} = \frac{1,893,841}{227,380} = 8.33 \text{ ft.}$$

The distance that the resultant E strikes from the center is, $b = 8.33 - \frac{1}{2}(13.5) = 1.58$ ft.

Graphic Solution.—The resultant pressure on the plane B-6 is $P = $ area $\triangle SeN \times 100 = 95{,}200$ lbs., which gives a unit pressure of 680 lbs. at B, and 146 lbs. at 2. The pressure on the plane B-2 is $P' = \frac{1}{2}(680 + 146)22 = 90{,}860$ lbs. Combining P' with the weight of the filling $= 135{,}930$ lbs., and with the weight of the wall $= 91{,}450$ lbs., gives a resultant pressure on the base A-$B = E = 244{,}900$ lbs. The vertical component of E is $F = 227{,}380$ lbs., and $b = 1.58$ ft.

Overturning.—The wall is safe as is shown by the direction of E.

Sliding.—The factor of safety against sliding is

$$f_s = \frac{227{,}380 \times \tan 30°}{90{,}860} = 1.44$$

Resultant Pressures.—The unit pressure on the toe from (49), Chapter III, is

$$p = \tfrac{1}{10}\left(\frac{F}{d} + \frac{6F.b}{d^2}\right) = 1{,}684 + 1{,}182 = 2{,}866 \text{ lbs. per sq. ft.}$$

The unit pressure on the heel is

$$p = \tfrac{1}{10}\left(\frac{F}{d} - \frac{6F.b}{d^2}\right) = 1{,}684 - 1{,}182 = 502 \text{ lbs. per sq. ft.}$$

Design of Foundation Slab.—The foundation slab will carry the filling on the heel and will transfer the vertical pressures to the soil on the toe.

Design of Heel Slab.—The load on the heel slab is due to 26 ft. of filling $= 26 \times 100 = 2{,}600$ lbs. per sq. ft. The maximum bending moment will occur in the slab if the wall is just on the point of overturning, so that the upward foundation pressures may be neglected. The bending moment at the middle of the slab will be $M = \frac{1}{8} \times 2{,}600 \times 8.5^2 \times 12 = 282{,}000$ in.-lbs. The thickness of the slab to carry the moment will be found from Fig. 2 and (6b), where $f_s = 16{,}000$, $f_c = 650$, and $p = 0.0078$, and $R = 107$.

$$d = \sqrt{\frac{M}{R.b}} = \sqrt{\frac{282{,}000}{107 \times 12}} = 14.8 \text{ in.} \qquad (6b)$$

The required thickness of the slab to carry shear is

$$d = \frac{V}{b.j.v} = \frac{2{,}600 \times 4.25}{12 \times 0.875 \times 40} = 26.3 \text{ in.} \tag{68}$$

A 24-in. slab with the reinforcing steel placed 3 in. from the bottom giving $d = 24 - 3 = 21$ ins., will be used. The maximum shear will from (68) then be

$$v = \frac{V}{b.j.d} = 50 \text{ lbs. per sq. in.,}$$

which is greater than allowed.

To carry the shear at the ends of the slab inclined bars $\frac{3}{4}''$ □ will be spaced 12 ins. center to center, as shown in Fig. 32a. The transverse reinforcement will be $\frac{3}{4}''$ □ bars spaced 18 ins. center to center, as shown in the design of the toe slab.

Steel in Heel Slab.—The required value of R from (6b) is $R = M/b.d^2 = 282{,}000/12 \times 441 = 53.3$. From Fig. 2 with $f_s = 16{,}000$, and $R = 53.3$, we find $p = 0.0037$, and $f_c = 425$.

The area of steel is $A = p.b.d = 0.0037 \times 12 \times 21 = 0.93$ sq. in. per foot of slab. The spacing for $\frac{3}{4}''$ □ bars with area, $a = 0.5625$ sq. in. will be $s = \dfrac{12a}{A} = \dfrac{12 \times 0.5625}{0.93} = 7.26$ ins. The spacing of $\frac{3}{4}''$ □ bars required by bond stress using $u = 100$ lbs. per sq. in., for the reason that most of the bars will be continuous, is

$$s = \frac{12u.j.d.o}{V} = \frac{12 \times 100 \times 0.875 \times 21 \times 3}{2{,}600 \times 4.25} = 6.0 \text{ ins.}$$

The reinforcing steel will be $\frac{3}{4}''$ □ bars spaced 6 ins. center to center.

Design of Toe Slab.—The shear on section K-K' is

$$F' = \tfrac{1}{2}(1{,}990 + 2{,}866) \times 5 = 12{,}140 \text{ lbs.}$$

The maximum shear from (68) is

$$v = \frac{F'}{b.j.d} = \frac{12{,}140}{12 \times 0.875 \times 21} = 55 \text{ lbs. per sq. in.}$$

The allowable maximum shear is $v = 40$ lbs. per sq. in., so that a

7

fillet will be required to carry the shear.   The thickness d at K required
for shear is

$$d = \frac{F'}{b.j.v} = \frac{12,140}{12 \times 0.875 \times 40} = 29 \text{ ins.}$$

A fillet 12 ins. high and 18 ins. long will be used, making the effective depth, $d = 36 - 3 = 33$ ins.   The unit shear at the end of the 18-
in. fillet will be

$$v = \frac{F''}{b.j.d} = \frac{8,904}{12 \times 0.875 \times 24} = 40.4 \text{ lbs. per sq. in.}$$

Steel required to carry moment at K-K'.

The bending moment is

$$M = F' \times 2.6 \times 12 = 12,140 \times 2.6 \times 12 = 379,000 \text{ in.-lbs.}$$

Then the required value of R is

$$R = \frac{M}{b.d^2} = \frac{379,000}{12 \times 33^2} = 29 \qquad (6a)$$

With $R = 29$, and $f_s = 16,000$, from Fig. 2 we have $f_c = 300$, and
$p = 0.002$.   The steel required per lineal foot is $A = p.b.d = .002 \times 12 \times 33 = 0.792$ sq. in.

The reinforcing will be $\frac{3}{4}''$ □ bars spaced 6 ins. center to center,
giving an area of $A = 0.5625 \times 2 = 1.125$ sq. in. per lineal foot, and

$$p = \frac{A}{b.d} = \frac{1.125}{12 \times 33} = 0.00282$$

The bond stress will be from (67)

$$u = \frac{V}{j.d.\Sigma o} = \frac{12,140}{0.875 \times 33 \times 6} = 70 \text{ lbs. per sq. in.}$$

The stress in the steel at the end of the fillet is calculated from (6a)
as follows:

$$R = \frac{M}{b.d^2} = \frac{8,820 \times 1.8 \times 12}{12 \times 21^2} = \frac{190,500}{12 \times 441} = 36$$

From Fig. 2, with $R = 36$, and $f_s = 16,000$, we have $p = 0.0025$, and $f_c = 300$. The actual value of steel ratio is $p = 0.0045$. The bond stress at the end of the fillet from (67) is

$$u = \frac{8,820}{j.d.\Sigma o} = \frac{8,820}{0.875 \times 21 \times 6} = 80 \text{ lbs. per sq. in.}$$

The steel in the toe will be $\frac{3}{4}''$ $\square$ bars spaced 6 ins. center to center, two bars per lineal 18 inches being 7 ft. long and one bar being 13 ft. long and furnishing transverse reinforcement for the heel slab.

Design of Counterfort.—The pressure on the counterfort per lineal foot is $P = \frac{1}{2}(146 + 632)20 = 7,780$ lbs. The point of application of the pressure from (35), Chapter II, is

$$y = \frac{1}{3}\frac{26^2 + 26 \times 6 - 2 \times 6^2}{26 + 6} = 7.92 \text{ ft.}$$

The shear on the base of the counterfort for $h = 26$ ft. is

$$v = \frac{V}{b.j.d} = \frac{7,780 \times 10}{18 \times 0.875 \times 8.5 \times 12} = 49.8 \text{ lbs. per sq. in.}$$

The rods are bent up and stirrups are used, so the shear is safe.

Steel in Counterfort for $h = 26$ ft.

Bending moment at base is

$$M = 7,780 \times 7.92 \times 10 \times 12 = 7,394,000 \text{ in.-lbs.}$$

Effective depth of counterfort is $d = 8.5 \times \cos\alpha$, where α is the angle between the back of the counterfort and a vertical $= 18° \, 13'$. Then $d = 7.83$ ft. $= 94$ in. The value of R required to take moment from $(6a)$ is

$$R = \frac{M}{b.d^2} = \frac{7,394,000}{18 \times 94^2} = 47$$

From Fig. 2 with $f_s = 16,000$, and $R = 47$, $p = 0.0032$, and $A = p.b.d = 5.42$ sq. in. Use 6 bars $1''$ $\square$. $\Sigma o = 24''$

Bond stress from (67) is

$$u = \frac{V}{j.d.\Sigma o} = \frac{77,800}{0.875 \times 94 \times 24} = 39.4 \text{ lbs. per sq. in.}$$

Design of counterfort at $h = 21$ ft.

$$P = 49,200 \text{ lbs.} \quad y = 6.12 \text{ ft.}$$

Shear on counterfort at h = 21.

Effective depth is $d = 79.2$ ins.

Then the maximum shear from (68) is

$$v = \frac{P}{j.b.d} = \frac{49,200}{0.875 \times 18 \times 79.2} = 40 \text{ lbs. per sq. in.}$$

Steel in counterfort for h = 21 ft.

Effective depth is $d = 79.2 \times \cos \alpha = 75.2$ ins.

$$M = 49,200 \times 6.12 \times 12 = 3,610,000 \text{ in.-lbs.,}$$

and from (6a)

$$R = \frac{M}{b.d^2} = \frac{3,610,000}{18 \times 75.2^2} = 35.4$$

From Fig. 2, with $f_s = 16,000$, and $R = 35.4$, we have $p = 0.0024$. Then $A = 0.0024 \times 18 \times 75.2 = 3.25$ sq. in. Use 4 bars $1''$ □, and turn 2 bars in and hook around the horizontal reinforcement in the vertical slab.

Bond stress from (67) is

$$u = \frac{V}{j.d.\Sigma o} = \frac{49,200}{0.875 \times 75.2 \times 16} = 46.7 \text{ lbs. per sq. in.}$$

Design of counterfort at h = 16 ft.

$P = 29,400$ lbs., $y = 4.67$ ft., d for shear $= 59.3$ in., d for moment $= 56.4$ ins.

Shear from (68) is

$$v = \frac{29,400}{j.b.d} = 32 \text{ lbs. per sq. in.}$$

Moment is

$$M = 29,400 \times 4.67 \times 12 = 1,650,000 \text{ in.-lbs.}$$

$$R = \frac{M}{b.d^2} = \frac{1,650,000}{18 \times 56.4^2} = 28.8 \tag{6a}$$

From Fig. 2, $p = 0.002$. $A = p.b.d = 0.002 \times 18 \times 56.4 = 2.03$ sq. in. Use 2 bars $1''$ □ from $h = 16$ ft. to top, and turn 2 bars in and hook around horizontal reinforcing steel in vertical slab.

Bond stress from (67) is

$$u = \frac{V}{j.d.\Sigma o} = \frac{29,400}{0.875 \times 56.4 \times 8} = 74 \text{ lbs. per sq. in.}$$

The bars in the counterfort will be bent over and hooked around the horizontal reinforcement. The counterfort bars will be run down into the cut-off trench at the heel, and hooked to develop the tensile stress.

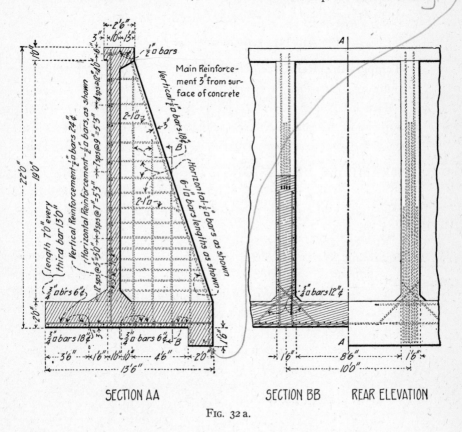

SECTION AA   SECTION BB   REAR ELEVATION

FIG. 32 a.

With a bond stress of $u = 100$ lbs. per sq. in., the length necessary to develop a stress of $f_s = 16,000$ lbs. per sq. in. is $l = \dfrac{16,000}{100 \times 4} = 40$ ins. The hooks are placed 2 ins. from the bottom, giving a length of 40 ins., which is safe. The vertical and horizontal reinforcement in the counterfort will be $\frac{1}{2}''$ □ bars spaced as shown in Fig. 32a. The vertical and horizontal bars are hooked on the ends as shown.

Pull of Vertical Slab on Counterfort.—The pull of the vertical slab per vertical foot of height at $h = 26$ ft. below the top of the wall, is $P = 8.5 \times 632 = 5,361$ lbs. With $f_s = 16,000$ lbs. per sq. in. the steel required per vertical foot will be $a = \dfrac{5,361}{16,000} = 0.335$ sq. in. The $\frac{1}{2}''$ □ bars spaced 10 ins. center to center and hooked around the horizontal bars in the slab Fig. 32a are ample.

Temperature Reinforcement.—The wall is fully reinforced for temperature by the steel carrying stress. In the vertical slab $\frac{1}{2}''$ □ bars spaced 24 ins. center to center will be used as spreaders and as temperature reinforcement. A few additional $\frac{1}{2}''$ □ bars will be added as shown.

EXAMPLES OF DESIGNS.—The following designs are given to illustrate the different solutions that may be made with reinforced concrete, and to bring out the merits and defects of different types of walls.

Retaining Walls for Track Elevation.—In track elevation it is usually desirable to place the face of the retaining wall on the right of way lines, and it often happens that it is not possible to extend the toe of the foundation beyond the face of the wall. It then becomes necessary to extend the heel back into the filling, and introduces new and interesting problems. In solving this problem at Elgin, Illinois, Mr. J. H. Prior, Asst. Engr., C. M. & St. P. R. R., developed the five designs in Fig. 33a to Fig. 33e. The allowable bearing on the foundation was 4,000 lbs. per sq. ft., and it was not possible to drive piles. The plain gravity, the cantilever and the counterfort reinforced walls are shown in the cuts and need no explanation. The cellular wall in Fig. 33d was formed of two longitudinal walls Q and R, connected by transverse walls S, 12' 0'' center to center, and all resting on a foundation slab. The cells thus formed were to be filled with earth.

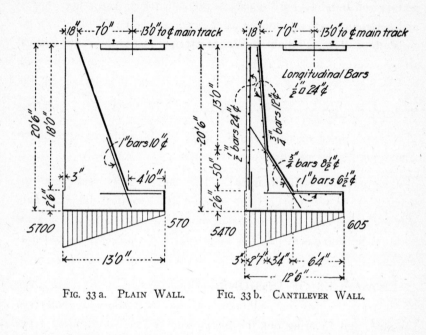

FIG. 33 a. PLAIN WALL. FIG. 33 b. CANTILEVER WALL.

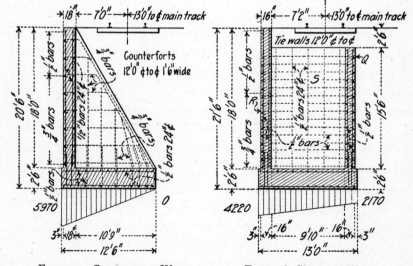

FIG. 33 c. COUNTERFORT WALL. FIG. 33 d. CELLULAR WALL.

The hollow retaining wall in Fig. 33*e* consists of a footing slab *Y*, which supports a longitudinal wall *T* and cross walls *U*, spaced 12′ 0″ center to center. The top slab *V* is carried on beam *X* and walls *T* and *U*.

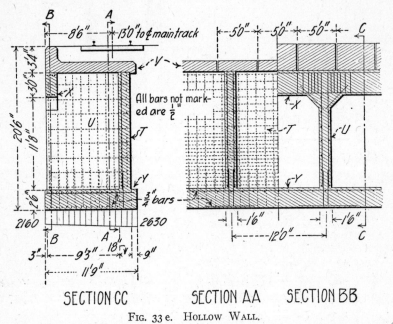

SECTION CC   SECTION AA   SECTION BB

FIG. 33 e.   HOLLOW WALL.

The pressures on the foundations are shown in the cuts for the five walls, the hollow wall having the smallest maximum stresses. The relative costs of the five walls, not including excavation, are given in Table VI_B.

The hollow retaining wall cost the most but was the type adopted and was built. The ratio of the horizontal and vertical forces acting on the wall is 0.41, which is very small, and shows that the wall might be unstable on a slippery material.

Reclamation Service Walls.—Standard plans prepared by the U. S. Reclamation Service for reinforced concrete walls are shown in Fig. 33*f*, Fig. 33*g*, and Fig. 33*h*. The following data were used in preparing the designs: Allowable stress in steel, $f_s = $ 15,000 lbs. per sq.

TABLE VIв.

Relative Costs per Lineal Foot of C. M. & St. P. R. R. Walls.

Item.	Price per Unit.	Plain Wall.		Reinforced. Cantilever.		Counterfort.		Cellular.		Hollow.	
		Units.	Cost.	Units.	Cost.	Units.	Cost.	Units.	Cost.	Units.	Cost.
Concrete footing	$6.00 cu. yd.	4.33	$25.98	1.15	$6.90	1.15	$6.90	1.20	$7.20	1.09	$6.54
" neatwork	7.50 " "	.....	......	1.80	13.50	1.44	10.80	2.12	15.90	1.67	12.50
" slabs	9.00 " "	.....	......	......	......	......	......	......	......	.62	5.58
Steel	2½ c. lb.	40. 8	1.02	148	3.70	151	3.78	270	6.75	250	6.25
Forms	$1.20 sq. yd.	4.12	4.95	4.12	4.95	6.4	7.78	10.25	12.30	9.9	11.88
Cost per lineal foot			$31.95		$29.05		$29.26		$42.15		$42.75
Cost of steel per cu. yd.			0.24		1.26		1.46		2.03		1.85
Cost of labor and materials per cu. yd.			7.14		8.59		9.85		10.65		10.80

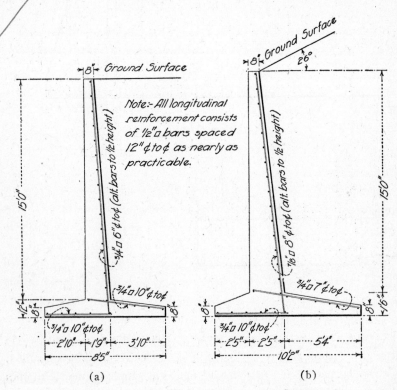

Note:- All longitudinal reinforcement consists of ½"□ bars spaced 12" ¢ to ¢ as nearly as practicable.

(a)   (b)

Fig. 33 f. Slab Walls, Reclamation Service.

in.; allowable stress in concrete, $f_c = 515$ lbs. per sq. in.; $n = 12$; shear on concrete, 60 lbs. per sq. in.; bond stress on bars, 60 lbs. per sq. in.; maximum pressure on foundations, 4,000 lbs. per sq. ft.; coefficient of

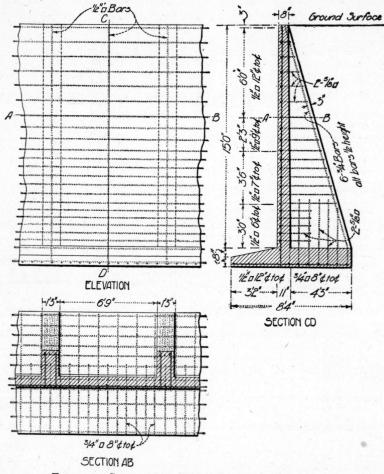

FIG. 33 g. COUNTERFORT WALL, RECLAMATION SERVICE.

friction between earth and concrete, 0.5; factor of safety against over-turning, 2; angle of repose of filling, $\phi = 26°$; weight of filling, $w = 100$ lbs. per cu. ft.; face slabs designed as simple beams; Rankine's solution used in calculating pressure of filling.

The designs are very simple and can be built at a relatively small cost, due to the small amount of bending of steel required. The fol-

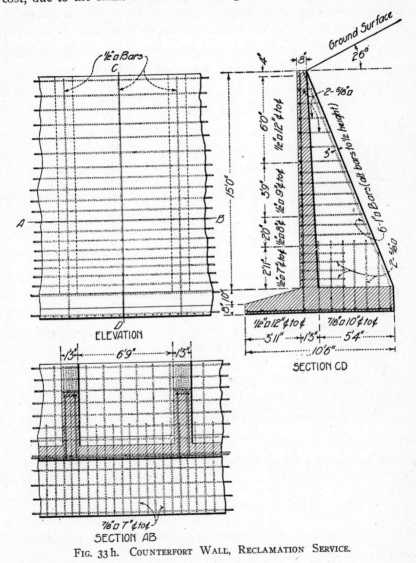

FIG. 33 h. COUNTERFORT WALL, RECLAMATION SERVICE.

lowing defects are apparent. (1) The vertical reinforcing bars in the slab walls will not develop sufficient bond stress at the bottom—the

vertical bars should be bent around the longitudinal bars. (2) The
horizontal temperature bars in the vertical slabs are all near the back
of the wall—temperature reinforcement should be near the exposed
face. (3) The counterfort wall is too low for economy—it is not economical to build a counterfort wall for a height of less than 18 to 20
feet. (4) The reinforcing bars in the counterforts are not well anchored at the bottom.

The quantities per lineal foot of wall for the four walls shown are
given in Table VIc.

TABLE VIc.

QUANTITIES IN RECLAMATION WALLS 15 FEET HIGH, PER LINEAL FOOT OF WALL.

Wall.	Concrete, cu. yds.	Steel Reinforcement, lbs.
Slab Wall, $\delta = 0$	0.978	92
Slab Wall, $\delta = 26°$	1.286	121
Counterfort Wall, $\delta = 0$	1.037	90
Counterfort Wall, $\delta = 26°$	1.418	144

Pittsburg, Pa., Walls.—The walls shown in Fig. 33i and Fig. 33j,
were designed by the Bureau of Construction of Pittsburg, Pa., and
were described by Mr. Chas. M. Reppert, Proceedings Western Society of Pennsylvania, October, 1910. The following data were used
in the design for the Dilworth Street wall, Fig. 33i: Angle of repose,
$\phi = 33°$ 42′; weight of filling, $w = 110$ lbs. per cu. ft.; plain concrete,
1:3:7; reinforced concrete, $1:2\frac{1}{2}:5$; ratio of moduli, $n = 15$; shear on
concrete, 40 lbs. per sq. in.; anchorage 40 to 50 diameters; stress in
steel, $f_s = 20,000$ lbs. per sq. in. The front wall slabs were designed
for $M = \frac{1}{15} w.l^2$ at the middle, and $M = -\frac{1}{12} w.l^2$ at the supports.
The counterforts were calculated for a spacing of 7.5 ft. and 9 ft., the
latter being found more economical. The counterforts are tied to the
front slabs by means of bars passing through holes punched in steel
angles, as shown in Fig. 33i. The counterfort reinforcing bars are run
into the cut-off wall or are bent around the transverse bars, and are
bent in at their tops.

The Michigan Street wall, Fig. 33j, was designed for twice the pressure developed by a surcharge of $5\frac{1}{2}$ feet and value of $\phi = 37°$ 30′.

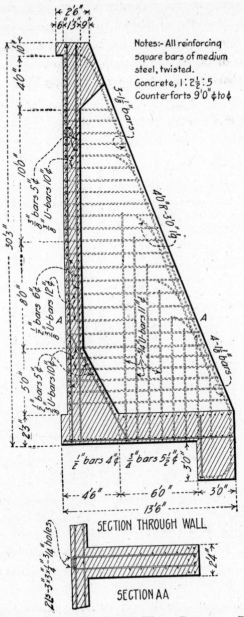

Notes:- All reinforcing
square bars of medium
steel, twisted.
Concrete, 1 : 2½ : 5
Counterforts 9'0" ¢ to ¢

SECTION THROUGH WALL

SECTION AA

FIG. 33 i. DILWORTH STREET WALL, PITTSBURG, PA.

The concrete used in this wall was 1:3:6. This wall is very substantial and is deserving of careful study where a very heavy wall is required. Temperature bars are placed near both surfaces of the vertical slab, a feature deserving of commendation.

The costs of both walls are given in Chapter VII.

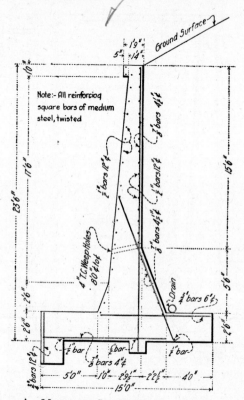

FIG. 33 j. MICHIGAN STREET WALL, PITTSBURG, PA.

Illinois Central R. R. Walls.—The retaining walls shown in Fig. 33k and Fig. 33l were designed by the Illinois Central R. R. for track elevation work in Chicago, Ill. Both walls were designed for a surcharge of 1,000 lbs. per sq. ft.; weight of filling, $w = 100$ lbs. per cu. ft.; weight of concrete, 150 lbs. per cu. ft., and the angle of repose, $\phi = 45°$. In Fig. 33l the author has calculated the pressures on the foundation for $\phi = 45°$ and for $\phi = 33°$ 42′; the resultant pressures striking near the center for $\phi = 45°$, and just inside the middle third for $\phi = 33°$ 42′. The designs are very carefully worked out and have many excellent features.

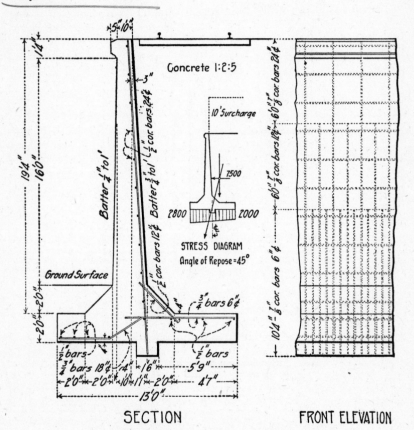

Concrete 1:2:5

10′ Surcharge

7500

2800   2000

STRESS DIAGRAM
Angle of Repose = 45°

Ground Surface

$\frac{3}{4}$ bars 6″ ⊄

$\frac{1}{2}$ bars
$\frac{3}{4}$ bars 18 ⊄

SECTION   FRONT ELEVATION

FIG. 33 k. SLAB WALL, ILLINOIS CENTRAL R. R.

In the design for the slab wall in Fig. 33k the vertical bars are extended into the cut-off wall, thus giving bond strength, and the cut-off wall at the same time giving additional resistance to sliding. The fillets at the base of the slab reinforced as shown, give additional strength at what is commonly the weakest place in a slab wall. The design could have been improved by placing horizontal temperature bars near the front face of the wall.

The design of the counterfort wall in Fig. 33*l* has been worked out

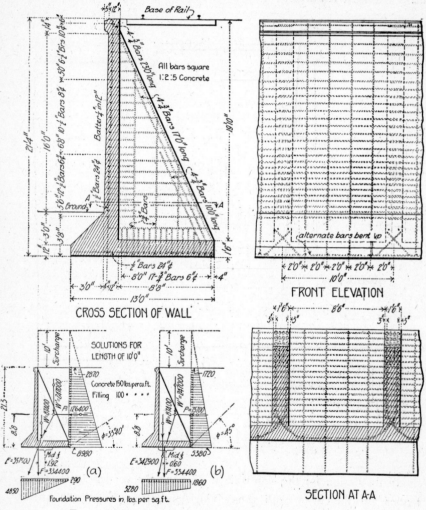

CROSS SECTION OF WALL

FRONT ELEVATION

SECTION AT A-A

Fig. 33 l. Counterfort Wall, Illinois Central R. R.

in great detail. The bars for the front slabs are carried back into the counterforts, the bottom bars are bent up into the counterforts, and the back counterfort bars are hooked around the horizontal bars in the foundation slab. The design could have been improved by increasing

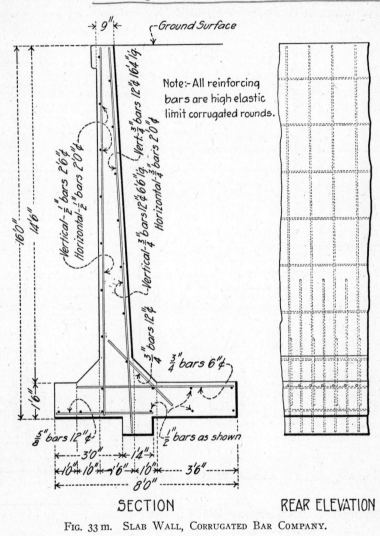

Note:- All reinforcing bars are high elastic limit corrugated rounds.

SECTION   REAR ELEVATION

FIG. 33 m. SLAB WALL, CORRUGATED BAR COMPANY.

the lengths of the inclined bars and bending them over to a rigid connection with the front slab. A cut-off wall at the heel to give additional bond for the counterfort bars would have been an improvement.

Bids were received on the two designs here shown and upon standard plain concrete walls similar to the section shown in Fig. 38; the
bids on the plain walls being smaller the reinforced concrete walls
were not built.

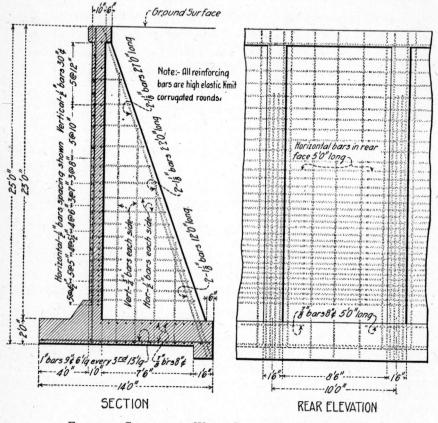

FIG. 33 n.   COUNTERFORT WALL, CORRUGATED BAR COMPANY.

Corrugated Bar Company Walls.—The retaining walls shown in
Fig. 33m and Fig. 33n were designed by the Corrugated Bar Company.
The following data were used in the design: Weight of filling, $w = 100$
lbs. per cu. ft.; angle of repose of filling, $\phi = 30°$; $n = 15$; stress in
steel, $f_s = 17,000$ lbs. per sq. in.; stress in concrete, $f_c = 700$ lbs. per

sq. in.; steel reinforcement, high steel corrugated bars with elastic limit 50,000 lbs. per sq. in.   The designs are quite satisfactory.

A cut-off wall placed at the heel of a wall as in Fig. 33n, gives an opportunity to imbed the inclined counterfort bars a sufficient length to develop the strength, while a cut-off wall at the toe increases the bearing capacity by preventing an outward flow of the footing material.   It would appear to be the best practice to use cut-off walls at both the toe and the heel where walls rest on poor soil.   The inclined counterfort bars in Fig. 33n should be hooked at the lower ends.

Specifications.—Specifications for reinforced concrete structures are given in Chapter IV, Appendix I.

P. 520

CHAPTER IVa.

Effect of Cohesion.—Stresses in Bracing of Trenches.—Stresses in Tunnels.

Effect of Cohesion.—In the preceding discussion it has been assumed that the filling is a granular mass without cohesion. This assumption is correct for dry sand, and is the assumption that should be made in the design of all retaining walls that are subject to vibration and surcharged loads, or are considered as permanent construction. In the design of temporary retaining walls and in the design of the bracing for deep trenches and for tunnels the effect of cohesion should be considered. In another place* the author has proposed a solution for calculating the stresses on the bracing in deep trenches. A method similar to Janssen's solution for the pressures in deep bins will be used in the calculation of the stresses on bracing in deep trenches, for loads on sewer pipe, and for temporary retaining walls. *P.307 — 310*

In clay, clayey sand and similar materials, the particles are held in equilibrium partly by friction and partly by cohesion. When the cohesion is sufficient to hold the mass in position the theoretical formulas for a granular mass do not apply, and when the granular mass is not of indefinite extent, as in a grain bin, the general formulas must be modified.

By experiment it has been found that the force of cohesion between two surfaces is: (1) directly proportional to the area of contact; (2) depends upon the nature of the surface, and (3) is independent of the normal pressure. If C is the resisting force of cohesion between two faces, A is the area of contact, and c is a quantity called the coefficient of cohesion, then

$$C = c.A \qquad (a)$$

And if $ABCD$, Fig. 34a, is the cross-section of a long trench, and BD

---

* Transactions, Am. Soc. C. E., Vol. LX, p. 67.

is the depth h at which the bank breaks down, it has been proved that

$$c = \frac{h.w\,(1 - \sin \phi)}{4 \cos \phi} \qquad\qquad (b)$$

Where h is the depth at which cohesion is destroyed by the weight of the earth, w is weight of a cubic foot of earth, and ϕ is the angle of internal friction of the earth.

If $w = 100$ lbs. per cu. ft., and $\phi = 30°$, then $c = 14.4\ h$.

The surface slope of the material will increase as h decreases, and will become nearly vertical at the surface of the earth, as is shown in Fig. 34a.

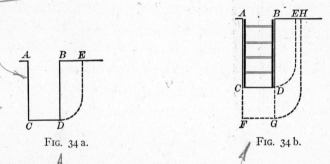

FIG. 34 a. FIG. 34 b.

Stresses in Bracing of Trenches.—If a trench be excavated in a material in which there is cohesion, the sides will stand vertically until the soil loses its cohesive power, or, if the trench be excavated rapidly a depth BD, Fig. 34a, will be reached where the weight of the earth will overcome both the cohesion and the friction, and the trench will cave in. When the slip occurs the cohesion is destroyed in the mass BDE, and, if the coefficient of cohesion is known, the equation of the curve DE can be calculated.

Now if sheeting be placed in the trench and properly braced, the mass BDE will be held in place, and there will be no active pressure on the sheeting until the depth, BG, Fig. 34b, is reached, where the weight of the mass BGH is sufficient to overcome the cohesion, friction, and initial stresses in the bracing, and the soil will break on the line GH.

It will be found that BH is not much larger than BE, which shows that the mass BED is held up mainly by the friction of the earth on the sheeting *BD,* and on the earth surface *HG.* The maximum pressure on the sheeting in a cohesive soil is thus seen to be due to the granular material between the sheeting and the earth surface *HG.* The problem of the calculation of stresses on bracing in deep trenches is then essentially the same as the calculation of the stresses in a deep bin.

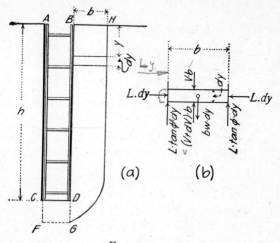

FIG. 34 c.

In Fig. 34*c.*

Let V = vertical unit pressure in lbs. per sq. ft. at depth y;

　L = lateral unit pressure in lbs. per sq. ft. at depth y;

　w = weight of earth in lbs. per cu. ft.;

　ϕ = angle of repose of earth;

　ϕ' = angle of friction of earth on sheeting;

　μ = tan ϕ = coefficient of friction of earth on earth;

　μ' = tan ϕ' = coefficient of friction of earth on the sheeting;

　A = b = area of horizontal section of broken earth one foot long;

　U = perimeter in feet of the section in contact with the sheeting and with the earth surface, taken as 2 lineal feet in the following analysis; *for each lineal foot of trench,*

　b = the distance in feet that the earth breaks back of the sheeting, the trench being assumed to be several times as long as deep.

on line HG

Now the weight of the earth between the section at y and $y + dy$ will be $b.w.dy$. The pressure on top of the section at y will be $V.b$, and the total pressure on the section having a depth $y + dy$ will be $(V + dV)b$; and the total frictional force acting on the sheeting and on the earth bank will be $L.dy(\tan\phi + \tan\phi')$.

These vertical forces are in equilibrium and

$$V.b - (V + dV)b + b.w.dy - L.dy(\tan\phi + \tan\phi') = 0 \qquad (1)$$

and

$$dV = \left[w - \frac{L}{b}(\tan\phi + \tan\phi')\right]dy \qquad (2)$$

Now at any point in a granular mass the lateral pressure is equal to the vertical pressure times k, a constant for the particular material and sheeting. For a granular mass of indefinite extent,

$$L = V\frac{(1 - \sin\phi)}{(1 + \sin\phi)} = k.V$$

(In grain bins it has been shown by tests that k can only be determined by experiment—see Chapter XVII.)

Substituting for L, $\tan\phi$, and $\tan\phi'$ in (2) we have

$$dV = \left[w - \frac{k.V}{b}(\mu + \mu')\right]dy \qquad (3)$$

Now let

$$n = k\frac{(\mu + \mu')}{b} \qquad (4)$$

and

$$\frac{dV}{w - n.V} = dy \qquad (5)$$

Integrating (5) between $y = 0$ and $y = h$, we have

$$\log(w - n.V) = -n.y + \log w,$$

and

$$\frac{w - n.V}{w} = e^{-n.y}$$

where e is the base of the Naperian system of logarithms.

Solving for V, we have

$$V = \frac{w}{n}(1 - e^{-n.y})$$

Substituting the value of n from (4)

$$V = \frac{w.b}{k(\mu + \mu')}(1 - e^{\frac{-k.y(\mu + \mu')}{b}}),\qquad(6)$$

and

$$L = \frac{w.b}{\mu + \mu'}(1 - e^{\frac{-k.y(\mu + \mu')}{b}})\qquad(7)$$

For timber sheeting with earth filling ϕ' may be taken equal to ϕ and

$$V = \frac{w.b}{2k.\mu}(1 - e^{\frac{-2k.\mu.y}{b}})\qquad(8)$$

$$L = \frac{w.b}{2\mu}(1 - e^{\frac{-2k.\mu.y}{b}})\qquad(9)$$

A table of natural logarithms is given in Table XXXIV, Chapter XVI.

The values of V and L for $b = 5$, 10, and 15 ft., $\phi = \phi' = 30°$, and $w = 100$ lbs., have been calculated for depths, h, from 0 to 120 ft., and are given in Fig. 34d.

Pressure on Sewers.—The pressures in Fig. 34d, where b is the width of the trench may be used for calculating the pressures on sewers and on water pipes laid in trenches, where the filling is clay, sand or gravel lightly tamped but not flooded. If the trench is flooded the pressures are closely those given by a fluid with the same specific gravity.

Temporary Retaining Walls.—Temporary retaining walls built to sustain a cohesive filling may be designed using Fig. 34d, or a diagram calculated for the proper value of ϕ. The distance b is determined by experiment or by observation on the bank, or as the excavation is made for the wall. It will be seen that the resultant pressure on a temporary retaining wall built to sustain cohesive material will be much less than that given by Rankine's solution, and also that the point of application of the resultant thrust will be at nearly one-half the height of the wall.

Pressures on Tunnels.—If $b=$ the width, and $h=$ depth of a tunnel driven in a granular material, the pressures on the sides of the tunnel may be calculated in the same manner as the stresses on the bracing of trenches in Fig. 34c, and the vertical pressures given in Fig. 34d will be the pressures on the roof of the tunnel.

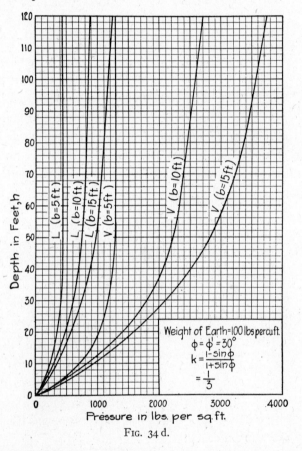

FIG. 34 d.

In Transactions, Am. Soc. C. E., Vol. 72, p. 403 (1911), Professor William Cain has used the method in Fig. 34c, taking into account the cohesion in the earth, and obtained results almost identical with those given in Fig. 34d; cohesion having no appreciable effect except on tunnels of small depth. As in the case of bins it will be seen that the vertical pressures show no appreciable increase after a depth of $2\frac{1}{2}$ to 3 times the width of the tunnel is reached.

In calculating the pressures on the bracing of trenches and deep tunnels the value of k should be determined by experiment. An approximate value may be obtained from the formula

$$k = (1 - \sin \phi)/(1 + \sin \phi) \qquad (10)$$

In a paper by Mr. J. C. Meem, M. Am. Soc. C. E., entitled "Bracing of Trenches and Tunnels, with Practical Formulas for Earth Pressures," Transactions, Am. Soc. C. E., Vol. LX, pp. 1 to 88, together with a discussion by the author and others, many important facts and data are given that are of great value to designing engineers. Mr. Meem proposes an algebraic solution of the problem, which, while interesting, has no theoretical basis. The stresses in the bracing of trenches and tunnels as given by Mr. Meem's formulas are less than those given in Fig. 34d. It should be remembered, however, that any theoretical method for calculating the stresses on the bracing of trenches or the pressure on tunnels can not be more accurate than the data upon which it is based; and since the conditions of the filling are variable the actual stresses and pressures may vary between wide limits.

STRESSES IN BRACING OF TRENCHES.—Retaining Wall Solution. Assuming that the filling is acting as a granular material as in Fig. 34c, the unit pressure at any depth, $h = y$, from the formula (150b), page 318, will be

$$L = \frac{w \cdot b}{\mu + \mu'} \left[1 - \frac{\sqrt{1 + \mu^2}}{\sqrt{\frac{2y}{b}(\mu + \mu') + 1 - \mu \cdot \mu'}} \right] \qquad (7a)$$

If $\mu = \mu'$

$$L = \frac{w \cdot b}{2\mu} \left[1 - \frac{\sqrt{1 + \mu^2}}{\sqrt{\frac{4y}{b}\mu + 1 - \mu^2}} \right] \qquad (9a)$$

Also as before $\qquad L = k \cdot V, \text{ and } V = L/k. \qquad (8a)$

CHAPTER V.

EXPERIMENTS ON RETAINING WALLS.

Experiments.—The preceding investigation has been based on the ideal condition of a granular mass and recourse must be had to experiments to check up the theoretical deductions. Experiments on earth pressures have been made by a large number of engineers, and a brief summary of the results will be given.

Experiments by M. M. L. Leygue.—These experiments which are described in detail in Cain's " Retaining Walls," were first published in " Annales des Ponts et Chaussees " in 1885. The experiments were made with dry sand, using a small model 1.22 to 1.3 feet long and 0.66 to 0.82 feet high, and appear to prove the following:

Cohesion.—That cohesion exists in a mass of sand but is very small and may be neglected.

Surface of Rupture.—All particles lying between the back of the wall and a convex surface (surface of rupture) moved parallel to the surface of rupture. The surface of rupture roughly bisected the angle between the back of the wall and the angle of repose of the sand; thus differing from theory for high surcharge.

Friction on the Wall.—The full friction was exerted on the back of the wall by the sand.

Ratio of Horizontal to Vertical Pressure.—Leygue found that the ratio of the horizontal to vertical pressure (k) for a vertical wall, varied from .30 for a horizontal surcharge to .65 for a surcharge sloping at the angle of repose of 33° 42′.

Center of Pressure.—Leygue obtained values of the distance of the point of application of the resultant pressure above the base varying from .296h to .375h, with an average of .34h.

Experiments by Sir Benjamin Baker.—These experiments were published in the Minutes of Proc. Inst. of C. E., Vol. LXV, p. 140.

The experiments showed that the coarser the materials the less lateral pressure. The lateral pressure for coal, shingle, ballast, and macadam material was about one-tenth the vertical pressure, and varied uniformly with it. The lateral pressure in clay was about one-fifth of the vertical, while in loose earth it varied from one-tenth to one-fifth.

Experiments by E. P. Goodrich.—In Trans. Am. Soc. C. E., Vol. LIII, pp. 272 to 304, Mr. Goodrich has recorded certain experiments made by him and has also discussed the principal experiments made by other experimenters. In his experiments he used the following apparatus:

1. A wooden model 3 ft. $\times$ 3 ft. and 6 ft. deep. The pressure of the moist sand was measured by means of a lever apparatus and a scale beam. The ratio of the horizontal to vertical pressure was about one-fifteenth plus 15 lbs. The arch action of the sand made the results of little value as applied to retaining walls.

2. An experiment was tried on sheet piling driven to form the face of a retaining wall. A box 6 ft. $\times$ 1 ft. $\times$ 15 ft., inside measurement, was built with one side open, which side was placed against the sheet piling and the other broad side received the pressure of the filling. The side which received the earth pressure was made of 3 $\times$ 10-in. yellow pine plank, 15 feet long. The deflection of this side was measured at intervals for three months when final settlement appeared to have taken place. The actual pressures of the earth on the wall were obtained by loading a similar plank with bricks. The results were also checked by comparing the observed deflections of the wall with calculated deflections. The material in the fill was fine beach sand weighing about 100 lbs. per cu. ft. These experiments showed that the horizontal pressure was about one-half the vertical pressure.

3. Experiments were made on the testing machine shown in Fig. 36. A cast iron cylinder was bored out to a diameter of 6 ins. and a depth of 5 ins. A plug was fitted in it and was attached to the head of an ordinary testing machine. A 1-in. hole was bored in one side of the cylinder near the bottom, and a plug was carefully fitted to the hole. The plug was just long enough to reach through the wall of the cylin-

der. The faced portion of the outside of the cylinder was fitted with hard rubber insulation opposite the 1-in. hole. On these hard rubber pieces were fitted pieces of copper which were connected to an electric

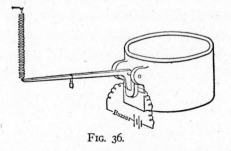

FIG. 36.

battery with an ordinary buzzer in the circuit. When the plug was pushed home the underside of the plug touched the copper and completed the circuit. If the plug was pushed slightly outward the circuit was broken and the buzzer stopped. Experiment showed that a movement of 0.001 inch was sufficient to break the circuit while a movement of 0.0002 was indicated by the tone of the buzzer. The pressure was measured by means of the steel-yard as shown.

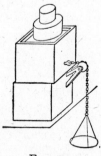

FIG. 37.

In making experiments the pressure was applied until the circuit was broken, when the weights on the steel-yard were moved out until the circuit was closed, the vertical pressure was then applied until the circuit was broken, weights were moved out on the steel-yard until the circuit was closed, and so on until the experiment was completed. The pressure was relieved in the reverse manner and the mean taken as the true values.

Internal Friction.—The angle of internal friction was obtained by means of the apparatus shown in Fig. 37. The two boxes are one foot in each internal dimension, but without tops, the lower one only having a bottom. In conducting an experiment the two boxes were filled with the earth to be tested and enough weights were added to the scale pan to start the upper box to sliding. It was then checked and jerked back into position, known weights were added to the top and weights were added to the scale pan until sliding took place. The angle of

internal friction was determined from Rankine's formula $\sin \phi = \dfrac{1 - r}{1 + r}$

The angle of surface slope was found by measuring the slope that the material assumed when loosely piled.*

The angles of internal friction, angles of surface slope and ratio of lateral to vertical pressure for various materials as determined by Goodrich and others are given in Table IX.

TABLE IX.
ANGLES OF INTERNAL FRICTION AND OF SURFACE SLOPE FOR DIFFERENT MATERIALS.

Ratio of Lateral to Vertical Pressure.	Kind of Material.	Observer.	Tangent of Angle of Internal Friction.	Tangent of Angle of Surface.	Observer.
Percentage.					
10..........	Coal, shingle, ballast, etc.	Baker.	1.423	1.11–0.70	Rankine.
	Bank sand.	Goodrich.	1.423	1.45–0.60 / 1.00–0.67 / 0.75–0.38	Goodrich. / Trautwine. / Rankine.
15..........	Rip-rap.	Goodrich.	1.097	1.00	Goodrich.
	Earth.	Baker.	1.097	0.66	Trautwine.
20..........	100-up quicksand.	Goodrich.	0.895		
	Clay.	Baker.	0.895	1.00	Rankine.
25..........	50-100 quicksand.	Goodrich.	0.750		
	Earth.	Steel.	0.750	0.66 / 0.58	Trautwine / Steel.
	Bank sand.	Wilson.	0.750	0.58–0.62	Wilson.
35..........	50-100 sand.	Goodrich.	0.549	0.85	Goodrich.
	Bank sand.	"	0.549	0.75–0.38	Rankine.
40..........	Clay.	"	0.474	1.00	Rankine.
	Cinders.	"	0.474	0.86	Goodrich.
	½ inch gravel.	"	0.474	0.66	Trautwine
50..........	¼ inch gravel.	"	0.350	0.85	Goodrich.
	Bank sand.	"	0.350	0.75–0.38	Rankine.
60..........	30-50 sand.	"	0.258	0.66	Goodrich.
70..........	20-30 sand.	"	0.179	0.75–0.38	Rankine.

* The angles of internal friction should be used in retaining wall calculations.

Compressibility of Soils.—Tests made on the compressibility of soils showed, (1) that layers immediately beneath the compressing disk were compressed more than the more distant ones, and that a compressed cone formed under the disk; (2) that an appreciable compression took place only with great loads; (3) that under extreme pressures garden earth and sand showed quite an elastic reaction; and (4) that clay, even when containing a small amount of water, would "crawl" and relieve the pressure by squeezing through openings in threads or sheets.

Results.—Goodrich discussed the foregoing experiments and experiments by Sir Benjamin Baker; G. H. Darwin,* A. A. Steel,† and George Wilson,‡ and arrived at the following conclusions:

Saturation.—The lateral pressure in materials which differ only in the percentage of saturation, varies as the ordinates to a curve of the fourth degree, possessing two minimums and one maximum between 0 and 100 per cent of saturation. The effect of moisture is more marked at heavy vertical pressure than at lesser ones.

Neither saturated nor loose dry materials are apt to exert the greatest lateral thrust, and, with slight saturation and rather moist conditions, the lateral thrust is apt to be relatively small.

In moist earths the first large application of pressure is likely to produce a permanent set which exerts lateral pressure at low repetitions of pressures.

Rankine's theory of conjugate pressures is correct when the proper angle of friction is found, and probably adaptations of his formulas will be of most practical value.

Professor William Cain's Discussion of Experiments.—In a paper printed in Transactions, Am. Soc. C. E., Vol. LXXII, p. 403 (1911), Professor William Cain discusses the experiments made on retaining

* Minutes of Proceedings, Inst. C. E., Vol. LXXI, p. 350.
† Engineering News, October 19, 1889, Vol. XLII, p. 261.
‡ Minutes of Proceedings, Inst. C. E., Vol. CXLIX, p. 208 (271).

walls by Lieutenant Hope, John C. Trautwine, Cure, Sir Benjamin
Baker, Leygue, Darwin and others.   He calculated the overturning
pressures using Cain's solution, and reached the following conclusions:

(1) "When wall friction and cohesion are included, the sliding
wedge theory is a reliable one, when the filling is a loosely aggregated
granular material, for any height of wall.

(2) "For experimental walls, from 6 to 10 feet high, or greater,
backed by sand, or any granular material possessing little cohesion, the
influence of cohesion may be neglected.

(3) "Many experiments that have been made on retaining walls
less than 1 foot high, have been analyzed by their authors on the suppo-
sition that cohesion can be neglected.   This hypothesis is so far from
the truth that the deductions are very misleading.

(4) "As it is difficult to ascertain accurately the coefficient of cohesion, and as it varies with the amount of moisture in the material,
small models should be discarded in future experiments and attention
should be confined to large ones.   Such walls should be made as light,
and with as wide a base as possible.   A triangular frame of wood on
an unyielding foundation seems to meet the conditions for precise
measurements.   The sliding wedge theory, omitting cohesion but including wall friction, is a good practical one for the design of retaining
walls backed by fresh earth, when the proper factor of safety is used."

Professor Cain makes the following remarks on the design of retaining walls: "It is plain that the wall should be designed for the
greatest thrust that can come on it at any time, and this in the majority
of cases will occur when the earth is recently deposited.   The cases
where the filling has shrunk away from the wall and afterwards rup-
tured (after saturation, perhaps) are too few in number to warrant
including them in a general scheme of design, even supposing that a
rational theory existed for such cases.   From the discussion of all the
experiments referred to in this paper, the conclusion may be fairly
drawn that the sliding wedge theory, involving wall friction, is a practical one for granular material of any kind subject to static loads.   In
a practical design, however, vibration due to a moving load should be

allowed for, also the effect of heavy rains. Both of these influences tend generally to lower the coefficient of friction and add to the weight of filling. The effect of vibration due to moving trains is most pronounced near the top of a retaining wall, and is evidently greater for a low wall than for a high one."

Criticisms of Theoretical Investigations.—The following criticisms of theoretical investigations of retaining walls are often made: (1) the theory of the granular mass neglects cohesion; (2) the "plane of rupture" is not a plane but a curved surface; (3) theoretical investigations do not apply to walls leaning toward the filling; (4) the direction of the thrust and the point of application of the resultant thrust are indeterminate; and (5) the conclusion is that inasmuch as something must be guessed at, why not guess at the size of the wall in the first place. These criticisms will be discussed in the above order.

1. Retaining walls are commonly built to carry a filling at the toe of a slope, or to carry a filling that carries traffic or a surcharge, and while the cohesion may be present in the beginning yet it may be destroyed at any time by vibration, by the percolation of water or other causes, and it has been repeatedly shown that the maximum theoretical stresses may be developed. The fact that many walls are standing that a theoretical investigation shows should fail, merely indicates, either that an error has been made in the data, or that the cohesion has not yet been destroyed. The proper design of engineering structures requires that the maximum conditions should be considered, and the fact that the structure stands is no sign of its proper design.

2. In Rankine's solution the plane of rupture is not considered, and the results are independent of any assumption as to the surface of rupture. In Weyrauch's solution he made the same assumptions as Rankine, and using the fiction of a "wedge of maximum thrust" deduced two formulas, one giving the direction of the thrust and the other giving the amount of the thrust. Weyrauch's solution gives results that are identical with those obtained by Rankine's solution and has the same limitations. The maximum pressures on a wall due to a granular mass occur before any movement takes place and the so-called

plane of rupture is simply a convenient fiction.   In a cohesive material the break is in a curve, as was shown in Chapter IVA.

3. That Rankine's solution modified by the author is perfectly general when properly applied has already been shown in Chapter IA.

4. The use of empirical rules leads to poor designs, in which the material is badly distributed, causing many walls to tip forward, due to excessive toe pressures.   In designing retaining walls on compressible foundations, the resultant thrust must be kept at or back of the center of the base to prevent excessive settlement at the toe, and a consequent tipping forward.

5. That the advocates of the empirical method are faint-hearted is shown by their almost universal use of some theoretical solution in the design of reinforced concrete retaining walls.   For the design of retaining walls Rankine's solution as modified by the author is the most satisfactory solution yet proposed.

Professor Cain has shown, Transactions, Am. Soc. C. E., Vol. LXXII, p. 403 (1911), that tests on retaining walls agree more nearly with the calculated pressures than has generally been believed.   In measuring the pressure of granular materials it is very difficult to devise a measuring apparatus that will give the true pressures.   Any measuring device that requires any appreciable movement of the pressure measuring surface in order to record the pressures will give unreliable results—see Chapter XVII.   The problem of determining the pressures of a cohesive material is a much more difficult one than the determination of the pressures of granular materials.   In addition, most tests on retaining walls have been made with material in a box, or with material of limited extent, so that the results are not comparable.   On the other hand the laws of granular materials as determined by experiments on bins show a remarkable uniformity of behavior. Due to the above difficulties the author believes that the experiments already made on retaining walls are of little value.

Author's Conclusions.—From the preceding experiments and discussion the following conclusions may be drawn:

(1) Rankine's solution as modified by the author to include walls

leaning toward the filling, furnishes the most rational theory yet proposed for the calculation of the pressure on retaining walls.

(2) Retaining walls in their normal condition sustain the pressure of the filling material at rest, and the calculation of the pressures on retaining walls is therefore a problem in statics. Bin walls sustain the pressure of a granular material of limited extent, the walls sustaining part of the load due to friction of the filling material upon the sides of the bins.

(3) A rational theory for the design of retaining walls should be based upon the laws of semi-fluids which can best be obtained by experiments made upon wheat, sand and similar materials in bins. The difficulty in measuring the exact pressures due to the influence of cohesion, and the movement of the filling are so great that experiments upon retaining walls have so far been of little value, and give no promise for the future.

CHAPTER VI.

EXAMPLES OF RETAINING WALLS.

Concrete Retaining Wall, Illinois Central R. R., Chicago, Ill.*—
The concrete retaining wall shown in Fig. 38 was built by the Illinois
Central R. R., on the lake front in Chicago in 1905. The wall is carried on piles 30 feet long, spaced 3 feet center to center parallel to
the wall, and 3 ft. 4⅞ ins. transversely. The wall is designed for an
8-ft. surcharge, with this surcharge the resultant load is 31,750 lbs. per
linear foot of wall, or 15.87 tons per pile.

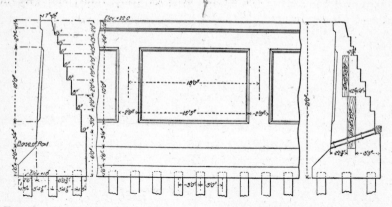

FIG. 38.—CONCRETE RETAINING WALL, ILLINOIS CENTRAL R. R., CHICAGO, ILL.

The concrete was mixed wet in the proportions 1 part Portland
cement, 3 parts sand, and 6 parts broken limestone. The front face
of the wall and the coping were finished with mortar as the concrete
was laid, the remainder of the concrete was left rough.

The concrete was laid in four courses. The first course extends
from the bottom up to the base of the rail, this course being laid without joints, continuously as possible. Between that level and the bottom

---

* Engineering Record, January 27, 1906.

of the panel is the second course, in which expansion joints are placed every 108 feet on the center line of the pilasters between the panels. The third course extends from the bottom of the panel to the bottom of the coping and contains expansion joints every 54 feet. The coping makes the fourth course and was laid before the third one was set. Each of the first three courses was sloped 2 inches on top and had a 6 × 12-in. timber laid in the top to make a key that would bond the adjacent faces of the courses together. A 6-in. drain tile was placed longitudinally along the back of the wall on the tread of the upper 9-in. step and connected at intervals with a pipe through the wall. The expansion joints were filled with one thickness of Hydrex felt, and the concrete was laid in alternate sections so that there are true parting planes at the expansion joints. The end of the section laid first was bulkheaded and vertical timbers were nailed to the inside of the bulkhead to form a key way for the end of the next section.

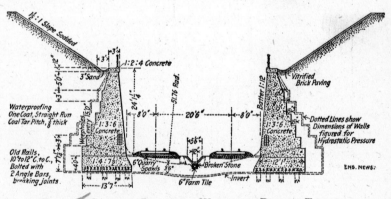

FIG. 39.—CONCRETE RETAINING WALLS FOR DETROIT TUNNEL.

Retaining Walls for Detroit Tunnel.*—The retaining walls shown in Fig. 39 were designed for the open cut approach of the proposed tunnel (1906) under the Detroit River for the Michigan Central R. R. It will be seen that the walls are braced apart by a concrete invert. The walls are made of concrete with the proportions 1 part Portland cement, 3 parts sand, and 6 parts broken stone, for the body and

* Engineering News, February 15, 1906.

1–4–7½ for the footing course. The footings are reinforced with old rails, 10 to 12 in. centers; the main body of the wall is not reinforced. The back of the walls are coated with a layer of tar ⅛-in. thick. Weep holes are provided through the wall every 15 feet. Transverse tar paper joints are made every 50 feet to provide for expansion.

Retaining Walls on the Pennsylvania Ave. Subway, Philadelphia, Pa.*—Fig. 40 shows a typical section of retaining wall with standard coping and French drain and weeper. Reduced heights were

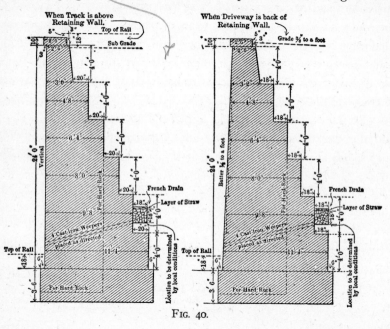

FIG. 40.

usually designed by cutting the standard section at the desired point. Wherever possible, the faces of all walls were given a batter of ½ in. per foot. The neat line was generally 18 ins. below the top of the rail. Unless otherwise ordered, the bed of the foundation was specified to be 5 ft. below the top of the rail in earth and soft rock, and 3 ft. below in hard rock. On lump-sum contracts, any masonry below these lines was paid for as additional masonry at the prices bid.

Specifications.—*Masonry.*—" All retaining walls shall consist of

* Trans. Am. Soc. C. E., Vol. 48, p. 470.

first-class Conshohocken or other approved stone of good shape and good flat beds ; no stone having less bed than face ; laid on their broadest faces as rubble work in Portland cement mortar.

"In walls of 5 ft. thickness or less, the stones shall average from 6 to 8 cu. ft. each, and the length of the headers shall be two-thirds of the thickness of the wall.   In walls over 5 ft. thick the stones shall average 12 cu. ft. each, and headers shall be at least 4 ft. long.   Generally, no stones of less than 4 cu. ft. shall be used, except for filling the interstices between the larger stones.   At least one-fifth of each face of all the walls shall be composed of headers placed so that those on one face come between those on the other ; and, where the thickness of the walls is such that the headers from opposite faces do not overlap, stones not less than 4 ft. long shall be set transversely in the heart of the wall to complete the bond.

"These walls must be built accurately to lines and levels given, and all exposed faces of the stone must be true and straight, and without prominent projections of the quarry faces.   The mortar in all joints on exposed faces shall be kept back one inch.

"Selected stone shall be used at all angles, and shall be neatly pitched to true lines and laid on hammer-dressed beds.   At all angles 1½-in. draft lines will be required.

"Grout shall be used in place of mortar, wherever directed by the Chief Engineer.

"The face and back of the wall shall be carried up together, over the whole wall, in approximately the same total height, except where otherwise specified.

"In rock-faced work, the faces of the stones shall have uniform projections not exceeding 3 ins., and in rough-pointed work not more than 1 in. beyond the neat lines, and in both cases they shall be pitched to a straight line at all the joints.

"The joints between all stones on the back of all retaining walls and abutments shall be carefully and thoroughly washed with Portland cement mortar so as to make the walls water-tight.

"In cases where rock adjoins the back of the wall, the wall is to be built up tight against the rock, and the joint thoroughly grouted with Portland cement grouting.

"All walls and abutments are to be thoroughly drained, wherever directed by the Chief Engineer, by means of 4-in. cast-iron pipe, built in the wall, or by openings left, as may be ordered. Wherever necessary, tile or French drains of broken stone, 18 × 18 ins., as shown on the drawings, shall be placed at the back of the wall. These drains and pipe will be paid for, per lineal foot, at the price given in the proposal for such work.

"All pointing shall be done with Portland cement mortar of an approved brand. The surfaces of all stone shall be thoroughly cleaned, the joints scraped out to the depth of at least an inch, and the whole thoroughly wetted before pointing is commenced."

Cement.—"In all cases where Portland cement mortar is specified, the mortar shall be composed of 1 part of Portland cement to 3 parts of sand.

"Mortar taken from the mixing box, and molded into briquettes, 1 sq. in. in cross-section, shall develop the following ultimate tensile strength:

AGE.	STRENGTH.
7 days (1 day in air, 6 days in water) 1 part of Portland cement to 3 parts of sand	100 lbs.
28 days (1 day in air, 27 days in water) 1 part of Portland cement to 3 parts of sand	150 lbs.

"Grout made of Portland cement shall be composed of 1 part of Portland cement to 2 parts of sand, except where the foundations are wet, when the quantity of sand shall be diminished, making the proportions 1 part of Portland cement to $1\frac{1}{2}$ parts of sand, which shall be used in the foundation masonry up to the neat lines if required.

"Portland cement shall have a specific gravity of not less than 3, and shall leave, by weight, a residue of not more than 1 per cent on a No. 50 sieve, 10 per cent on a No. 100 sieve, and 30 per cent on a No. 200 sieve.

"Pats of neat cement, $\frac{1}{2}$ in. thick, with thin edges, immersed in water, after 'hard set,' shall show no signs of 'checking' or disintegration.

"It shall require at least 30 minutes to develop initial set.

"Briquettes of cement, 1 sq. in. in cross-section, shall develop the following ultimate tensile strengths:

AGE.	STRENGTH.
24 hours (in water, after hard set)	175 lbs.
7 days (1 day in air, 6 days in water)	450 lbs.
28 days (1 day in air, 27 days in water)	550 lbs.
7 days (1 day in air, 6 days in water), 1 part of cement to 3 parts of standard quartz sand	160 lbs.
28 days (1 day in air, 27 days in water), 1 part of cement to 3 parts of standard quartz sand	220 lbs.

"All cements shall meet such additional requirements as to 'hot water,' 'set,' and 'chemical' tests as the Chief Engineer shall determine. The requirements for 'set' may be modified where the conditions are such as to make it advisable."

Retaining Wall at Black Lick, Ohio.*—The retaining wall shown in Fig. 41 was designed and constructed by Frank A. Bone, of Lebanon, Ohio, for the wing walls of a reinforced concrete arch. A patent has been granted Mr. Bone on this design.

The steel bents shown imbedded near the back of the wall are built up of plates and angles; are placed 4 feet apart and are connected to a 2 × 2-in. angle at the bottom. Small angle brackets are riveted to the upright bents to prevent slipping of the bond. The 4 × ¼-in. plate extending toward the toe is an anchor. The plate is twisted to get a better hold on the concrete. The steel framework is designed to take all the tensile stresses in the wall.

The concrete is composed of 1¼ barrels of cement to ½ cu. yd. of sand and 1 cu. yd. of crushed limestone, with one-third the whole volume of large-sized sound freestone imbedded in the concrete. The walls have a coat of plaster on each side.

* Engineering News, March, 1902.

The patent on the above cantilever retaining wall granted to Frank
A. Bone, No. 705,732, July 29, 1902, application filed April 21, 1899,
was decided against Mr. Bone in the United States District Court at
Marion, Indiana, January 16, 1916. The decision of the lower court
was affirmed by the United States District Court of Appeals for the
Seventh District, October 2, 1917. The principal anticipation was a
reinforced concrete retaining wall designed by P. Planat, and described
in La Construction Moderne, September 26, 1896. For a very complete discussion of the Bone patent and the chief anticipations, see
Engineering News, February 10, 1916.

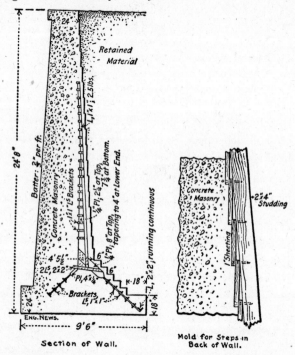

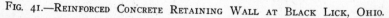

FIG. 41.—REINFORCED CONCRETE RETAINING WALL AT BLACK LICK, OHIO.

**Concrete Retaining Walls at New York Central Terminal, New
York.***—The concrete is composed of 1 part Portland cement, 3
parts sand, and 6 parts broken stone. The concrete was mixed by a
Ransome mixer. It was mixed very wet and required no ramming.
One-man stones were placed in the molds, and the mortar was care-

* Engineering Record, January 6, 1906.

fully spaded around the sides of the molds. The wall was made in full height sections 52 ft. long, with open, vertical, transverse, expansion joints ⅛-in. thick between them.

The molds were built with 2-in. pine planks, ship-lapped ½ inch and laid ⅛ inch apart to allow for swelling. They were lined on the face with thin steel plates, and secured by vertical spruce joists and remov-

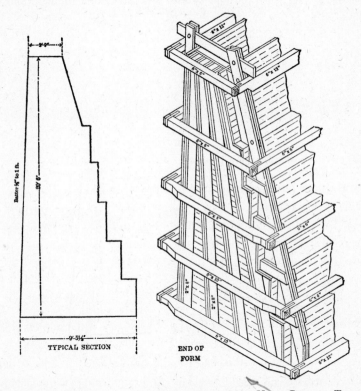

FIG. 42.—CONCRETE RETAINING WALL AND FORM, NEW YORK CENTRAL TERMINAL, NEW YORK.

able horizontal yellow pine waling pieces, bolted on as shown in Fig. 42. The waling pieces were fastened at the corners by angle straps of 2 × ½-inch iron. The longitudinal waling pieces were tied together through the molds with 2 bars ½-in. diameter, placed midway between the ends.

In placing the concrete three molds were used, one being in use, one standing, and one being erected.

Reinforced Concrete Retaining Walls, C. B. & Q. Ry., Galesburg, Ill.*—The retaining walls are of solid sections up to 12 ft. 6 ins., and beyond that they are of tee and counterfort section. The details of the wall are shown in Fig. 43.

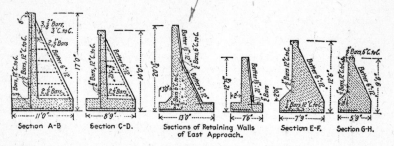

Fig. 43.—Reinforced Concrete Retaining Walls for Subway, Galesburg, Ill.

Gravel concrete was used, and had the proportions 1 part Portland cement, to 6 parts gravel. The concrete was mixed very wet and was poured like water, thoroughly filling the forms and surrounding the reinforcing bars. The concrete was found to be very dense. The forms were of matched lumber, not lined, and the only attempt at facing the exposed surfaces was to work the face of the concrete with a hoe, so as to press back the stones and show a cement facing.

Reinforced Concrete Retaining Walls for Philadelphia Rapid Transit Co. Tunnel, Philadelphia, Pa.†—The retaining walls were built in 30-ft. sections, with broad footing courses and specially designed reinforcement for each section. The sections forming the portal have ⅜-in. longitudinal horizontal rods on 2 ft. centers, near their central vertical plane, and near the middle of their footing courses to bind them to the walls of the subway, and are the only part of the retaining walls containing reinforcement in those portions. The bulk of the reinforcement in them is in the same position as in the remainder of the

* Engineering News, February 8, 1906.
† Engineering Record, February 25, 1906.

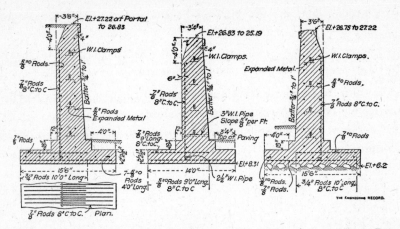

FIG. 44.—REINFORCED CONCRETE RETAINING WALLS FOR PHILADELPHIA RAPID
TRANSIT COMPANY SUBWAY.

walls, and is made of $\frac{7}{8}$-in. horizontal and vertical bars 6 inches inside
their back faces. The horizontal bars are on 2-ft. centers. The vertical bars are 8 inches apart and extend from 4 feet below the top of
the wall to within 6 inches of the toe of the footing, where they bend
at right angles toward the face and continue horizontal to within 6
inches of the toe of the footing. A piece of $2\frac{1}{2}$ in. gas pipe 7 inches
long and filled with concrete is placed in each bend transverse to the
rod, and the rod is wired to it to relieve the crushing tendency in the
concrete at the point of the bend by an upward pull. Horizontal $\frac{3}{4}$-in.
rods 10 feet long are placed in the same plane with the horizontal portion of the vertical rods, with one end 6 inches from the heel of the footing course, and alternate with those rods on 8-in. centers. Six inches
below the top of the lower footing course, which is $2\frac{1}{2}$ feet deep, and of
a width of about nine-tenths the height of the wall in a section, are
placed transverse horizontal, $\frac{7}{8}$-in. rods 10 feet long parallel to the $\frac{3}{4}$-in.
rods below them. Clamps are placed at the joints between the sections
which prevent unequal lateral motion of adjoining sections, but permit
difference of settlement. The clamps are made of three $5'' \times 12'' \times \frac{3}{4}''$
steel plates. The middle plate is set in one section vertically and the

two outside plates are set in the adjacent section. The clamps are spaced 3 feet apart vertically.

The concrete was composed of 1 part Portland cement, 2½ parts gravel or coarse sand, and 5 parts crushed granite or trap rock.

Reinforced Concrete Retaining Wall at Bridge 123, Great Northern Ry.[*]—The reinforced concrete retaining wall shown in Fig. 45 was designed to hold a sliding embankment at Bridge 123, Kalispel Division, Great Northern Ry. The filling was saturated and rested on

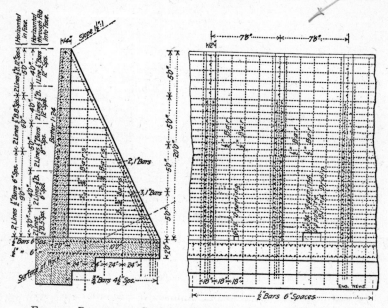

FIG. 45.—REINFORCED CONCRETE RETAINING WALL AT BRIDGE 123.

a soapstone ledge. The filling was drained by an elaborate system of drains back of the wall. The water was led around the end of the wall, and through holes in the wall. Tamped shell rock filling was deposited back of the wall as shown in Fig. 46. The soapstone was excavated and the wall was placed in a trench as shown in Fig. 46. The concrete was composed of 1 part Portland cement, 2½ parts sand, and 4 parts crushed rock in the wall, and 5 parts crushed rock in the foun-

[*] Engineering News, May 6, 1906.

dation. The concrete was mixed very wet so that tamping was not necessary. The facing was put on by means of a steel blade $4'' \times 6''$ $\times \frac{1}{4}''$ forged on the end of a steel bar $4\frac{1}{2}$ feet long, the rock being simply forced away from the forms with this tool.

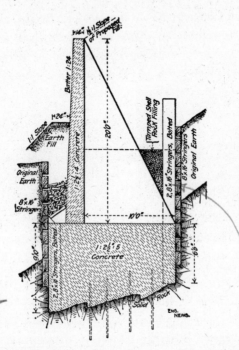

FIG. 46.—SECTION OF WALL SHOWING FOUNDATION.

The reinforcement consisted of Johnson corrugated bars, arranged as shown in Fig. 45.

To take the pressure of the filling during erection a heavy framing was used in the trench.

A view of the complete wall is shown in Fig. 47. P. 144.

Hennebique System Retaining Wall.*—The retaining wall shown in Fig. 48 was built at the Paris Exposition of 1900 to support a temporary sunken street near the gardens of Trocadero. The Hennebique System was employed. The retaining wall is divided into

* Engineering News, February 15, 1900.

FIG. 47.—REINFORCED CONCRETE RETAINING WALL AT BRIDGE 123.

panels 19.7′ long, and each of these panels is made of reinforced concrete, from the back of which project three buttresses of similar construction. The facing and buttresses are connected by two beams of
reinforced concrete. Another buttress projects from the face of the
wall and is located a certain distance below the street level. This construction is clearly shown in Fig. 48.

By this arrangement of horizontal beams the earth filling rests on
the retaining wall and resists overturning. In the calculation the angle
of repose of earth was taken as 35°, and the weight of the earth was
taken at 112 lbs. per cu. ft. The allowable pressure on soil at the toe
was taken at 2048 lbs. per sq. ft.

The imbedded metal work of the vertical face consists of two
series of vertical bars combined with one series of horizontal bars, the
spaces, between which, decrease toward the top of the wall. These
vertical bars are bent over at right angles at the top to give support
for a coping of the same construction as the facing. The reinforce-

ment of the buttresses consist of inclined bars, tied together by straps, and supported by horizontal bars. The horizontal beams are made up of bars in both directions, spaced 5 bars to the square meter; the beams are further strengthened at the edges by flanges. The concrete was of the proportions of 1¼ barrels of cement to 1 cu. yd. of sand and gravel.

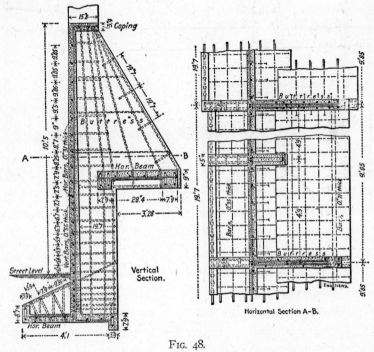

FIG. 48.

Retaining Walls, Railway Terminal Station, Atlanta, Ga.*—The retaining wall to support the embankment approaching the train shed is of novel construction. This type of wall was made necessary owing to the impossibility of securing an adjacent piece of property.

The plan of the wall is given in Fig. 49 and various sections are given in Fig. 50. It will be seen that the usual solid counterforts are replaced by a framework of reinforced concrete beams, ties, and struts. The drawings explain the details of construction.

It will be seen in Fig. 49 that reinforced concrete piles support the

* Engineering News, April 12, 1906.

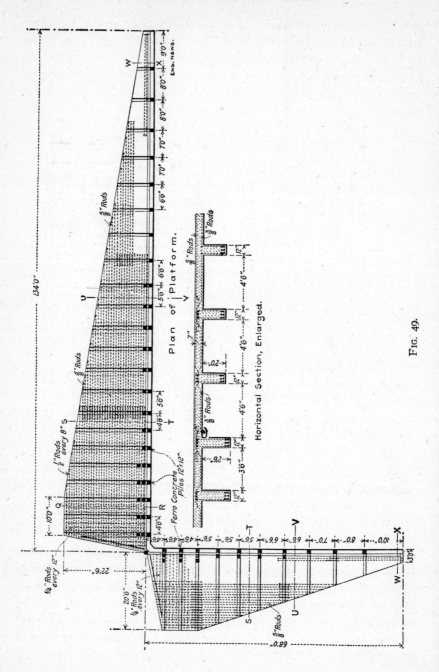

FIG. 49.

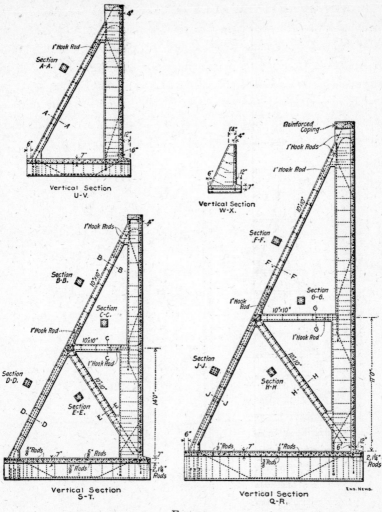

FIG. 50.

toe of the retaining wall. These piles are 12 × 12 ins. square and 10 ft. long. The piles are reinforced with four 1⅛-in. round rods tied up with binders. The piles were concreted horizontally on the ground, and were allowed to set 15 days. They were then driven with an ordinary pile driver weighing 3,500 lbs., dropping 9 feet. The tops were protected with a cast-iron cap with a sawdust cushion between the metal and the concrete.

PLAIN GRAVITY WALLS.—The sections of 27 plain gravity
see retaining walls are shown in the folding plate, Fig. 50a. Fig. 50a
was prepared from data collected by Mr. Frank H. Carter, Assoc.
M. Am. Soc. C. E., after correspondence with the author. All the
data available are given in the drawings. It is evident that the walls
note must have been designed for widely varying conditions. A study of
the designs shows that the ratio of base to height is a poor guide, and
that the design of each retaining wall is a problem in itself.

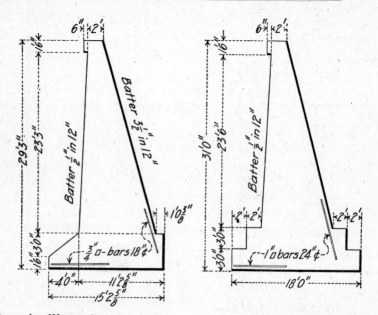

FIG. 50 b.—WEST ALAMEDA AVENUE   FIG. 50 c.—SAN CARLOS ARCH RE-
SUBWAY RETAINING WALL.   TAINING WALL.

The design for a standard retaining wall used by the C. B. & Q.
R. R. is shown in Fig. 51a.

**Retaining Wall for West Alameda Avenue Subway, Denver,
Colorado.**—The retaining wall in Fig. 50b was designed by the author
for West Alameda Avenue Subway, Denver, Colo. The calculations
for this wall are given in Fig. 28 and Fig. 28a, and the specifications
are given in Chapter III. *P.64.*   *P.67.*   *P.74–78.*

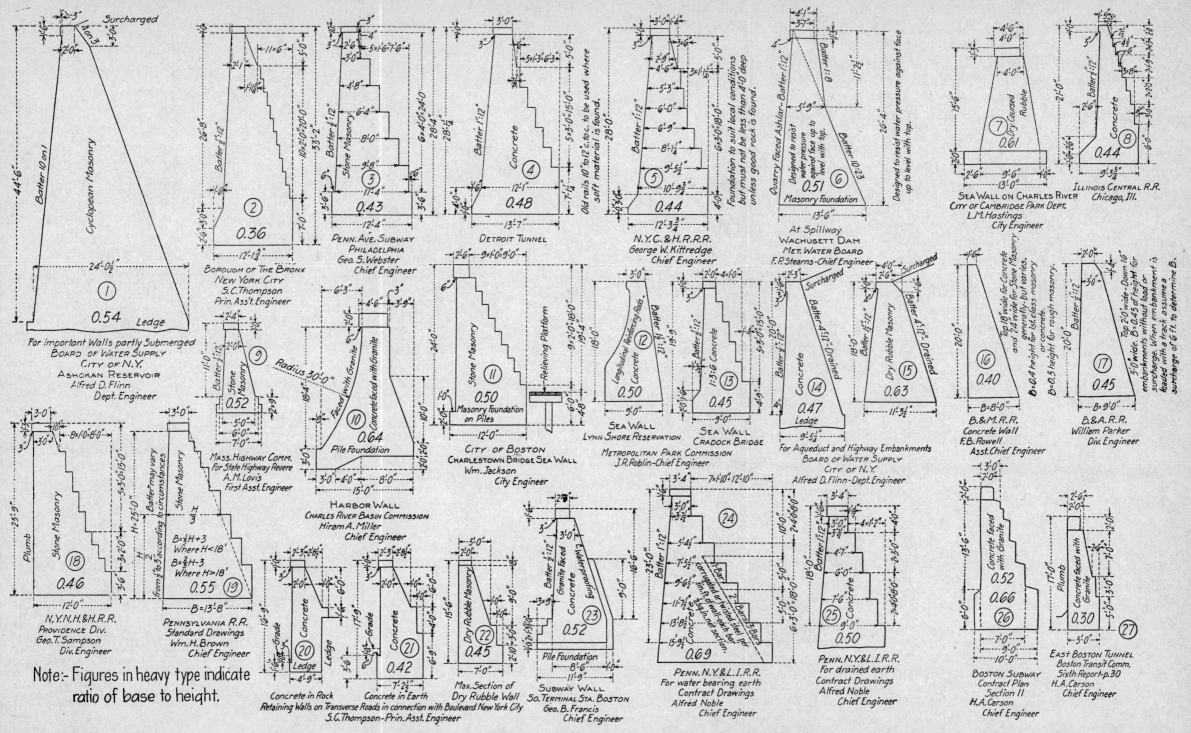

Fig. 50 a.

Retaining Wall for San Carlos Arch.—The retaining wall in Fig. 50c is a wing wall for the two 60-ft. concrete arch bridges built by the Colorado and Southern R. R. and the Denver and Rio Grande R. R. over the St. Charles River at San Carlos, Colorado. The wall was designed for an angle of repose of $\phi = 33° \ 42'$, and a surcharge of $\delta = \phi = 33° \ 42'$, the remainder of the data being the same as for the Alameda Avenue Subway walls. The maximum pressures are 9,600 lbs. and 700 lbs. on the toe and heel, respectively. The foundation was a good quality of limestone. The wall was built of 1-3-5 Portland cement concrete. Crocker and Ketchum were consulting engineers on the arch, the author being in charge of the design.

CHAPTER VII.

METHODS OF CONSTRUCTION AND COST OF RETAINING WALLS.

Cost of Masonry Retaining Walls.—The cost of masonry walls varies between wide limits, depending upon the cost of stone, cost of quarrying, cost of dressing, cost of laying, cost of mortar, cost of superintendence, cost of tools, cost of maintenance and depreciation of plant. Space will not permit a discussion of all the above items.

Cost of Stone.—The price of stone is usually quoted f. o. b. at the quarry, and varies with the stone and location.

Cost of Quarrying.—After the quarry has been opened in limestone, two-man stone for rubble wall can usually be quarried for from ¼ to ½ the cost of the daily wages of a quarry laborer per cu. yd. Stones ranging from ½ to 1 cu. yd., that have to be blasted, will cost per cu. yd., from ½ to 2 times the cost of the daily wages of one man. Dimension stones that have to be wedged out will cost twice as much as the large stones that can be blasted. This estimate is high for sand stone and low for granite.

Cost of Dressing.—Rubble is roughly scabbled when it is laid and there is no special charge for dressing. Dimension stones, if dressed to lay with quarry finish and fairly close joints, will cost from $1.00 to $3.00 per cu. yd. Bush-hammering costs about 25 cents per sq. ft.

Cost of Laying.—One mason and a helper can lay from 4 to 5 cu. yds. of small rubble in a day of 8 hours. If a derrick is necessary and some dressing required, one mason and a helper will lay only from 2 to 3 cu. yds. of heavy rubble or 1½ to 2 cu. yds. of dimension stone in a day of 8 hours.

Cost of Mortar.—The amount of mortar required varies with the specifications and the stone used. Rubble masonry is from 20 to 35 per cent mortar. Dimension stone masonry is from 10 to 15 per cent mortar. Knowing the cost of cement and sand, the cost of the mortar can be estimated.

150

Miscellaneous Costs.—The cost of superintendence, tools, maintenance and depreciation of plant, etc., can only be estimated on the particular work. These costs may vary from 5 to 20 per cent of the cost above.

Actual Cost of Stone Masonry Retaining Walls.—The cost of quarrying and laying limestone on the Chicago Sanitary Canal is given by James W. Beardsley as follows:* The limestone occurred in uniform strata, so that the beds required no dressing. The walls were 4 feet wide on top, with a thickness at the bottom of one-half the height, which averaged 24 feet. The stone was laid in courses 12 to 18 inches thick. The stone was scabbled and carefully placed in position on the natural beds, so as to break joints. The stone was laid in mortar composed of 1 part natural cement and 1 part sand. The mortar occupied only $13\frac{1}{4}$ per cent of the wall. The stone was handled with guy derricks having a capacity of 6 to 10 tons, and a boom 40 to 60 feet long, operated by a hoisting engine. The cost given does not include general superintendence, installation of plant, plant maintenance, power, delays, etc.

Retaining walls were built on four sections, the tabulated costs of which are given in the original article.

The total cost of the masonry per cubic yard was as follows:

Quarry force	$0.73
Wall force	1.03
Sand, at $1.35 per cu. yd.	0.13
Cement, at $0.60 per bbl.	0.24
Total	$2.13

If the full cost of the plant is charged to the work the cost would be $2.13 + 0.32 = $2.45 per cubic yard. The contract price was $3.25 per cubic yard. The total cost of the masonry in these walls is very low.

Concrete Retaining Walls. Methods of Constructing Forms.—Forms for retaining wall may be built in sections, or may be built up each time they are used. The former method is much the cheaper,

* Journal Western Society of Engineers, December, 1898.

especially for plain concrete walls where the sections between expansion joints are of equal length.

The forms used on the Grand Central Terminal walls, New York City, are shown in Fig. 42. The sections were made 52 feet long and were shifted by a locomotive crane. The cost of shifting the forms

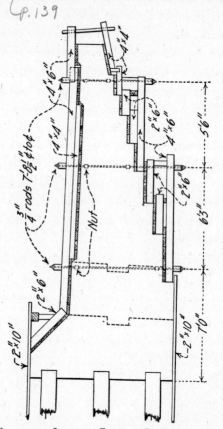

FIG. 51.—FORMS FOR ILLINOIS CENTRAL R. R. RETAINING WALL.

was approximately $0.12 per cu. yd. The concrete was mixed on a travelling tower, and was run directly into the forms, at an actual cost of $0.42 per cu. yd. for mixing and placing, not including cost of plant and superintendence.

The forms for the Illinois Central R. R. retaining wall shown in

Fig. 38 are shown in Fig. 51. The forms were built in sections 54 feet long. The forms were cross-braced by ¾ inch rods spaced 7' 8½" center to center as shown. When the forms were taken down the ends of these rods were unscrewed, the main portion of the rod being left in the wall. The forms were made of 2" plank surfaced on the inside.

The forms used on the C. B. & Q. R. R. walls shown in Fig. 51*a* are shown in Fig. 51*b*. The studs, coping and bottom forms for the face, and the back forming are sectional, while ordinary sheeting is

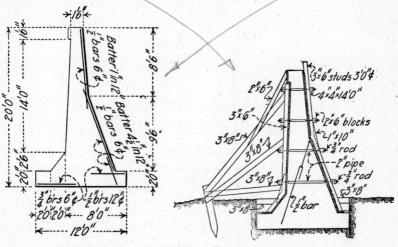

FIG. 51 a.—RETAINING WALL, C. B. & Q. R. R.

FIG. 51 b.—FORMS FOR RETAINING WALL, C. B. & Q. R. R.

used between the coping and bottom forms. No attempt was made to use sectional forms on the face of the wall, because the sections soon become badly warped, making a rough wall. The concrete had a tendency to lift the forms and they were tied to bars imbedded in the footings as shown. The sectional forms were 12' 0" long, while the studs were spaced 3' 0" center to center.

The forms used by the Chicago and Northwestern R. R. on track elevation in Chicago are shown in Fig. 51*c*. The forms were built in sections 35 feet long. The 2" × 8" braces were used to hold the sides of the forms apart and were removed as the concrete was put in place.

The 2″ pipe used to cover the rod bracing was old boiler flues and rejected pipe.

Ingredients in Concrete.—The proportions of concrete materials should be stated in terms of the volume of the cement. The volume of one barrel or four bags of cement is taken as 3.8 cu. ft., and the sand

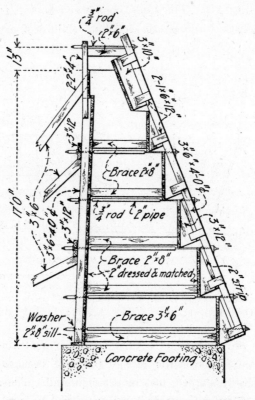

FIG. 51 c.—FORMS FOR C. & N. W. R. R. WALL.

and aggregate are measured loose. Concrete mixed one part cement, 2 parts sand, and 4 parts stone is commonly called 1 : 2 : 4 concrete. The proportions should be such that there should be more than enough cement paste to fill the voids in the sand, and more than enough mortar to fill the voids in the stone. With voids in sand and stone varying from 40 to 45 per cent, the quantities of the ingredients are closely given by Fuller's rule, where

c = number of parts of cement;

s = number of parts of sand;

g = number of parts of gravel or stone.

Then $\dfrac{11}{c + s + g} = p$ = number of barrels of Portland cement required for one cu. yd. concrete.

$\dfrac{p \times s \times 3.8}{27}$ = number of cu. yds. sand required for one cu. yd. concrete.

$\dfrac{p \times g \times 3.8}{27}$ = number of cu. yds. gravel or stone required for one cu. yd. concrete.

The materials for one cu. yd. of 1 : 2 : 4 concrete will then be: Portland cement 1.57 barrels, sand 0.44 cu. yds., gravel or stone 0.88 cu. yds.

The proportions for plain walls commonly vary from 1 : 2½ : 5 to 1 : 3 : 6, while the proportions for reinforced walls vary from 1 : 2 : 4 to 1 : 2½ : 5.

Mixing and Placing Concrete.—For mixing concrete a batch mixer in which the materials can be definitely proportioned and thoroughly mixed is to be preferred. In cold weather the concrete materials should be heated by the addition of boiling water to the mixer. To prevent scalding the cement the sand, aggregate and hot water should first be placed in the mixer and, after giving it several turns to remove the frost, the cement should be added and the mixing completed.

The author uses the following specifications for placing concrete in cold or freezing weather. "When the temperature of the air during the time of mixing and placing is below 40° Fah. the water used in mixing the concrete shall be heated to such a temperature, that the temperature of the concrete when deposited in the forms shall not be less than 60° Fah. Care shall be used not to scald the cement."

Where the wall is in a cut and the materials can be delivered on the bank, the mixer may be installed on the bank above and the concrete wheeled or chuted to place. Concrete should not be chuted in freezing weather. In building the West Alamda Avenue Subway retaining walls, Denver, Colo., the gravel and sand were taken from the cut, the concrete was mixed in mixers installed at the foot of movable towers, and the concrete was raised in a skip elevator and chuted into place.

On railroad work the mixer may be mounted on a flat car, the materials may be delivered on other cars, and the concrete is dumped or chuted directly into place.

For specifications for reinforced concrete construction, see Appendix I.

Cost of Reinforced Concrete Retaining Walls.—The cost of reinforced concrete may be divided into cost of cement, cost of sand, cost of broken stone, cost of forms, cost of laying, cost of reinforcement, and cost of superintending, etc.

Cost of Materials.—The cost of concrete materials varies with the location and must be obtained before preparing an estimate of cost. Portland cement (1911) costs about $1.00 per barrel f. o. b. plant; sand can usually be obtained delivered on wagons at $0.75 to $1.00 per cu. yd.; broken stone can usually be obtained at $1.00 to $1.50 per cu. yd. f. o. b. crusher.

Cost of Forms.—The cost of the timber for forms should be obtained locally. Lumber can be used several times, commonly from 3 to 5 times where forms are torn down each time, and almost indefinitely where forms can be used without change; so that the first cost of lumber should be distributed over all the concrete laid with the forms. The amount of lumber per cubic yard varies with the type of wall, being very much greater for reinforced than for plain walls. A carpenter and a helper should be able to place one M ft. B. M. in two days of 8 hours each, making the cost from $8 to $10 per M ft. B. M.

Cost of Mixing and Placing.—With men at $1.50 per day and a foreman at $3.00 per day, concrete should be mixed and rammed into place for from $1.00 to $1.25 per cu. yd. If the reinforcement is troublesome or the wall narrow the cost may be higher. This does not include facing which will cost more. If machine mixers are used the cost is less on large work.

Cost of Reinforcing Steel.—The cost of steel bars delivered at the work will depend upon the mill price and cost of transportation to the site. The cost of bending and placing steel reinforcing will vary from $5.00 to $15.00 per ton, depending upon the amount of bending and other conditions.

Actual Cost of Plain Concrete Retaining Walls.—The cost of building concrete retaining walls on the Chicago Sanitary Canal is given by James W. Beardsley as follows:* The walls were 4 feet wide on top, with a thickness at the base of one-half the height, which averaged 10 feet for Section 14, and 22 feet for Section 15. The concrete was 1 natural cement, 1½ sand, and 4 broken stone, faced and coped with 1 : 3 Portland cement mortar 3 inches thick. The costs given do not include general superintendence, installation of plant, plant maintenance, insurance, delays, etc. The Portland cement on Section 14 was 9.3 per cent of the total cement used, and on Section 15, 5.2 per cent.

Section 14.—On Section 14 stone was obtained from the spoil bank of the canal, hauled 100 feet in wheelbarrows to an Austin jaw crusher, which discharged the stone into the bins from which it was fed into a Sooysmith mixer. Both the crusher and the mixer were mounted on a flat car, the cement, sand and stone were raised by a belt elevator so arranged as to discharge into the mixer in the proper proportions. The cement and sand were hauled to the bins in wagons.

Supports for the concrete forms were made by setting vertical posts 9 inches in front of the face of the wall and 8 feet apart, the foot of the post being held in place by a dowel pin set three or four inches into the rock. Wooden braces held the posts in place longitudinally and tie rods connected them with a line of similar posts at the back of the wall. The forms were 16 feet long and 2 feet high. Two one-foot courses were laid, and after an interval of twenty-four hours the forms were drawn, cleaned and reset.

*Journal Western Society of Engineers, December, 1898.

The Portland cement facing was placed by using plates of iron held three inches from the forms by blocks; as the course was completed this plate was withdrawn and the mortar tamped into place. There were 23,568 cubic yards of concrete masonry on Section 14. The contract prices per cubic yard on Section 14 were: excavation, 38 cents; concrete masonry, $2.74; back filling, 14 cents. Utica cement is rated at 65 cents per bbl.; Portland cement, $2.25 per bbl., and sand at $1.35 per cubic yard.

Section 15.—The quarry was 1,000 feet from the No. 7 Gates crusher. The rock was hauled to the crusher on $4\frac{1}{2}$ ton cars by a light locomotive on a standard gage track. A mixer of the spiral screw type was used, operated by an engine and boiler mounted on a separate car. The output of the crusher was about 210 cu yds. in 10 hours. The output of the mixer was about 100 cu. yds. in 10 hours. The concrete was deposited as on Section 14. There were 44,811 cubic yards of concrete masonry on Section 15. The contract price for concrete masonry on Section 15 was $3.40 per cubic yard. A comparison of the costs on the two sections is given in Table X. The costs are very low on account of the low cost of stone and cement, and the size of wall.

TABLE X.

COMPARISON OF COSTS OF CONCRETE MASONRY ON SECTIONS 14 AND 15, CHICAGO SANITARY CANAL.

	Section 14. Cost per Cubic Yard.	Section 15. Cost per Cubic Yard.		Section 14. Cost per Cubic Yard.	Section 15. Cost per Cubic Yard.
General	$ .078	$ .082	Cement, natural	$ .863	$ .930
Wall	.108	.116	Cement, Portland	.305	.180
Mixing	.121	.250	Sand	.465	.476
Timbering	.150	.142	Plant	.407	.567
Transportation	.142	.081			
Crushing	.073	.128			
Quarrying	.303	.275			
Total	$ .975	$1.074	Total	$3.015	$3.227

The costs of a plain concrete retaining wall are given in Table XI, and of reinforced concrete retaining walls in Table XII and Table XIII.

TABLE XI.

COST OF A PLAIN CONCRETE RETAINING WALL, BUILT BY D. L. & W. R. R.,
SCRANTON, PA., IN 1907; 500 CU. YDS. OF CONCRETE.*

Items of Expense.	Cost.	
	Per cubic yard.	Per cent of Total.
Broken stone @ $0.70 per ton.	$0.72	16.7
Sand @ $0.55 per cu. yd.	0.24	5.4
Cement @ $0.85 per bbl.	1.06	24.6
Lumber charged @ ¾ value.	.48	11.3
Labor — Mixing and placing concrete.	1.03	23.4
Labor — building forms.	.53	12.3
Labor — unloading materials	.17	3.8
Depreciation of wheelbarrows and tools	.04	1.0
Superintendence — 30 hr. @ 50 ct.	.03	0.6
Office expense — $20.00	.04	0.9
	$4.34	100.0

TABLE XII.

COST OF REINFORCED CONCRETE WALLS, PITTSBURG, PA.; CHAS. M. REPPERT, IN
PROCEEDINGS ENGINEER'S SOC. WEST. PENN., OCTOBER, 1910.
35 ft. Reinforced Concrete Wall, Counterfort Type.

Item.	Quantity per lineal foot.	Unit price.	Cost per cu. yd. concrete 7.08 cu. yd.	Cost per lineal foot.
Excavation, cu. yd.	9.33	$0.645	$0.85	$6.02
Reinforced concrete, cu. yd.	6.38	6.68	6.02	42.62
Plain concrete, cu. yd.	0.70	4.00	.40	2.80
Steel reinforcement, lb	604	.0245	2.09	14.80
Structural steel, lb.	43.8	.022	.13	.96
			$9.49	$67.20

Estimated cost of plain concrete wall 20 per cent more than estimated cost of reinforced wall.

30 ft. Reinforced Concrete Wall, Counterfort Type, Fig 33i.

Item.	Quantity per lineal foot.	Unit price.	Cost per cu. yd. concrete 5.02 cu. yd.	Cost per lineal foot.
Excavation, cu. yd.	5.70	$0.533	$0.60	$3.04
Reinforced concrete, cu. yd.	4.38	6.88	6.00	30.13
Plain concrete, cu. yd.	0.64	4.20	0.54	2.70
Steel reinforcement, lb.	382	0.277	2.11	10.58
Structural steel, lb.	38	0.22	0.17	.84
			$9.42	$47.29

Estimated cost of plain concrete wall 15 per cent more than estimated cost of reinforced wall.

*Data by Mr. C. C. Williams, who was in charge of work.

TABLE XII (*continued*).

21.5 ft. Reinforced Concrete Wall, Counterfort Type.

Item.	Quantity per lineal foot.	Unit price.	Cost per cu. yd. concrete 2.98 cu. yd.	Cost per lineal foot.
Excavation, cu. yd....................	3.15	$0.596	$0.64	$1.88
Reinforced concrete, cu. yd	2.50	6.806	5.70	16.99
Plain concrete, cu. yd.	.48	4.47	0.72	2.15
Steel reinforcement, lb	204	0.278	1.90	5.68
Structural steel, lb...................	26	0.22	.19	0.57
			$9.15	$27.27

note { Estimated cost of plain concrete wall 18 per cent more, and estimated cost cantilever type same as estimated cost counterfort type.

Cost Michigan St. Wall, 23′ 6″ high, Cantilever Type, Fig. 33 j.

Reinforced Concrete, 3.3 cu. yds. per lineal foot......@ $8.00 = $26.40

Reinforcing Steel, 405 lbs. per lineal foot............@ $ .04 = 16.20

Total per lineal foot....................................$40.60

TABLE XIII.

Cost of Reinforced Concrete Retaining Walls for Track Elevation in Chicago, 1907.

Items of Expense.	Cost per cu. yd. of Concrete.	
Excavation, 4528 cu yds. including pumping, sheet piling' and cutting off piles		$0.54
Piling, 14,616 lin. ft., piles 10 cts. and driving 18 cts. per lin. ft..		0.72
Concrete, 5608 cu. yd.		
Cement..	$1.75	
Gravel	.03	
Reinforcing steel...	.62	
Forms	.56	
Cost of materials.		2.96
Labor, Building forms...	1.10	
Removing forms	.23	
Mixing, placing and cleaning concrete....................	1.02	
Placing reinforcement..	.05	
Equipment, etc.	.34	
Cost of labor..		2.74
Total cost per cu. yd............................		$6.96

Comparison of Plain and Reinforced Concrete Retaining Walls.

—(1) In designing a reinforced concrete retaining wall for the Great Northern Ry., Seattle, Wash., Mr. C. F. Graff made a comparative design of plain and reinforced concrete retaining walls. The plain wall had a thickness of 0.4 the height, a front batter of 1 in 12, and was stepped on the back as shown in Fig. 51d. The reinforced concrete wall was designed as shown in Fig. 51d. With steel at 4½ cents per lb. in place, and concrete at $6.00 per cu. yd. in place, the reinforced concrete wall was 20.4 per cent cheaper for a wall 12 feet high; 36.4 per cent cheaper for a wall 22½ feet high; 43.3 per cent cheaper for a wall 32½ feet high; and 45 per cent cheaper for a wall 42½ feet high.

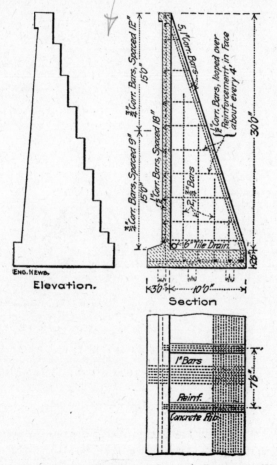

Elevation.

Section

FIG. 51 d.—PLAIN AND REINFORCED CONCRETE RETAINING WALLS.

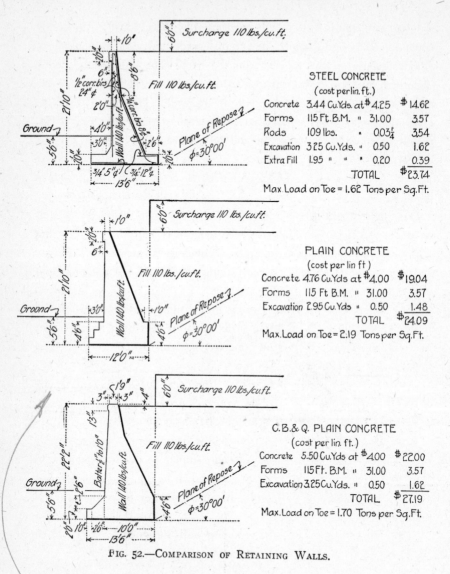

STEEL CONCRETE
(cost per lin. ft.)

Concrete	3.44 Cu.Yds. at $4.25	$14.62
Forms	115 Ft. B.M. " 31.00	3.57
Rods	109 lbs. " .003¾	3.54
Excavation	3.25 Cu.Yds. " 0.50	1.62
Extra Fill	1.95 " " 0.20	0.39
	TOTAL	$23.74

Max. Load on Toe = 1.62 Tons per Sq. Ft.

PLAIN CONCRETE
(cost per lin ft)

Concrete	4.76 Cu.Yds. at $4.00	$19.04
Forms	115 Ft B.M. " 31.00	3.57
Excavation	2.95 Cu.Yds " 0.50	1.48
	TOTAL	$24.09

Max. Load on Toe = 2.19 Tons per Sq. Ft.

C.B.& Q. PLAIN CONCRETE
(cost per lin. ft.)

Concrete	5.50 Cu.Yds at $4.00	$22.00
Forms	115 Ft. B.M. " 31.00	3.57
Excavation	3.25 Cu.Yds. " 0.50	1.62
	TOTAL	$27.19

Max. Load on Toe = 1.70 Tons per Sq. Ft.

FIG. 52.—COMPARISON OF RETAINING WALLS.

(2) The walls shown in Fig. 52 were described in the Journal of the Western Society of Engineers, June, 1907, by Mr. T. L. Condron. The reinforced concrete wall is very much like the C. B. & Q. R. R. wall in Fig. 51a, and is cheaper than the plain wall which gives the same toe pressure. P. 153

(3) The wall in Fig. 51a is a wall used by the C. B. & Q. R. R. for track elevation in Chicago. The walls were supported by piles more closely spaced on the toe than on the heel. The cost of the walls, including concrete, reinforcing steel, excavation, and piles was $9.00 for each cu. yd. of concrete actually in the wall. The cost of the concrete alone was $6.23 per cu. yd. The cost of plain retaining walls, including concrete, excavation, and piling, was $5.55 per cu. yd. of concrete. The cost of the concrete alone in the plain walls was $5.03 per cu. yd. The estimated cost of a C. B. & Q. R. R. plain wall is given in Fig. 52.

(4) A reinforced concrete wall of the slab type, 21 feet high and 11 ft. by 1½ ft. base, and 500 feet long, was built in 1907 by the Union Railway Company, Memphis, Tennessee, at a cost of $8.82 per cu. yd. of concrete, including reinforcing and forms, but not including excavation.

(5) Mr. J. G. Sullivan, Asst. Chief Engineer, Canadian Pacific R. R., states that " for retaining walls up to 35 feet high from bottom of foundation slab, reinforced concrete is about 25 per cent cheaper than monolithic concrete."

(6) Mr. Alex. Bonnyman, Chief Engineer, Atlantic, Birmingham & Atlantic R. R., states: " By the contract prices we figure that there is a saving in reinforced concrete walls of about 25 per cent."

(7) The Illinois Central R. R. is now using plain concrete retaining walls on track elevation in Chicago similar to the walls shown in Fig. 38. The reinforced concrete wall shown in Fig. 33l was designed for this work but was not built, due to the lower price bid for the plain wall.

(8) For estimated costs of retaining walls designed by the C. M. & St. P. R. R., see Table VIB, Chapter IV.

CHAPTER VIIA.

Notes on Design of Retaining Walls and Pressures in Sand Boxes.

DESIGN OF RETAINING WALLS AND ABUTMENTS.*—

The Committee believes that the intelligent use of theoretical formulas leads to economical and proper design, and therefore recommends that Rankine's formulas which consider that the filling is a granular mass of indefinite extent, without cohesion, be used in the design of retaining walls. It is recommended that retaining walls be designed (*a*) for a level surcharge, or (*b*) for a sloping surcharge at the angle of repose, or (*c*) for a level surcharge with a uniform surcharge loading. Formulas based on Rankine are given for vertical walls, walls leaning away from the filling, and for walls leaning toward the filling.

The use of a fixed ratio of width to height leads to a neglect of the distribution of the pressure on the foundation. This is a question of great importance, since it is well established that movements from the original alignment, due to unequal settlement, form a defect more common than any other. The Committee feels that attention should be called to the importance of making a study of each case in designing a wall, particularly of the weight and character of the filling, and the amount and distribution of the pressure on the bed of foundations.

DESIGN OF RETAINING WALLS.—The following nomenclature is recommended:

$\phi =$ the angle of repose of the filling.
$\theta =$ the angle between the back of the wall and a horizontal line passing through the heel of the wall and extending from the back into the fill.
$\delta =$ angle of surcharge, the angle between a horizontal line and the surface of the filling. (It is recommended that values of $\delta = 0$ or $\delta = \phi$ be used.)
$\lambda =$ the angle between the resultant thrust, P, and a horizontal line.
$h =$ vertical height of the wall in feet.
$h' =$ height of surcharge in feet.
$l =$ width of the base of the wall in feet.

* Report of the masonry committee of American Railway Engineering Association, adopted March 22, 1917.

$e =$ distance from the center of the base to the intersection of the resultant thrust, E, and the base.

$a = l/2 - e =$ distance from toe of wall to intersection of the resultant thrust, E, and the base.

$P =$ the resultant earth pressure per foot of length of wall.

$E =$ the resultant of the earth pressure and the weight of the wall.

$F =$ vertical component of resultant E.

$w =$ the weight of the filling per cubic foot.

$w_1 =$ the weight of the masonry per foot of length.

$W =$ total weight of the wall per foot of length.

p_1 and $p_2 =$ pressure per square foot on the foundation, due to F, at toe and heel, respectively.

Formulas.—The following formulas for vertical walls or for walls leaning away from the filling are based on Rankine's Theory, as given in Howe's "Retaining Walls," and in Ketchum's "Walls, Bins and Grain Elevators"; and the formulas for walls leaning toward the filling are based on a modification of Rankine's Theory, as given in Ketchum's "Walls, Bins and Grain Elevators."

For vertical walls with horizontal surcharge the pressure, P, is given by the formula

$$P = \tfrac{1}{2}wh^2 \frac{1 - \sin \phi}{1 + \sin \phi} = \tfrac{1}{2}wh^2 \tan^2 \left(45° - \frac{\phi}{2} \right) \qquad (1)$$

where P is parallel to the top surface, is normal to the wall, and is applied at one-third the height of the wall above the base.

For vertical walls with a positive surcharge, δ, the pressure, P, is given by the formula

$$P = \tfrac{1}{2}wh^2 \cos \delta \frac{\cos \delta - \sqrt{\cos^2 \delta - \cos^2 \phi}}{\cos \delta + \sqrt{\cos^2 \delta - \cos^2 \phi}} \qquad (2)$$

where P is parallel to the top surface of the filling, makes an angle δ with a normal to the back of the wall, and is applied at one-third the height of the wall above the base. Where the surcharge is equal to the angle of repose, ϕ, formula (2) becomes

$$P = \tfrac{1}{2} wh^2 \cos \phi \qquad (3)$$

For a vertical wall with a loaded surcharge the resultant pressure on the back of the wall will be given by the formula

$$P = \tfrac{1}{2} wh (h + 2h') \frac{1 - \sin \phi}{1 + \sin \phi} \qquad (4)$$

where h is the height of the wall and h' the equivalent height of surcharge, equals surcharge per square foot divided by w, the weight per cubic foot of the filling.

The resultant pressure is horizontal and is applied at a distance from the base of the wall equal to

$$y = \frac{h^2 + 3hh'}{3(h + 2h')} \tag{5}$$

[handwritten: + for. (35) P. 47 where H = h + h']

(a) In calculating the surcharge due to a track the entire load shall be taken as distributed uniformly over a width of 14 feet for a single track or tracks spaced more than 14 feet centers, and the distance center to center of tracks where tracks are spaced less than 14 feet.

(b) In calculating the pressure on a retaining wall where the filling carries permanent tracks or structures, the full effect of the loaded surcharge shall be considered where the edge of the distributed load or the structure is vertically above the back edge of the heel of the wall. The effect of the loaded surcharge may be neglected where the edge of the distributed load or the structure is at a distance from the vertical line through the back edge of the heel of the wall equal to h, the height of the wall. For intermediate position the equivalent uniform surcharge load is to be taken as proportional. For example, for a track with the edge of the distributed load at a distance, h/2, from the vertical line through the back edge of the heel of the wall, the equivalent uniform surcharge load is one-half the normal distributed load distributed over the filling. Case 15, Fig. 2, explains the distribution. The height of surcharge loading will be equal to the load per linear foot divided by b (b = 14 feet for a single track railway). Where the edge of the distributed load cannot come nearer to the vertical line through the back of the heel of the wall than h — x, the equivalent uniformly distributed load in terms of heights is

[handwritten: By proportion, see fig. 2. P.164d,]

$$h_x' = h'\frac{x}{h}.$$

[handwritten: $h_x' : h' = x' : h$, $h_x' = h'\frac{x}{h}$]

For walls leaning forward or walls with the base extending into the filling, the pressure of the filling on a vertical plane through back of the heel of the wall, as calculated above, is to be combined with the wedge of filling contained between this vertical plane and the back of the wall.

For walls leaning toward the filling the resultant pressure, P, will be horizontal for a wall without surcharge or with a horizontal loaded surcharge, and will make an angle, λ, with the horizontal for a wall with a sloping surcharge. The values of λ will vary from δ, where the wall is vertical, to zero, where Rankine's Theory shows that the resultant pressure is horizontal. Values of λ are given in cases 10 and 11, Fig. 1. Values of K, where P = ½ wh² K, are given in cases 10 and 11, Fig. 1.

The formulas for the different cases above are given in cases 1 to 9, Fig. 1.

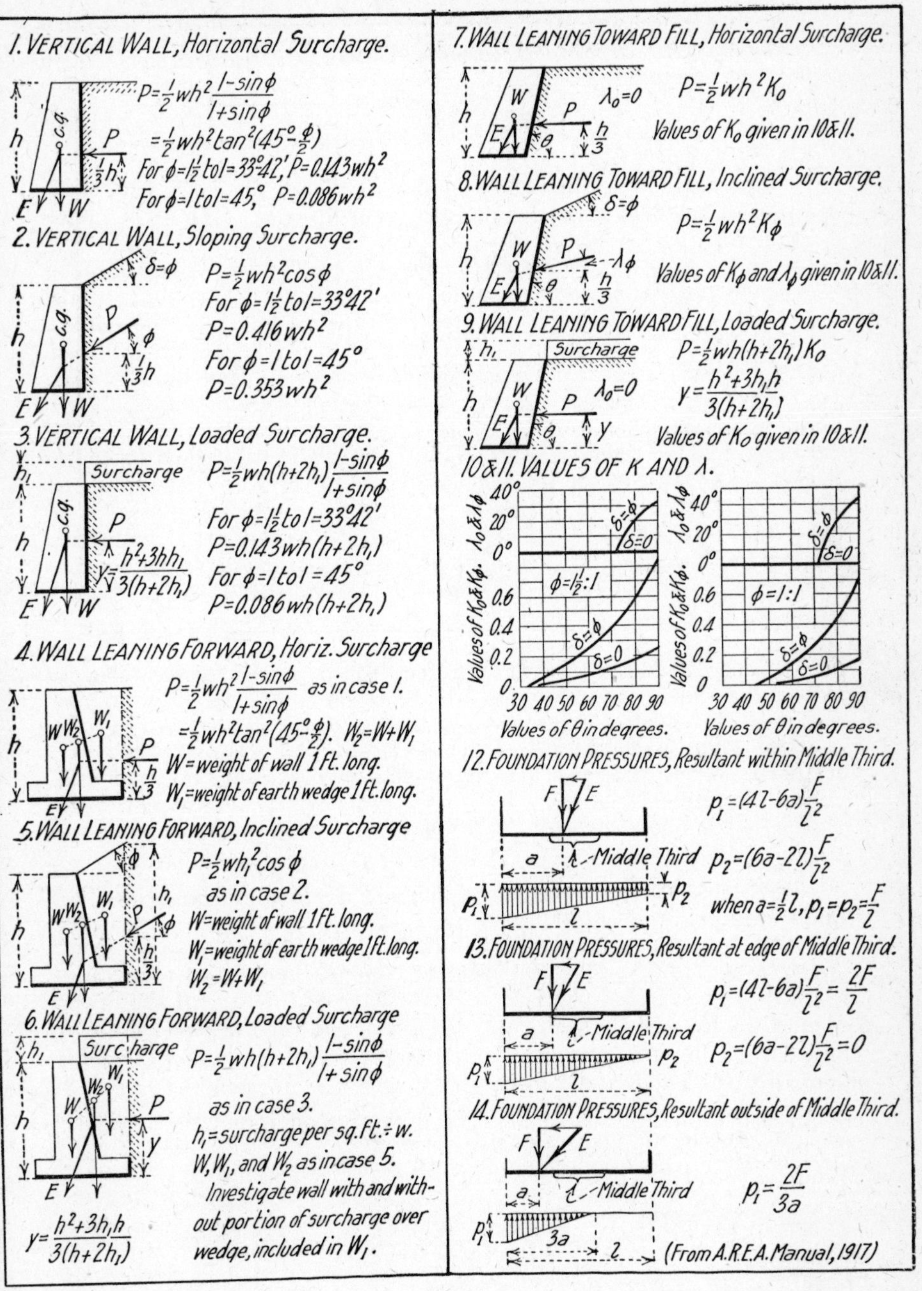

1. VERTICAL WALL, Horizontal Surcharge.

$$P = \tfrac{1}{2}wh^2\frac{1-\sin\phi}{1+\sin\phi}$$
$$= \tfrac{1}{2}wh^2\tan^2(45°-\tfrac{\phi}{2})$$
For $\phi=1\tfrac{1}{2}$ to $1=33°42'$, $P=0.143wh^2$
For $\phi=1$ to $1=45°$, $P=0.086wh^2$

2. VERTICAL WALL, Sloping Surcharge.

$$P=\tfrac{1}{2}wh^2\cos\phi$$
For $\phi=1\tfrac{1}{2}$ to $1=33°42'$
$P=0.416wh^2$
For $\phi=1$ to $1=45°$
$P=0.353wh^2$

3. VERTICAL WALL, Loaded Surcharge.

$$P=\tfrac{1}{2}wh(h+2h_1)\frac{1-\sin\phi}{1+\sin\phi}$$
For $\phi=1\tfrac{1}{2}$ to $1=33°42'$
$P=0.143wh(h+2h_1)$
$y=\dfrac{h^2+3hh_1}{3(h+2h_1)}$
For $\phi=1$ to $1=45°$
$P=0.086wh(h+2h_1)$

4. WALL LEANING FORWARD, Horiz. Surcharge

$$P=\tfrac{1}{2}wh^2\frac{1-\sin\phi}{1+\sin\phi} \text{ as in case 1.}$$
$$=\tfrac{1}{2}wh^2\tan^2(45°-\tfrac{\phi}{2}). \quad W_2=W+W_1.$$
$W=$ weight of wall 1 ft. long.
$W_1=$ weight of earth wedge 1 ft. long.

5. WALL LEANING FORWARD, Inclined Surcharge

$$P=\tfrac{1}{2}wh^2\cos\phi$$
as in case 2.
$W=$ weight of wall 1 ft. long.
$W_1=$ weight of earth wedge 1 ft. long.
$W_2=W+W_1.$

6. WALL LEANING FORWARD, Loaded Surcharge

$$P=\tfrac{1}{2}wh(h+2h_1)\frac{1-\sin\phi}{1+\sin\phi}$$
as in case 3.
$h_1=$ surcharge per sq. ft. $\div$ w.
$W, W_1,$ and W_2 as in case 5.
Investigate wall with and without portion of surcharge over wedge, included in W_1.
$$y=\frac{h^2+3h_1h}{3(h+2h_1)}$$

7. WALL LEANING TOWARD FILL, Horizontal Surcharge.

$\lambda_0=0$
$$P=\tfrac{1}{2}wh^2K_0$$
Values of K_0 given in 10 & 11.

8. WALL LEANING TOWARD FILL, Inclined Surcharge.

$\delta=\phi$
$$P=\tfrac{1}{2}wh^2K_\phi$$
Values of K_ϕ and λ_ϕ given in 10 & 11.

9. WALL LEANING TOWARD FILL, Loaded Surcharge.

$\lambda_0=0$
$$P=\tfrac{1}{2}wh(h+2h_1)K_0$$
$$y=\frac{h^2+3h_1h}{3(h+2h_1)}$$
Values of K_0 given in 10 & 11.

10 & 11. VALUES OF K AND λ.

Values of K_0 & λ_0 — $\phi=1\tfrac{1}{2}:1$ — $\delta=\phi$, $\delta=0$
Values of θ in degrees. 30 40 50 60 70 80 90

Values of K_0 & λ_0 — $\phi=1:1$ — $\delta=\phi$, $\delta=0$
Values of θ in degrees. 30 40 50 60 70 80 90

12. FOUNDATION PRESSURES, Resultant within Middle Third.

$$p_1=(4l-6a)\frac{F}{l^2}$$
$$p_2=(6a-2l)\frac{F}{l^2}$$
when $a=\tfrac{1}{2}l$, $p_1=p_2=\dfrac{F}{l}$

13. FOUNDATION PRESSURES, Resultant at edge of Middle Third.

$$p_1=(4l-6a)\frac{F}{l^2}=\frac{2F}{l}$$
$$p_2=(6a-2l)\frac{F}{l^2}=0$$

14. FOUNDATION PRESSURES, Resultant outside of Middle Third.

$$p_1=\frac{2F}{3a}$$

(From A.R.E.A. Manual, 1917)

FIG. I.

see fig of Case 12. P. 1

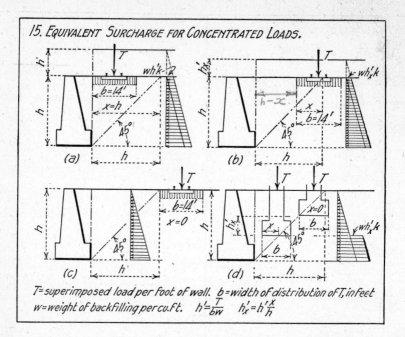

FIG. 2. EQUIVALENT SURCHARGE FOR CONCENTRATED LOADS.

Discussion of Formulas.—Cases 1 to 3 are for vertical walls without heels. The pressure, P, is the same as the pressure on a vertical plane in the filling. Vertical walls with heels come under cases 4 to 6.

Cases 4 to 6 are for walls with heels. The wall may be vertical or may lean forward, or may lean backward, as long as the upper edge of the back of the wall is in front of the vertical plane through the edge of the heel.

Cases 7 to 9 are for walls without heels. Walls with heels come under cases 4 to 6 as long as the upper edge of the back of the wall is in front of the vertical plane through the edge of the heel; if the upper edge of the back of the wall extends back of the vertical plane through the edge of the heel, the problem can be solved by combining the solutions of cases 4 to 6 and 7 to 9.

Pressure on Foundations.—The pressures on foundations will be calculated by the following formulas:
Where a is equal to or greater than $l/3$.
Pressure at the toe

see fig of Case 12. P. 164 c.
$$p_1 = (4l - 6a)\frac{F}{l^2} \tag{6}$$

$P = \dfrac{F}{l} =$ unit pressure due to direct vertical force F. ('y- same

$p' = \dfrac{6F\left(\frac{l}{2} - a\right)}{l^2} = \dfrac{6F(l-2a)}{2l^2} = \dfrac{3F(l-2a)}{l^2} =$ unit pressure on toe

$p_1 = p + p'$ =

$$p - p' = \frac{F}{l} - \frac{3F(l-2a)}{l^2} = \frac{Fl - 3Fl + 6Fa}{l^2} = \frac{6Fa - 2Fl}{l^2}$$

$$= \frac{F}{l^2}(6a - 2l)$$

'f fig. 9 case 13 & Case 14, P. 164 c.

Pressure at the heel is

$$p_2 = (6a - 2l)\frac{F}{l^2}$$

$$P_1 = \left(4l - 6a\right)\frac{F}{l^2}$$

$$P_1 = \frac{(4 \times 3a - 6a)F}{(3a)^2} = \frac{6aF}{(3a)^2} \qquad (7)$$

Where a is less than $l/3$, the pressure at the toe is

$$p_1 = \frac{2F}{3a}$$

$$P_1 = \frac{2F}{3a} \qquad (8)$$

Principles for Design of Retaining Walls.—The following principles should be observed in the design and construction of retaining walls.

1. For usual conditions of the filling use an angle of repose of 1½ to 1 ($\phi = 33° 42'$). For dry sand or similar material, a slope of 1 to 1 ($\phi = 45°$) may be used.

2. The maximum pressure at the toe of the retaining wall should never exceed the safe bearing pressure on the material considered.

3. When the retaining wall rests on a compressible material, where settlement may be expected, the resultant thrust, E, should strike at the middle or back of the middle of the base of the wall so that the wall will settle toward the filling ($a =$ or $> l/2$).

4. When the retaining wall rests on a material where settlement may not be expected the resultant thrust, E, should not strike outside the middle third of the base ($a =$ or $> l/3$), except as noted in (5) below.

5. Where the retaining wall rests on solid rock or is carried on piles the resultant thrust, E, may strike slightly outside the middle third, provided the wall is safe against overturning, and also provided the maximum allowable pressure is not exceeded.

6. In order that the retaining wall may be safe against sliding, the frictional resistance of the base, combined with the abutting resistance of the earth in front of the wall, must be greater than the horizontal thrust on the back of the wall.

7. The filling back of the wall should be carefully drained so that the wall may not be subjected to hydrostatic pressure.

8. The foundation for a retaining wall should always be placed below frost line.

9. A careful study should be made of the conditions in the design of each wall, and it should be remembered that no theoretical formulas can be more than an aid to the judgment of the experienced designer. The main value of theoretical formulas is in obtaining economical proportions, in obtaining a proper distribution of the stresses, and in making experience already gained more valuable.

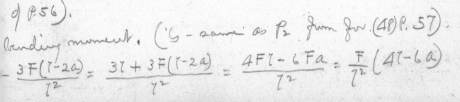

d (P. 56).

Bending moment. ('S - same as P_2 from for. (48) P. 57).

$$\frac{3F(l-2a)}{l^2} = \frac{3l + 3F(l-2a)}{l^2} = \frac{4Fl - 6Fa}{l^2} = \frac{F}{l^2}(4l - 6a)$$

PRESSURE IN SAND BOXES.—Sand boxes in which the sand can be withdrawn are used to lower centers of arches, for camber blocking in erecting trusses, and as a substitute for powerful jacks in lowering structures. Sand boxes are usually steel plate cylinders with a plate bottom connected to the cylinder by an angle on the outside, the rivets on the inside of the cylinder being counter-sunk. The load is applied through a plunger which fits the steel cylinder with sufficient clearance and rests on the sand filling. The load is lowered by permitting the sand to run out of holes in the side of the cylinder near the bottom or in the plate bottom. A clean, dry sand with uniform size grains should be used. Fine sand is commonly less compressible and also flows more freely than a coarse sand.

The sand box is a deep bin in which the lateral and vertical pressures at any point are due to a pressure p lb. per sq. ft. on top of the bin in addition to the pressures due to the granular material itself. The derivation of the formula for vertical pressure in Fig. 3 is the same as for deep bins, except that in equation (5) when $y=0$, $V=p$, resulting in equation (6). In solving equations (11) and (12) hyperbolic logarithms must be used. Hyperbolic logarithms are given on page 313, also on 322 of Ketchum's Structural Engineers' Handbook. Equation (13) is equation (12) reduced to common or Briggs logarithms. The relation between vertical and lateral pressure is $L = k \cdot V$, where $k = (1 - \sin\phi)/(1 + \sin\phi)$.

PRESSURE ON SAND BOXES

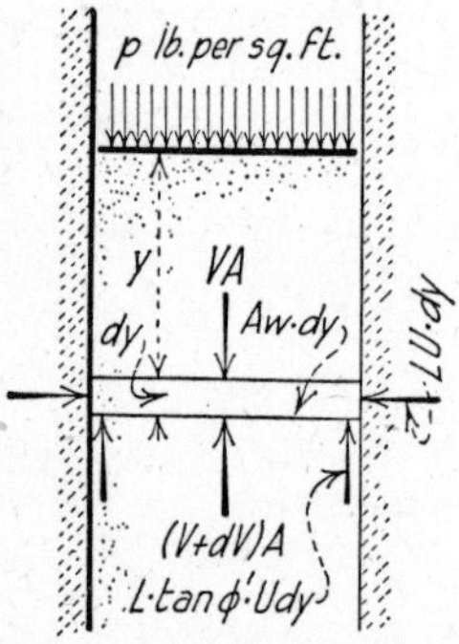

p lb. per sq. ft.

y VA

dy $Aw \cdot dy$

$(V+dV)A$

$L \cdot \tan\phi \cdot Udy$

ϕ' = angle of friction of sand on walls. $\mu' = \tan\phi'$.
w = weight of sand per cu. ft.
V = vertical pressure, lb./sq. ft
L = lateral pressure, lb./sq. ft
A = area of box in sq. ft
U = circumference of box in ft

$$V \cdot A - (V+dV)A + Aw \cdot dy - L \cdot \tan\phi' \cdot U \cdot dy = 0 \qquad (1)$$

$$dV = (w - L \cdot \tan\phi' \tfrac{U}{A})dy \qquad (2)$$

but $L = k \cdot V$ $\tan\phi' = \mu'$ $\dfrac{A}{U} = R$

$$dV = (w - \tfrac{kV\mu'}{R})dy \qquad (3)$$

Let $n = k\mu' \div R$ then $dV = (w - nV)dy$

$$\frac{dV}{w - nV} = dy \qquad (4)$$

Integrating (4) $Log(w-nV) = -ny + C$ (5)
when $y=0$, $V=p$, and $C = Log(w-np)$, and

$$Log(w-nV) = -ny + Log(w+np) \qquad (6)$$

$$Log\left(\frac{w-nV}{w-np}\right) = -ny \quad (7). \quad \frac{w-nV}{w-np} = e^{-ny} \qquad (8)$$

and $nV = w - (w-np)e^{-ny}$ (9)

$$V = \frac{w}{n}(1 - e^{-ny}) + pe^{-ny} \qquad (10)$$

$$= \frac{wR}{k\mu'}\left(1 - e^{-\frac{k\mu'y}{R}}\right) + pe^{-\frac{k\mu'y}{R}} \qquad (11)$$

$$L = kV = \frac{wR}{\mu'}\left(1 - e^{-\frac{k\mu'y}{R}}\right) + kpe^{-\frac{k\mu'y}{R}} \qquad (12)$$

$$= \frac{wR}{\mu'}\left(1 - \frac{1}{2.303 \cdot log_{10}\left(\frac{k\mu'y}{R}\right)}\right) + kp \cdot \frac{1}{2.303 \cdot log_{10}\frac{k\mu'y}{R}} \qquad (13)$$

FIG. 3. PRESSURE IN SAND BOXES.

APPROXIMATE DESIGN OF REINFORCED CONCRETE RETAINING WALLS.

The formulas and curves shown in Figs. 4 and 5 give the approximate dimensions, foundation pressures, and factors of safety for most types of reinforced concrete retaining walls, including the cantilever wall, and the counterfort wall.

These formulas and curves are based on the assumption that the wall and the filling have the same weight per cubic foot, and the weight of the toe is neglected. This is shown by the shaded areas in the figures. The values given by the formulas and curves are sufficiently accurate for determining the general dimensions of a wall preliminary to design.

Two sets of formulas are given. In Fig. 4 the resultant pressure on the foundation passes through the outside edge of the middle third of the base and in Fig. 5 the resultant pressure passes through the center of the base. See Principles of Design in first part of this chapter.

Four cases have been considered: (a) the ground surface horizontal; (b) the ground surface sloping at the angle of repose; (c) a loaded surcharge up to a point vertically over the edge of the heel but not extending over the heel; and (d) a loaded surcharge extending over the heel. The loaded surcharge is taken as equivalent to some vertical load, such as loaded tracks, bins, etc.

The factor of safety against sliding is given by the nearly vertical lines crossing the solid curves. The angle of friction is taken as $\phi' = 33° 42'$ ($1\frac{1}{2}$ to 1) in all cases. The effect of a cut-off was not considered. The factor of safety against overturning is always safe in this type of wall.

Two sets of curves are given for each case, one with the angle of repose as $\phi = 33° 42'$ ($1\frac{1}{2}$ to 1) and one with the angle of repose as $\phi = 45° 00'$ (1 to 1). See Principles of Design in first part of this chapter.

The curves show that, except in the case with sloping surcharge, the smallest width of base will be obtained when the front of the vertical slab is at a distance of two-thirds the width of the base from the heel when the resultant cuts the base at the edge of the middle third, and when the front of the vertical slab is at the center of the base when the resultant cuts the base at the center.

PROBLEM 1. INVESTIGATION OF MASONRY WALL.

Problem.—Given a plain masonry retaining wall with dimensions as shown in figure in Problem 1 and a surcharge at an angle of 15° 00'. Find the magnitude and direction of the pressure against the wall, the unit pressure at the heel and toe, and the factors of safety against sliding and overturning. Use Rankine's Method in finding the resultant pressure against the wall and check by Coulomb's Method. The weight of earth is to be assumed as 100 lb. per cu. ft., the angle of repose and the angle of friction 30° 00', and the angle of surcharge 15° 00'.

Solution.—To find the pressure against the wall by Rankine's Method proceed as follows: Draw AO parallel to the surface of the ground and at any convenient point O in AO draw OD at right angles to AO. Draw OM vertical and locate M by striking the arc DM with O as a center. Draw OC making an angle $\phi = 30°$ with OD. At any point e in OD describe an arc tangent to OC and cutting OM at f. Draw ef. Through M draw MG parallel to ef. Bisect the angle DGM and draw GR'. To determine the semi-major axis of the ellipse of stress draw OR parallel to GR' and make $OM_1 = OG + GM$. To determine the semi-minor axis draw OX perpendicular to OR and equal to $OG - GM$. To calculate the unit pressure against the wall at A draw OG' at right angles to the back of the wall AB and make $OG' = OG$, draw $G's$ perpendicular to OR and make $st = Os$, draw $G't$ and lay off GM' equal to GM, then $M'O$ acting as shown is the intensity of stress at A. To determine the magnitude of this stress $M'O$ measure its length, using the same scale as that used in laying off the wall, and multiply this length by the weight of a cubic foot of earth (100 in this case) and the result will be the intensity of pressure at A measured in pounds per sq. ft. on the surface AB. This is found to be $p = 8.25 \times 100 = 825$ lb. per sq. ft. The intensity of pressure at B is evidently zero and since the pressure varies as the

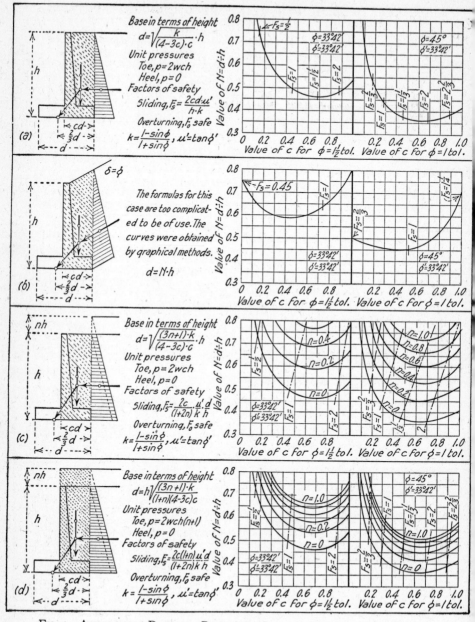

FIG. 4. APPROXIMATE DESIGN OF REINFORCED CONCRETE RETAINING WALLS. (Resultant thrust at outer edge of middle third of base.)

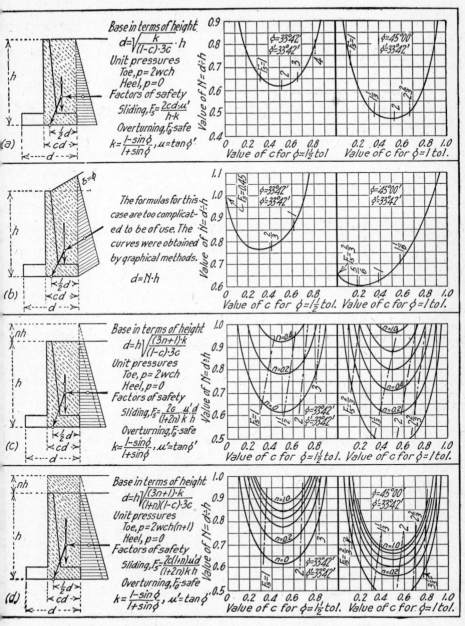

Fig. 5. Approximate Design of Reinforced Concrete Retaining Walls. (Resultant thrust at center of base.)

depth the total pressure P against the back of the wall AB will be $\frac{1}{2}p \times$ length $AB = \frac{1}{2} \times 825 \times 20.5 = 8,260$ lb. The line of action of P is parallel to OM' and the angle λ is measured and found to be 25° 20'.

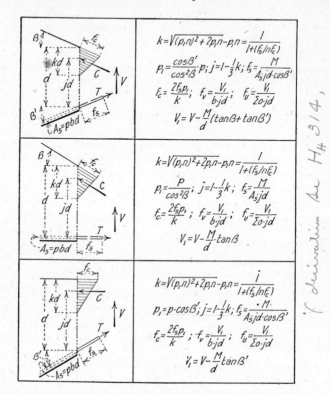

FIG. 6. STRESSES IN WEDGE-SHAPED REINFORCED CONCRETE BEAMS.

To find the pressure against the wall by Coulomb's Method proceed as follows: The pressure against the vertical plane AB' must first be found and this pressure combined with the weight of the wedge ABB' to find the pressure against AB. This procedure is necessary because Coulomb's method gives the magnitude of the pressure but not its direction, and since it is known that for a vertical plane the pressure is parallel to the ground surface, the magnitude and direction of the resultant pressure can be found by combining the pressure against AB' with the weight of the wedge ABB'. Draw AB' vertical and AD making an angle of $\phi = 30°$ with the horizontal, the point D being the intersection of this line, and the ground surface. Through B' draw BM making an angle $\delta = 15°$ with BF the normal to AD. Locate O bisecting the line AD and with O as a center and AO as a radius describe the semicircle ACD. Draw MC normal to AD and with A as a center and a radius AC describe the arc CN. Draw EN parallel to $B'M$. With N as a center and radius EN describe the arc ES. Then the total pressure against AB' is $P' = $ area $SEN.w = \frac{1}{2} \times 12.65 \times 12.20 \times 100 = 7,700$ lb. acting at $\frac{1}{3}$ the height AB' above A. Combine P' with W', the weight of the wedge, acting through its centroid, and find $P = 8,250$, the resultant pressure against AB. The angle λ is measured and found to be 25° 16'.

These two methods should give the same result. The results obtained in this problem are seen to check very closely.

To find the unit pressure at the heel and toe combine $P = 8,260$ with the weight of the wall $W = 14,250$, acting through its centroid, giving the resultant $E = 19,230$, as shown in the problem under Rankine's Method. This resultant E cuts the base at a distance $b = 1.80'$ from the center, which is outside of the middle third. The unit pressure at the heel and toe are found as shown under Coulomb's Method and are o and 6,060 pounds per square foot respectively. The factor of safety against sliding is equal to $QU \div RU = 1.50$, and against overturning is $SU \div RU = 2.95$.

Results.—The results of this investigation show that the wall is unsatisfactory, for the resultant pressure on the base falls outside of the middle third. The unit pressures are not excessive if the foundation is dry sand or clay.

PROBLEM 2. INVESTIGATION OF CANTILEVER WALL.

Problem.—Make a complete investigation of the reinforced concrete retaining wall with a horizontal surcharge shown in Problem 2. The weight of the wall is 150 lb. per cu. ft. and the earth 100 lb. per cu. ft. The angle of repose is 30° 00'. (p. 164 o)

Solution.—The first step in the solution is to determine the pressure acting against the back of the wall. This pressure is found by combining the pressure P' against the vertical plane $A'B'$, acting at one-third of the height, with the weight W' of the wedge of earth resting on the heel acting through the center of gravity G' of the wedge. The calculations are shown on the problem.

The resultant pressure on the foundation $R = 22,600$ lb. is found by combining the pressure P on the wall with the weight of the wall W acting through the center of gravity G. This resultant pressure R cuts the base at a distance of $e = 1.35'$ from the center of the base. The unit pressure at the heel and toe are calculated as shown and are 517 and 2,945 lb. per sq. ft. respectively.

The wall is divided into three cantilever beams which must be investigated, i. e., the vertical slab, the heel, and the toe. Three sections, $A–A$, $B–B$ and $C–C$, on the vertical slab must be investigated on account of the change in steel area at these sections. The intensity of stress at $A–A$ is $p = w \cdot h \cdot k = 100 \times 6 \times 0.333 = 200$ lb. per sq. in. where $k = 1 - \sin \phi \div 1 + \sin \phi = 0.333$. The total pressure on the cantilever above $A–A$ is $P_A = \frac{1}{2} \times 200 \times 6 = 600$ lb. acting 2.0 ft. above $A–A$. These values are recorded in the table. The shear at $A–A$ is $V = P_A = 600$ lb. The bending moment at $A–A$ is $M = 600 \times 2 = 1,200$ ft. lb. $= 14,400$ in. lb. The dimensions, steel area, etc., at this section are as given in the table. The values of k and j may be taken from a diagram or calculated from the formula that $k = \sqrt{p^2 \cdot n^2 + 2p \cdot n} - p \cdot n$ and $j = 1 - \frac{1}{3}k$ where $n = 15$. The unit stresses can now be calculated from the formulas given in the table and are there recorded. The other sections of the vertical slab are investigated in a similar manner.

The resultant pressure on the toe is obtained by subtracting the downward force due to the weight of the toe from the upward force due to the foundation pressures. This gives a resultant pressure upward as shown graphically by the shaded area in (f) on the problem. The shear at the section is given by the portion of the shaded area to the left of the section, and the moment by the moment of this area about the section. These values are recorded in the table. The stresses at $D–D$ are found in the same way as explained for $A–A$. On account of the fillet the stresses at the section $E–E$ must be found by using the formulas for wedge-shaped beams, Fig. 6.

The resultant pressure on the heel is obtained by subtracting the downward force due to the weight of the heel and the earth on the heel from the upward force due to foundation pressures. This gives a resultant pressure acting downward as shown by the shaded area in (f). The unit stresses at $F–F$ and $G–G$ are found as in a similar manner to that explained for the sections $D–D$ and $E–E$. In investigating the section $G–G$ the horizontal steel was neglected, for since it is so near the neutral axis it would be carrying very little stress, and the solution considering this steel is quite laborious. The unit stress in steel at this section would be somewhat less than the value of 16,300 lb. per sq. in. given in the table. In investigating the section $F-F$ the diagonal steel was neglected, for if the section had been taken a little to the right of its present position the steel would be so near the neutral axis that it would not be effective and the moment would have been reduced but a small amount.

The required length of embedment beyond the section of zero moment is figured for a stress of 16,000 lb. per sq. in. in the steel and a bond stress of 80 lb. per sq. in. if the ends are not hooked, and 120 lb. per sq. in. if hooked.

The factor of safety against overturning is always safe in this type of wall. The factor of safety of sliding, neglecting the cut-off, is equal to the ratio of $V \cdot \tan \phi'$ to $P = 21,100 \times 0.577 \div 8,067 = 1.51$.

The percentage of temperature reinforcement in the vertical slab is $0.25 \div 16.2 \times 12 = 0.0013$, using the section $B-B$ as an average section. This should be at least 0.0033 to conform to the best practice.

Results.—The results of the investigation are shown on the problem. The wall is found to be satisfactory in every respect except for the temperature reinforcement.

See Prob. 3. P. 164 P

PROBLEM 3. DESIGN OF A CANTILEVER WALL.

Problem.—Design a cantilever wall having a total height of 20 ft. with tracks spaced 14 ft. running parallel to the wall and carrying Cooper's E 50 loading. The weight of concrete is 150 lb. per cu. ft. and of earth 100 lb. per cu. ft. The angle of repose and the angle of internal friction are $1\frac{1}{2}$ to 1 ($33° 42'$). The allowable unit stresses are tension in steel 16,000 lb. per sq. in., compression in concrete 650 lb. per sq. in., allowable bond stress 80 lb. per sq. in. if ends of bars are not hooked, and 120 lb. per sq. in. if hooked, $n = 15$. The allowable pressure on the foundations is 2 tons per sq. ft.

Solution.—The effect of the train load may be taken care of by using an equivalent surcharge. The axles are spaced 5 ft. and the axle load is 50,000 lb., and since the tracks are spaced 14 ft., the load per square foot is $50,000 / (5 \times 14) = 720$ lb. This is equivalent to a surcharge $720 \div 100 = 7.2$ ft. high. A height of 8 ft. will be used. It is not necessary to consider impact in figuring the earth pressure due to engine loads. Two cases must be considered: (1) when the first track is not loaded and there is therefore no live load over the heel, and (2) when all of the tracks are loaded and there is therefore a live load over the heel. The first case is usually the more severe. See first part of this chapter.

The width of base which will make the resultant pressure on the base pass through the outer edge of the middle third may be determined for Case 1 from the diagram in (c) Fig. 4, for $n = 0.4$ to be $d = 13.7$ ft. For Case 2 from diagram (d) in Fig. 4, for $n = 0.4$, $d = 11.7$ ft. Case 1 gives the maximum width of base. Use $d = 14$ ft.

The minimum top width which should be used is 12 in. and for a wall of this size the base slab should be about 2 ft. thick. In some cases it may be more economical to use a thickness of 12 in. at the heel and toe and taper the base slab up to the required thickness at the junction of the base and the vertical slab.

In designing this type of wall the section may be considered as divided into three cantilever beams, i. e., the vertical slab, the heel, and the toe. The first step is to determine the thickness of the vertical slab where it joins the base. This section will be called $C-C$. The effect of the fillet will be neglected for this section. The horizontal pressure on the vertical slab is the same as on the portion of the plane $A'B$ between $C-C$ and the top of the wall. The unit pressure a depth of $18 + 8 = 26$ ft. from the top of the surcharge is $p = w \cdot h \cdot k = 100 \times 26 \times 0.286 = 744$ lb. per sq. ft. The unit pressure at the top of the wall or 8 ft. below the top of the surcharge is $p = 100 \times 8 \times 0.286 = 229$. The total pressure above the section $C-C$ is $P_c = \frac{1}{2}(229 + 744) \times 18 = 8,750$ lb. per foot length of wall. The distance from $C-C$ to the line of action of P_c may be found graphically or calculated from the formula

$$ y = \frac{2a + b}{a + b} \cdot \frac{h}{3} = \frac{2 \times 229 + 744}{229 \times 744} \cdot \frac{18}{3} = 7.40 \text{ ft.} $$

Derived in same way as Prob. 35. P. 47.

where a and v are the bases of the trapezoid and h the height. The values of P_c and y are recorded in the table. The shear at the section is $V = P_c = 8,750$ lb. and the moment is $M = 8,750 \times 7.40 = 64,800$ ft.-lb. $= 777,000$ in.-lb. Using an allowable unit shear of 40 lb. per sq. in., which corresponds to an average shear of 35 lb. per sq. in., the thickness required by shear is $d = V \div 35b = 8,750 \div 35 \times 12 = 20.8$ in. The coefficient of resistance for $f_s = 16,000$ and $f_c = 650$ is 107.5; the depth required for a moment of 777,000 in.-lb. is therefore

$$d = \sqrt{777,000 \div 107.5 \times 12} = 24.5 \text{ in.}$$

A depth of 25 in. will be adopted with 3 in. of concrete outside of the steel, making a total depth of 28 in. The dimensions of the vertical slab are now known, the batter of the face being taken as 6 in. in 18 ft. The front of the vertical slab is placed at a distance of $\frac{2}{3} \times 14 = 9.33$ ft. from A', or 4 ft. 8 in. from the toe.

The foundation pressures at the heel and toe will now be found. The unit horizontal pressure at A' is $p = w \cdot h \cdot k = 100 \times 28 \times 0.286 = 800$ lb. per sq. ft. The total pressure against $A'B'$ is $P = \frac{1}{2}(229 + 800) \times 20 = 10,290$ lb. for both cases. The distance of P from the base is found to be 8.16 ft. as explained for P_c. It is evident that there can be no horizontal pressure acting above the top of the wall for there is nothing for it to act against. In finding the resultant pressure on the wall the horizontal pressure P is combined with the weight over the heel W' acting through its centroid. This pressure on the wall is combined with the weight of the wall acting through its centroid. This resultant pressure cuts the base at a distance from the center of $e = 2.07$ ft. for Case 1 and 0.86 ft. for Case 2. The unit pressures at the toe and heel are now calculated as shown on the problem. These are all within the allowable pressure and the resultant pressure on the foundations strikes within the middle third so the width of base is satisfactory.

The resultant pressure on the toe is found by subtracting the downward force due to the weight of the toe from the upward force due to the foundation pressures. This pressure is shown by the shaded area in the foundation pressure diagram. The shear at the section $D-D$ is equal to portion of this area to the left of the section and the bending moment is equal to the moment of this portion of the area about the section. The values of the shear and moment for these two cases are recorded in the table, and the depth, steel area, and unit stresses are worked out as explained for the section $C-C$. Section $E-E$ is worked out in a similar manner but it is found that a fillet is required so the formulas for wedge-shaped beams must be used.

The resultant pressure on the heel is found by subtracting the downward force due to the weight of the heel and the load on the heel, from the upward force due to foundation pressures. This gives a resultant force downward as shown by the shaded areas in the foundation pressure diagrams. The shear and moment at the sections $F-F$ and $G-G$ were calculated as explained for $D-D$. A fillet is not necessary but one will be put in to correspond with that on the front of the wall. The reinforcements in this fillet will be made nominal and the effect of the fillet will be neglected in the calculations assuming all of the tension to be carried on the horizontal steel. The diagonal steel in the fillet will carry a high unit stress but this will have no effect on the strength of the wall.

The calculations for all sections of the wall are given in the table. The minimum factor of safety against sliding is for Case 1 where the resultant pressure on the foundation makes an angle of 65° with the horizontal, giving a factor of safety of $\tan 33° 42' \div \tan (90° - 65°) = 0.667 \div 0.466 = 1.43$, neglecting the effect of the cut-off. The cut-off will increase the factor of safety against sliding very materially. Walls of this type are always safe against overturning.

All bars must be embedded 50 diameters beyond the section of zero moment if ends are not hooked and 33 diameters if ends are hooked.

Working drawings based on the calculations given in the table are shown in the problem.

11*

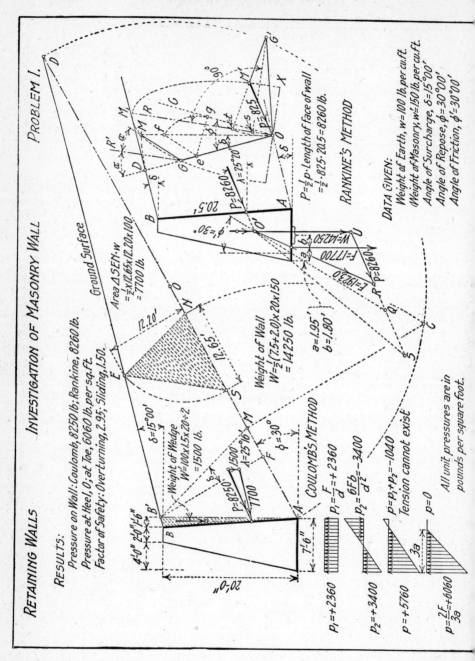

RETAINING WALLS   INVESTIGATION OF MASONRY WALL   PROBLEM I.

RESULTS:
Pressure on Wall: Coulomb, 8250 lb.; Rankine, 8260 lb.
Pressure at Heel, 0; at Toe, 6060 lb. per sq. ft.
Factor of Safety: Overturning, 2.95; Sliding, 1.50.

Ground Surface

Area △SEN∙w
= ½×12.65×12.20×100.
= 7700 lb.

12.20'

12.65'

Weight of Wall
W = ½(7.5+2.0)×20×150
= 14250 lb.

a = 1.95'
b = 1.80'

Weight of Wedge
W = 100×1.5×20÷2
= 1500 lb.

δ = 15°00'

φ = 30°

Λ = 25°16'

P = 8250
7700

1500

B   B'

A

7'-6"

B

20'-0"

4'-0" 2'-0" 1'-6"

COULOMB'S METHOD

$p_1 = \dfrac{F}{d} = +2360$

$p_2 = \dfrac{6Fb}{d'^2} = -3400$

$p = p_1 + p_2 = -1040$

Tension cannot exist

$p = 0$

$p = \dfrac{2F}{3a} = +6060$

$p_1 = +2360$

$p_2 = +3400$

$p = +5760$

3a

All unit pressures are in
pounds per square foot.

P = ½ p. length of face of wall
= ½ · 825 · 20.5 = 8260 lb.

RANKINE'S METHOD

DATA GIVEN:
Weight of Earth, w = 100 lb. per cu. ft.
Weight of Masonry, w = 150 lb. per cu. ft.
Angle of Surcharge, δ = 15°00'
Angle of Repose, φ = 30°00'
Angle of Friction, φ' = 30°00'

Λ = 25°20'

P = 8260

φ' = 30°

O'

A

W = 14250

F = 17700

F = 19230

R = 8260

p = 825

90°

δ

20.5'

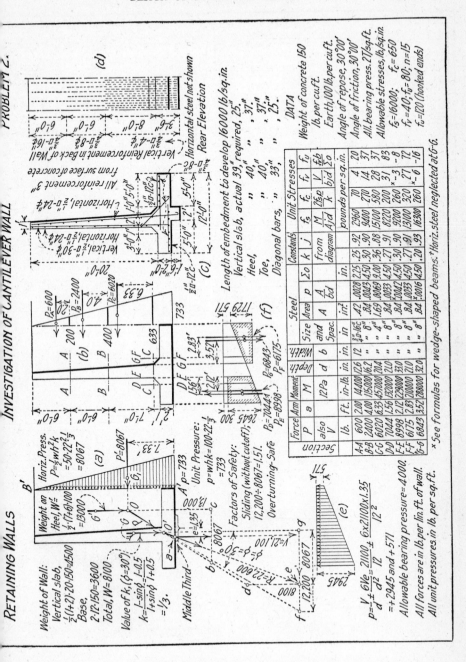

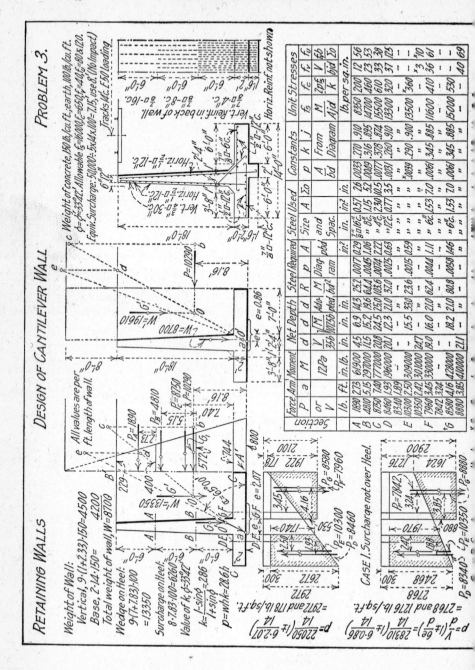

RETAINING WALLS   DESIGN OF CANTILEVER WALL   PROBLEM 3.

PART II.

THE DESIGN OF COAL BINS, ORE BINS, ETC.

Introduction.—Bins are designed to contain materials which are more or less nearly in a granular condition. Dry sand, screened anthracite coal, etc., are almost ideal semi-fluids, while bituminous coal, ashes, etc., are in a variable condition. Coal bins, ore bins, ash bins, etc., will be considered in Part II, while grain bins and grain elevators will be considered in Part III. The bins discussed in Part II are for the greater part shallow bins (bins where the plane of rupture cuts the free surface of the filling), while the bins discussed in Part III are deep bins (bins where the plane of rupture cuts the side of the bin).

CHAPTER VIII.

TYPES OF COAL BINS, ORE BINS, ETC.

Introduction.—Bins for coal, ore, etc., are made of different materials and are of different types. (a) Timber was formerly quite generally used on account of low cost and ease of construction. With more permanent construction fire-proof bins were required and bins are now made (b) of steel with timber cribbed lining, (c) of steel with plate lining, (d) of steel with reinforced concrete lining, and (e) of reinforced concrete.

The material to be confined in the bin is usually delivered into the top of the bin either by dumping directly from cars or by means of conveyors, and is drawn from the bottom through gates, operated by hand levers or by power-driven mechanism. Coal bins, ore bins, etc., are made of several types. The most used are (1) the suspension bunker; (2) the hopper bin; and (3) the circular bin.

1. **Suspension Bunkers.**—Suspension bunkers are made by suspending a steel plate or framework from two side girders; the weight of the filling causing the sides to assume the curve of the equilibrium polygon; the stresses in the plates of a true suspension bunker for a full load being pure tensile stresses.

A Berquist suspension bunker is shown in Fig. 53 and illustrates the method of construction. This bunker is lined with a concrete lining about $1\frac{1}{2}''$ thick, reinforced with wire netting, to protect the metal from the action of the lime.

A suspension bunker constructed of ferroinclave, built by the Brown Hoisting Machinery Co., Cleveland, Ohio, is shown in Fig. 54. The special corrugated sheets are fastened to and are supported by the angle framework. Both sides are then plastered with Portland cement mortar as in making walls and floors (see the Design of Steel Mill Buildings, Chapter XXII).

FIG. 53. BERQUIST SUSPENSION BUNKER FOR LIME.

FIG. 54. BROWN HOISTING MACHINERY CO.'S FERROINCLAVE SUSPENSION BUNKER.

For additional examples of suspension bunker bins with complete details see Chapter XII.

2. **Hopper Bins.**—Hopper bins are made of timber, steel, and reinforced concrete. A steel hopper bin built by the Minneapolis Steel & Machinery Co., Minneapolis, Minn., for the Cananea Copper Co., Sonora, Mexico, is shown in Fig. 55. The bins carry the railway

FIG. 55.   STEEL HOPPER ORE BIN, CANANEA COPPER CO.

tracks, the ore being dumped directly into the bins, then passing through gates to conveyors. Details of these bins are given in Fig. 103, Chapter XII.

Fig. 56 shows a general cross section of coke and stone bins recently erected for the Lackawanna Steel Company at Buffalo, N. Y. These bins are described by E. W. Pittman in Proc. West. Soc. Penna., June, 1906, as follows:

"These bins are divided into panels of 12′ 6″ center to center of columns, with a double partition at every panel point, leaving the clear length of each pocket about 11′ 6″. The general features of the coke and stone bins are the same, lighter sections being used for the coke bins. Diaphragms are placed between the partitions to prevent the plates from buckling under the action of the normal thrust. These diaphragms also perform the functions of a beam in transmitting the normal thrust to the floor at the bottom and to the transverse channel at the top when one pocket is filled and the adjacent one empty. The bins are lined throughout with $\frac{3}{8}''$ plates. All rivets in the floor are countersunk.

"Deliveries into these bins are made directly from bottom dumping

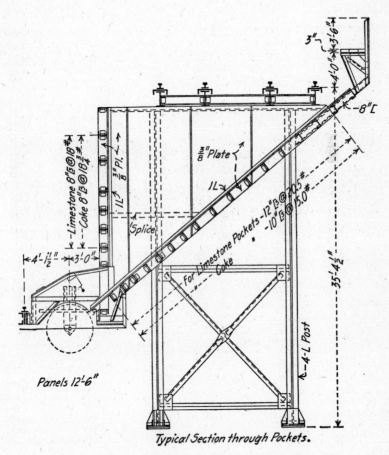

FIG. 56. COKE AND STONE BINS, LACKAWANNA STEEL CO.

cars which run on the tracks above, and also from buckets operated from a conveyor bridge.

"The gates at the bottoms of the bins are of special construction. They are cylindrical and are revolved by a system of shafting and gears. There is an opening in the side of the drum, and when the drum is revolved this opening comes opposite the opening in the bottom of the bin and the drum is filled. When the drum is further revolved and the opening turned down, its load of material is dumped into a larry for transportation to a furnace skip. At the same time communication between the bin and drum is shut off. The most notable feature of these gates is that they measure the material delivered to the larries. The larries are suspended from the tracks shown in cross section on either side of the gates."

FIG. 57.   LOCOMOTIVE COALING STATION AT SAARBRUCKEN, GERMANY.

A locomotive coaling station in which the coal bins are made of steel with hopper bottoms is shown in Fig. 57. For additional examples of hopper bottom bins with complete details see Chapter XII.

3. **Circular Bins.**—Circular bins are made of both steel and reinforced concrete. Steel bins are made with spherical or conical bottoms, while reinforced concrete bins usually have conical bottoms resting on the ground or on columns.

A circular ore bin with a hemispherical bottom, built by the Minneapolis Steel & Machinery Co. at Globe, Arizona, is shown in Fig.

58. Details of this bin are given in Fig. 119 to Fig. 120, Chapter XII.

Another bin made by the same company is shown in Fig. 59. In this bin a masonry wall forms one side of the bin, the other three

FIG. 58. CIRCULAR ORE BIN, GLOBE, ARIZONA (SEE DETAIL OF GATE IN FIG. 97 b).
(Bin set up and photographed at bridge shop.)

sides being formed by plates curved as shown and anchored to the masonry.

Circular steel ore bins have been used in steel rock houses recently constructed for the Ahmeek, the Franklin, and Baltic Mining Companies in the Lake Superior mining district.

For additional examples of circular bins see Chapter XII.

FIG. 59.   STEEL ORE BINS, CANANEA, MEXICO.

CHAPTER IX.

STRESSES IN BINS.

Introduction.—In this chapter the stresses will be calculated (1) in bin walls; (2) in hopper bins; (3) in suspension bunkers; (4) in conical bin bottoms; (5) in spherical bin bottoms; (6) in circular girders; and (7) in columns. For the calculation of the stresses in deep bins due to a granular material see Chapter XVI.

1. STRESSES IN BIN WALLS.—The problem of the calculation of the pressures on bin walls is the same as the problem of the calculation of pressures on retaining walls. The forces acting on bin walls depend upon the weight, angle of repose, moisture, etc., of the material, which are variable factors, but are less variable than for the filling of retaining walls.

For plane bin walls the formulas developed for retaining walls are directly applicable. The graphic solutions will be found the simplest and most direct for any particular case. Algebraic solutions will be given for six cases which frequently occur in practice. The pressures on plane bin walls will be calculated for bituminous coal, anthracite coal, sand, and ashes, using the data given in an article by R. W. Dull in Engineering News, July 21, 1904. Cases 1 to 6 and Tables XVI to XXII, inclusive, are essentially the same as given in the foregoing article. The same nomenclature will be used as in retaining walls except that P' will be used to indicate the pressure obtained by means of Cain's formulas when $z = \phi'$, N' will indicate the normal component of P', and N will indicate the normal pressure on the wall when $\phi' = 0$. This analysis applies to shallow bins, only.*

Case 1. Vertical Wall, Surface Level. Angle $z = \phi'$.

$$P' = \tfrac{1}{2}w.h^2 \frac{\cos^2 \phi}{\cos \phi' \left(1 + \sqrt{\dfrac{\sin (\phi + \phi') \sin \phi}{\cos \phi'}} \right)^2} \tag{63}$$

---

* A shallow bin is one where the plane of rupture cuts the free surface of the filling.

$$N' = P'. \cos \phi' \qquad (64)$$

If $\phi' = \phi$

$$P' = \tfrac{1}{2}w.h^2 \frac{\cos \phi}{(1 + \sin \phi \sqrt{2})^2} \qquad (65)$$

$$N' = P'. \cos \phi \qquad (66)$$

If $\phi' = 0$, which corresponds to a smooth wall,

$$N = \tfrac{1}{2}w.h^2. \tan^2 \left(45° - \frac{\phi}{2}\right) \qquad (67)$$

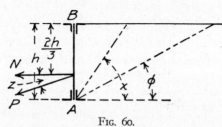

FIG. 60.

TABLE XVI.

CONSTANTS FOR STEEL PLATE BINS, CASE I.

Material.	ϕ Degrees.	ϕ' Degrees.	W Lbs. Per Cu. Ft.	P' Lbs.	N' Lbs.	N Lbs.
Bituminous coal.	35	18	50	$6.13h^2$	$5.83h^2$	$6.75h^2$
Anthracite coal.	27	16	52	$8.73h^2$	$8.39h^2$	$9.77h^2$
Sand.	34	18	90	$11.50h^2$	$10.93h^2$	$12.72h^2$
Ashes.	40	31	40	$4.02h^2$	$3.44h^2$	$4.34h^2$

Case 2. Vertical Wall, Surface Surcharged at angle δ. *Angle* $z = \phi'$.

$$P' = \tfrac{1}{2}w.h^2 \frac{\cos^2 \phi}{\cos \phi' \left(1 + \sqrt{\dfrac{\sin (\phi + \phi') \sin (\phi - \delta)}{\cos \phi' . \cos \delta}}\right)^2} \qquad (68)$$

$$N' = P'. \cos \phi' \qquad (69)$$

If $\delta = \phi$

$$P' = \tfrac{1}{2}w.h^2 \frac{\cos^2 \phi}{\cos \phi'} \qquad (70)$$

$$N' = P' \cdot \cos \phi' = \tfrac{1}{2}w.h^2 \cdot \cos^2 \phi \qquad (71)$$

If $\qquad\qquad \phi' = 0$

$$N = \tfrac{1}{2}w.h^2 \cdot \cos^2 \phi \qquad (72)$$

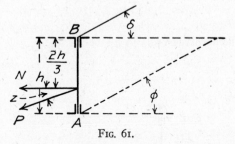

FIG. 61.

TABLE XVII.

CONSTANTS FOR STEEL PLATE BINS, CASE 2. $\delta = \phi$.

Material.	ϕ Degrees.	ϕ' Degrees.	W Lbs. Per Cu. Ft.	P' Lbs.	N' Lbs.	N Lbs.
Bituminous coal.	35	18	50	$17.65h^2$	$16.75h^2$	$16.75h^2$
Anthracite coal.	27	16	52	$21.45h^2$	$20.50h^2$	$20.50h^2$
Sand.	34	18	90	$32.50h^2$	$30.90h^2$	$30.90h^2$
Ashes.	40	31	40	$13.70h^2$	$11.73h^2$	$11.73h^2$

Case 3. Vertical Wall, Surcharge Negative = δ. Angle z = φ′.

$$P' = \tfrac{1}{2}w.h^2 \dfrac{\cos^2 \phi}{\cos \phi' \left(1 + \sqrt{\dfrac{\sin (\phi + \phi') \sin (\phi + \delta)}{\cos \phi' \cdot \cos \delta}}\right)^2} \qquad (73)$$

$$N' = P' \cdot \cos \phi' \qquad (74)$$

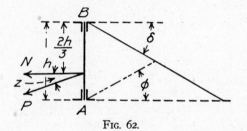

FIG. 62.

If $\phi' = 0$

$$N = \tfrac{1}{2}w.h^2 \frac{\cos^2 \phi}{\left(1 + \sqrt{\dfrac{\sin \phi \sin (\phi + \delta)}{\cos \delta}}\right)^2} \qquad (75)$$

TABLE XVIII.

CONSTANTS FOR STEEL PLATE BINS, CASE 3. $\delta = -\phi$.

Material.	ϕ Degrees.	ϕ' Degrees.	W Lbs. Per Cu. Ft.	P' Lbs.	N' Lbs.	N Lbs.
Bituminous coal.	35	18	50	$4.49h^2$	$4.27h^2$	$5.13h^2$
Anthracite coal.	27	16	52	$6.64h^2$	$6.38h^2$	$7.64h^2$
Sand.	34	18	90	$8.44h^2$	$8.00h^2$	$9.61h^2$
Ashes.	40	31	40	$2.85h^2$	$2.45h^2$	$3.23h^2$

Case 4.   Wall Sloping Outward. $\theta < 90° + \phi'$.   *Surface Level.*

$$P' = \tfrac{1}{2}w.h^2 \frac{\sin^2 (\theta - \phi)}{\sin (\phi' + \theta) \sin^2 \theta \left(1 + \sqrt{\dfrac{\sin (\phi + \phi') \sin \phi}{\sin (\phi' + \theta) \sin \theta}}\right)^2} \qquad (76)$$

$$N' = P' . \cos \phi' \qquad (77)$$

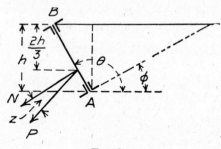

FIG. 63.

Case 5.   Wall Sloping Outward. $\theta < 90° + \phi'$.   *Surface Surcharged.*

$$P' = \tfrac{1}{2}w.h^2 \frac{\sin^2 (\theta - \phi)}{\sin (\phi' + \theta) \sin^2 \theta \left(1 + \sqrt{\dfrac{\sin (\phi + \phi') \sin (\phi - \delta)}{\sin (\phi' + \theta) \sin (\theta - \delta)}}\right)^2} \qquad (78)$$

$$N' = P' . \cos \phi' \qquad (79)$$

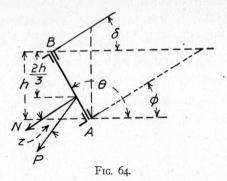

Fig. 64.

Case 6. Wall Sloping Outward. $\theta > 90° + \phi'$. *Surface Level.*

$$P = \tfrac{1}{2}w.h^2 . \tan^2 \left(45° - \frac{\phi}{2}\right)$$

$$W = weight \triangle ABC = \frac{w . \tan\theta . h^2}{2}$$

$$E = \sqrt{W^2 + P^2}$$

$$= \tfrac{1}{2}w.h^2 \sqrt{\tan^2\theta + \tan^4\left(45° - \frac{\phi}{2}\right)} \qquad (80)$$

$$\tan(\theta + z - 90°) = \frac{\tan\theta}{\tan^2\left(45° - \frac{\phi}{2}\right)} \qquad (81)$$

$$Q = E . \cos z \qquad (82)$$

$$T = E . \sin z \qquad (83)$$

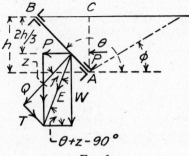

Fig. 65.

For a wall sloping outwards, and sloping surface the use of formulas is cumbersome and the calculations can be more easily made by graphic methods as explained on succeeding pages.

Tables of Pressure on Vertical Bin Walls.*—The normal pressure on vertical bin walls as calculated by the preceding formulas for bituminous coal, anthracite coal, sand, and ashes are given in Table XIX, Table XX, Table XXI, and Table XXII, respectively. In the tables column 1 gives the normal pressure for a smooth vertical wall and horizontal surcharge, while column 4 gives the normal pressure on a rough wall with an angle of friction $= \phi'$. Column 2 gives the normal pressure for a smooth vertical wall and a surcharge $= \phi$, while column 5 gives the normal pressure on a rough wall with an angle of friction $= \phi'$. Column 3 gives the normal pressure for a smooth vertical wall and a negative surcharge $= -\phi$, while column 6 gives the normal pressure on a rough wall with an angle of friction $= \phi'$. It will be seen that the pressures in columns 2 and 5 are identical. For a vertical wall with $\delta = \phi$, the normal pressures as given by Rankine's and Cain's formulas are identical. To prove this substitute $\delta = \phi$ in (8), multiply by $\cos \phi$ and compare with (41).

The total pressures are given for a wall one foot long in all cases.

Note.—These tables apply to shallow bins only (bins where the plane of rupture cuts the free surface of the filling). For the calculation of the stresses in deep bins (bins where the plane of rupture cuts the side of the bin) see Part III.

* Link Belt Machinery Co.'s Standards; R. W. Dull, Engineering News, July 21, 194.

TABLE XIX.

TOTAL PRESSURE IN POUNDS FOR DEPTH "h" FOR BITUMINOUS COAL. Wall One Foot Long.

$$w = 50 \text{ lbs.}, \quad \phi = 35°.$$

Depth h in Feet	Smooth Wall, φ'=0			Rough Wall, Angle of Friction = φ'		
	1	2	3	4	5	6
	$\phi'=0$	$\delta=\phi$	$\delta=-\phi$	$\phi'=18°$	$\delta=\phi$	$\delta=-\phi$
1	6.75	16.75	5.13	5.83	16.75	4.27
2	27	67	20.5	23.32	67	17.1
3	60.75	150.75	46.2	52.47	150.75	38.4
4	108	268	82	93.4	268	68.3
5	168.75	418.75	128	145.7	418.75	107
6	243	603	184.5	209.4	603	156
7	333	821	257	286	821	209
8	432	1,072	328	373	1,072	273
9	547	1,357	415	472	1,357	346
10	675	1,675	513	583	1,675	427
11	817	2,027	615	705	2,027	516
12	972	2,412	738	840	2,412	615
13	1,141	2,831	866	985	2,831	722
14	1,323	3,283	1,005	1,143	3,283	838
15	1,519	3,769	1,152	1,312	3,769	960
16	1,728	4,288	1,311	1,492	4,288	1,093
17	1,951	4,841	1,480	1,685	4,841	1,232
18	2,187	5,427	1,660	1,889	5,427	1,382
19	2,437	6,047	1,852	2,105	6,047	1,541
20	2,700	6,700	2,052	2,332	6,700	1,708
21	2,977	7,387	2,262	2,571	7,387	1,883
22	3,267	8,102	2,483	2,821	8,102	2,067
23	3,571	8,861	2,560	3,084	8,861	2,259
24	3,888	9,648	2,810	3,358	9,648	2,460
25	4,219	10,469	3,206	3,644	10,469	2,669
26	4,563	11,323	3,468	3,941	11,323	2,887
27	4,923	12,211	3,740	4,250	12,211	3,113
28	5,292	13,142	4,022	4,570	13,142	3,348
29	5,677	14,087	4,314	4,903	14,087	3,591
30	6,075	15,075	4,617	5,247	15,075	3,843

TABLE XX.

TOTAL PRESSURE IN POUNDS FOR DEPTH "h" FOR ANTHRACITE COAL.
Wall One Foot Long.

$w = 52$ lbs., $\phi = 27°$.

Depth h in Feet	Smooth Wall, $\phi'=0$			Rough Wall, Angle of Friction $=\phi'$		
	1	2	3	4	5	6
	$\phi'=0$	$\delta=\phi$	$\delta=-\phi$	$\phi'=16°$	$\delta=\phi$	$\delta=-\phi$
1	9.75	20.5	7.64	8.39	20.5	6.38
2	39.0	82.0	30.6	33.5	82.0	25.5
3	87.8	184.5	68.8	75.5	184.5	57.5
4	156	328	122.2	134.2	328	102.0
5	244	513	191	210	513	159.5
6	351	738	267	302	738	230
7	478	1,005	374	411	1,005	313
8	624	1,312	489	536	1,312	402
9	790	1,661	619	680	1,661	517
10	975	2,050	764	839	2,050	638
11	1,180	2,481	925	1,014	2,481	773
12	1,405	2,952	1,100	1,209	2,952	920
13	1,648	3,465	1,290	1,418	3,465	1,080
14	1,910	4,018	1,497	1,643	4,018	1,250
15	2,193	4,613	1,720	1,887	4,613	1,436
16	2,500	5,248	1,953	2,145	5,248	1,636
17	2,808	5,945	2,207	2,421	5,945	1,845
18	3,160	6,642	2,471	2,718	6,642	2,064
19	3,521	7,400	2,758	3,030	7,400	2,310
20	3,902	8,200	3,053	3,350	8,200	2,554
21	4,303	9,041	3,372	3,700	9,041	2,820
22	4,718	9,922	3,701	4,061	9,922	3,086
23	5,156	10,845	4,040	4,438	10,845	3,372
24	5,611	11,808	4,398	4,833	11,808	3,680
25	6,097	12,813	4,770	5,244	12,813	3,985
26	6,600	13,858	5,160	5,672	13,858	4,521
27	7,112	14,945	5,560	6,116	14,945	4,650
28	7,638	16,072	5,979	6,578	16,072	5,000
29	8,202	17,241	6,421	7,056	17,241	5,370
30	8,775	18,450	6,880	7,551	18,450	5,742

TABLE XXI.

TOTAL PRESSURE IN POUNDS FOR DEPTH "h" FOR SAND.
Wall One Foot Long.

$w = 90$ lbs., $\phi = 34°$.

Depth h in Feet	Smooth Wall, $\phi'=0$			Rough Wall, Angle of Friction = ϕ'		
	1	2	3	4	5	6
	$\phi'=0$	$\delta=\phi$	$\delta=-\phi$	$\phi'=18°$	$\delta=\phi$	$\delta=-\phi$
1	12.72	30.9	9.61	10.93	30.9	8
2	50.8	123.6	38.4	43.7	123.6	32
3	114.5	278	86.40	98.5	278	72
4	203.7	494	113.8	175	494	128
5	318	772	240	273	772	200
6	458	1,117	346	394	1,113	288
7	624	1,515	471	535	1,515	392
8	815	1,980	615	700	1,980	512
9	1,030	2,500	778	885	2,500	648
10	1,272	3,090	961	1,093	3,090	800
11	1,540	3,740	1,162	1,345	3,740	968
12	1,833	4,450	1,383	1,575	4,450	1,152
13	2,150	5,230	1,624	1,848	5,230	1,352
14	2,495	6,060	1,880	2,160	6,060	1,568
15	2,862	6,960	2,160	2,460	6,960	1,800
16	3,256	7,910	2,460	2,798	7,910	2,048
17	3,676	8,930	2,777	3,159	8,930	2,312
18	4,121	10,012	3,114	3,541	10,012	2,592
19	4,592	11,155	3,469	3,946	11,155	2,888
20	5,088	12,360	3,844	4,372	12,360	3,200
21	5,610	13,627	4,238	4,820	13,627	3,528
22	6,156	14,956	4,651	5,290	14,956	3,872
23	6,729	16,346	5,084	5,782	16,346	4,232
24	7,327	17,798	5,535	6,296	17,798	4,608
25	7,950	19,313	6,006	6,831	19,313	5,000
26	8,599	20,889	6,496	7,389	20,889	5,408
27	9,273	22,526	7,006	7,968	22,526	5,832
28	9,972	24,225	7,534	8,569	24,225	6,272
29	10,698	25,987	8,082	9,192	25,987	6,728
30	11,448	27,810	8,649	9,837	27,810	7,200

TABLE XXII.

TOTAL PRESSURE IN POUNDS FOR DEPTH "h" FOR ASHES.

Wall One Foot Long.

$w = 40$ lbs., $\phi = 40°$.

Depth h in Feet	Smooth Wall, $\phi' = 0$			Rough Wall, Angle of Friction $= \phi'$		
	1	2	3	4	5	6
	$\phi' = 0$	$\delta = \phi$	$\delta = -\phi$	$\phi' = 31°$	$\delta = \phi$	$\delta = -\phi$
1	4.35	11.73	3.23	3.44	11.73	2.45
2	17.4	47	12.9	13.76	47	9.80
3	39.2	105.7	29.01	30.96	105.7	22.05
4	69.6	188	31.7	55.04	188	39.20
5	108.7	294	80.8	86	294	61.2
6	156.4	423	116	124	423	88.2
7	213	576	158	168	576	120
8	278	751	207	220	751	157
9	352	952	261	279	952	199
10	435	1,173	323	344	1,173	245
11	526	1,420	391	416	1,420	296
12	626	1,690	465	495	1,690	353
13	735	1,985	546	581	1,985	414
14	852	2,300	634	674	2,300	480
15	978	2,640	726	774	2,640	550
16	1,113	3,010	828	881	3,010	627
17	1,257	3,400	934	994	3,400	708
18	1,408	3,803	1,045	1,115	3,803	794
19	1,527	4,240	1,165	1,242	4,240	884
20	1,740	4,700	1,290	1,376	4,700	980
21	1,920	5,181	1,423	1,517	5,181	1,080
22	2,100	5,677	1,561	1,665	5,677	1,186
23	2,300	6,215	1,706	1,820	6,215	1,296
24	2,506	6,756	1,860	1,981	6,756	1,411
25	2,720	7,331	2,017	2,150	7,331	1,531
26	2,940	7,929	2,180	2,325	7,929	1,656
27	3,165	8,551	2,352	2,508	8,551	1,786
28	3,406	9,196	2,530	2,697	9,196	1,921
29	3,660	9,865	2,718	2,893	9,865	2,060
30	3,915	10,557	2,910	3,096	10,557	2,205

Pressure Exerted by Coal Against Vertical Retaining Walls, per Foot of Length by Trautwine's Formulas.—The Link Belt Engineering Co. uses Trautwine's formulas for calculating the pressure of coal. The solutions and tables for anthracite and bituminous coal based on these formulas follow:

Anthracite Coal.—Angle of repose of coal $= 27°$.
Weight of anthracite coal per cubic foot $= 52.1$ lbs.
For Surface Horizontal.—Fig. 66.

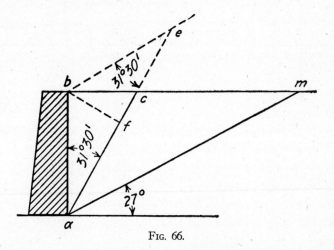

Fig. 66.

$$\text{Horizontal pressure} = \frac{\text{weight of the triangle } a\,c\,b \times b\,c}{a\,b}$$

$$= \frac{52.1 \times a\,b \times b\,c \times b\,c}{2\,a\,b} = 26.05\,(b\,c)^2, \quad (84)$$

or, the presure varies directly as the square of the depth, d.

When the Surface Slope is Equal to the Angle of Repose.—Fig. 66.

$$\text{Horizontal pressure} = \frac{\text{weight of the triangle } a\,e\,b \times b\,c}{a\,b}$$

$$= \frac{52.1 \times b\,f \times a\,f \times b\,c}{a\,b} = 52.1\,(b\,f)^2, \quad (85)$$

again, the presure varies directly as the square of the depth, d.

TABLE XXIII.

PRESSURE OF ANTHRACITE COAL ON VERTICAL BIN WALLS CALCULATED BY
TRAUTWINE'S FORMULAS.*

Depth in Ft.	Horizontal Surface.		Sloping Surface.		Depth in Ft.	Horizontal Surface.		Sloping Surface.	
	Total Pressure.	Pressure on Lowest Foot.	Total Pressure.	Pressure on Lowest Foot.		Total Pressure.	Pressure on Lowest Foot.	Total Pressure.	Pressure on Lowest Foot.
1	9.78	9.78	14.22	14.22	26	6,611	498	9,612	725
2	39	29	56.88	42.66	27	7,129	518	10,366	753
3	88	48	127.98	71	28	7,667	537	11,149	782
4	156	68	227	99	29	8,225	557	11,988	810
5	244	88	355	127	30	8,802	577	12,797	839
6	352	107	511	156	31	9,398	596	13,665	867
7	479	127	696	184	32	10,015	616	14,561	895
8	625	146	910	213	33	10,650	635	15,486	924
9	792	166	1,151	241	34	11,306	655	16,439	952
10	978	185	1,422	270	35	11,980	674	17,420	981
11	1,183	205	1,720	298	36	12,675	694	18,429	1,009
12	1,408	224	2,047	327	37	13,389	713	19,467	1,038
13	1,652	244	2,403	355	38	14,123	733	20,533	1,066
14	1,916	264	2,787	383	39	14,875	753	21,629	1,095
15	2,200	283	3,199	412	40	15,648	772	22,752	1,123
16	2,503	303	3,640	440	41	16,440	792	23,904	1,151
17	2,826	322	4,109	469	42	17,252	811	25,084	1,180
18	3,168	342	4,607	497	43	18,083	830	26,293	1,208
19	3,530	361	5,133	526	44	18,934	850	27,530	1,237
20	3,912	381	5,688	554	45	19,804	870	28,793	1,265
21	4,313	400	6,271	583	46	20,695	889	30,090	1,294
22	4,733	420	6,882	611	47	21,605	909	31,412	1,322
23	5,173	440	7,522	639	48	22,533	929	32,763	1,350
24	5,633	459	8,190	668	49	23,482	948	34,143	1,379
25	6,112	479	8,887	696	50	24,450	968	35,550	1,407

Surface horizontal $\begin{cases} \text{Total pressure} = 9.78\,d^2. \\ \text{Pressure on lowest foot} = 9.78(2d-1). \end{cases}$

Surface sloping $\begin{cases} \text{Total pressure} = 14.22\,d^2. \\ \text{Pressure on lowest foot} = 14.22(2d-1). \end{cases}$

Bituminous Coal.—Angle of repose of bituminous coal $= 35°$.
Weight of bituminous coal per cubic foot $= 47$ lbs.

From Fig. 67 in the same manner as for anthracite coal we have:

Surface horizontal $\begin{cases} \text{Total pressure} = 6.37\,d^2. \\ \text{Pressure on lowest foot} = 6.37(2d-\text{L}). \end{cases}$

* Link Belt Engineering Co.

TABLE XXIV.

PRESSURE OF BITUMINOUS COAL ON VERTICAL BIN WALLS CALCULATED BY
TRAUTWINE'S FORMULAS.*

Depth in Ft.	Horizontal Surface.		Sloping Surface.		Depth in Ft.	Horizontal Surface.		Sloping Surface.	
	Total Pressure.	Pressure on Lowest Foot.	Total Pressure.	Pressure on Lowest Foot.		Total Pressure.	Pressure on Lowest Foot.	Total Pressure.	Pressure on Lowest Foot.
1	6.4	6.4	10	10	26	4,305	325	6,760	510
2	25	19	40	30	27	4,641	338	7,290	530
3	57	32	90	50	28	4,993	350	7,840	550
4	102	45	160	70	29	5,358	363	8,410	570
5	159	57	250	90	30	5,732	376	9,000	590
6	229	70	360	110	31	6,122	389	9,610	610
7	312	83	490	130	32	6,523	401	10,240	630
8	407	96	640	150	33	6,935	414	10,890	650
9	516	108	810	170	34	7,362	427	11,560	670
10	637	121	1,000	190	35	7,778	440	12,250	690
11	770	134	1,210	210	36	8,253	452	12,960	710
12	917	146	1,440	230	37	8,754	465	13,690	730
13	1,076	159	1,690	250	38	9,193	478	14,440	750
14	1,248	172	1,960	270	39	9,682	490	15,210	770
15	1,433	185	2,250	290	40	10,192	503	16,000	790
16	1,630	197	2,560	310	41	10,669	516	16,810	810
17	1,840	210	2,890	330	42	11,236	529	17,640	830
18	2,063	223	3,240	350	43	11,797	541	18,490	850
19	2,298	236	3,610	370	44	12,331	554	19,360	870
20	2,548	248	4,000	390	45	12,968	567	20,250	890
21	2,809	261	4,410	410	46	13,478	580	21,160	910
22	3,083	274	4,840	430	47	14,100	592	22,090	930
23	3,369	287	5,290	450	48	14,679	605	23,040	950
24	3,669	299	5,760	470	49	15,275	618	24,010	970
25	3,981	312	6,250	490	50	15,925	631	25,000	990

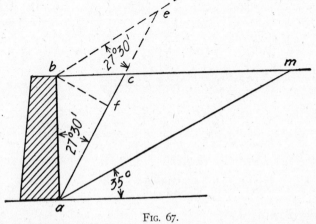

FIG. 67.

* Link Belt Engineering Co.

Surface sloping　$\begin{cases} \text{Total pressure} = 10\,d^2. \\ \text{Pressure on lowest foot} = 10(2d - 1). \end{cases}$

The pressures on vertical walls based on the above formulas are given for anthracite coal in Table XXIII and for bituminous coal in Table XXIV.

2. STRESSES IN HOPPER BINS.

The stresses in hopper bins can be most easily calculated by graphic methods or by a combination of algebraic and graphic methods.　In the following solutions the bins are shallow so that the angle of rupture cuts the top surface of the material within the bin, and the bin walls are assumed as smooth.　The following çases will be considered: (1) top surface level; (2) top surface heaped; (3) top surface surcharged.　The bin and data are assumed practically as in the Paterson, N. J., bin, the failure of which in 1897 brought out a spirited discussion in Engineering News.

1. Hopper Bin, Top Surface Level.

The bin is 32' 0" wide, 18' 0" high, and the pockets are 17' 0" long.　The bin will be assumed to be filled with coal weighing 58 lbs. per cu. ft., and having an angle of

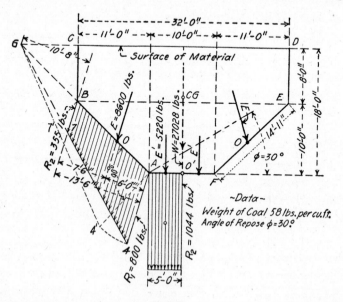

Fig. 68.

repose of $\phi = 30°$. (Anthracite coal is commonly assumed to weigh 52.1 lbs. per cu. ft., and to have an angle of repose of 27°.) The analysis will be made for a section of the bin 1 ft. long.

(a) *First Method.*—In Fig. 68 it is required to calculate the pressure on the inclined side *A-B*. The direction of maximum pressure in the filling will be vertical and will be $p = w.y = 58 \times 18 = 1044$ lbs. per sq. ft. This is the unit pressure on the bottom *A-F*, and the

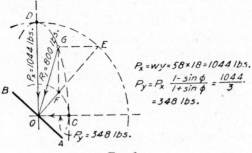

$P_x = w.y = 58 \times 18 = 1044 \ lbs.$

$P_y = P_x \dfrac{1 - \sin \phi}{1 + \sin \phi} = \dfrac{1044}{3}.$

$= 348 \ lbs.$

FIG. 69.

resultant pressure on the left half of the bottom will be $E' = 1044 \times 5 = 5220$ lbs. To calculate the pressure on the side *A-B*, construct the ellipse of stress at the point *A*, as in Fig. 69, and determine the unit pressure on the plane *A-B* at *A*. The ellipse of stress at point *A* is constructed in Fig. 69 as follows: Lay off $OD = 1044$ lbs.; and $OC = 1044 \times \dfrac{1 - \sin \phi}{1 + \sin \phi} = 348$ lbs. Now draw *AB* in Fig. 69, and draw *OF* normal to *A-B*. Construct circles with radii *OD* and *OC*, then *G* is a point on the ellipse of stress, by construction, and $OG = R_1 = 800$ lbs. $=$ the pressure on the plane *A-B* in Fig. 68. Now in Fig. 68 lay off *A*4 to represent the unit stress, R_1, at *A* on the plane *A-B*, and draw line 4*G*. The pressure at *B* on the plane *A-B* will be 355 lbs. per sq. ft., and may be calculated from the pressure area or calculated by an ellipse of stress as in Fig. 69. The total pressure on the side *A-B* will be equal to the area of the quadrilateral *A-B-7'-4'* and will act through the center of gravity of quadrilateral *A-B-7-4*, and is $E = 8,600$ lbs. The pressure on side *C-B* at *B* may be calculated by means of the ellipse of stress and is $=8\times 58\times \dfrac{1-\sin\phi}{1+\sin\phi}=155$ lbs. per sq. ft.

(b) *Second Method.*—In Fig. 70 the total pressure on the plane $A\text{-}H$ is $P_1=\tfrac{1}{2}w.h^2\dfrac{1-\sin\phi}{1+\sin\phi}=3{,}130$ lbs., acting horizontally through a point 12′ 0″ below the top surface. Now to find the pressure P_2 on the plane $G\text{-}A$ produce P_1 until it intersects the line $O2=$ weight of triangle $AHG=10{,}440$ lbs. at O, and by construction $O1=P_2=$

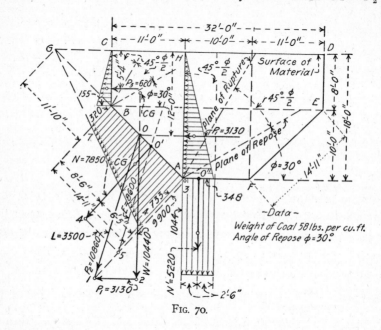

FIG. 70.

10,860 lbs. P_2 is parallel to E in Fig. 70. The normal pressure on $A\text{-}G$ is 9,900 lbs. Now 9,900 lbs. acts through the center of gravity of triangle $AG4$, and is equal to the area of $AG4$. The normal pressure at A is 733 lbs. per sq. ft. and the normal pressure at B is 320 lbs. per sq. ft., and the normal pressure on $A\text{-}B$ acts through the center of gravity of the shaded area and is $N=7{,}850$ lbs. Also by construction $E=8{,}600$ lbs. as before. The pressures on bottom $A\text{-}F$ and wall $B\text{-}C$ are found as in the first solution. Solutions (a) and (b) give identical results.

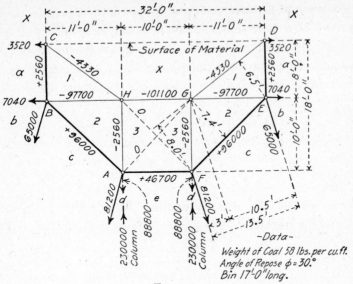

FIG. 71 a.

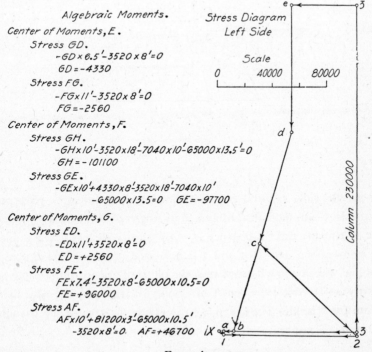

Algebraic Moments.

Center of Moments, E.
   Stress GD.
      $-GD \times 6.5' - 3520 \times 8' = 0$
      $GD = -4330$
   Stress FG.
      $-FG \times 11' - 3520 \times 8' = 0$
      $FG = -2560$

Center of Moments, F.
   Stress GH.
      $-GH \times 10' - 3520 \times 18 - 7040 \times 10' - 65000 \times 13.5' = 0$
      $GH = -101100$
   Stress GE.
      $-GE \times 10' + 4330 \times 8' - 3520 \times 18 - 7040 \times 10'$
         $-65000 \times 13.5 = 0 \quad GE = -97700$

Center of Moments, G.
   Stress ED.
      $-ED \times 11' + 3520 \times 8' = 0$
      $ED = +2560$
   Stress FE.
      $FE \times 7.4' - 3520 \times 8' - 65000 \times 10.5 = 0$
      $FE = +96000$
   Stress AF.
      $AF \times 10' + 81200 \times 3' - 65000 \times 10.5'$
         $-3520 \times 8' = 0. \quad AF = +46700$

Stress Diagram
Left Side

Scale
0   40000   80000

FIG. 71 b.

Calculation of Stresses in Framework.—The loads on the bin walls are carried by transverse framework as in Fig. 71, spaced 17′ 0″ center to center. The loads at the joints act parallel to the pressures as previously calculated, the loads being found in the same manner as for a simple beam loaded with a similar loading. To calculate the stresses by graphic resolution in Fig. 71 b, lay off loads $x\text{-}a = 3{,}520$ lbs., $a\text{-}b = 7{,}040$ lbs., $b\text{-}c = 65{,}000$ lbs., $c\text{-}d = 81{,}200$ lbs., and $d\text{-}e = 88{,}800$ lbs. Then beginning at joint C construct the diagram in the usual manner. The stresses may also be calculated by algebraic moments as explained in Fig. 71 b.

Center of Gravity of a Trapezoid.—To calculate the center of gravity of the trapezoid 1–2–3–4 in Fig. 72 proceed as follows: Bisect

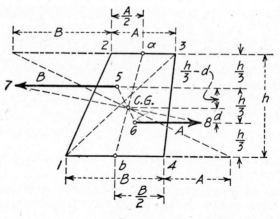

FIG. 72.

the parallel sides 1–4 and 2–3 and draw bisecting line $a\text{-}b$. Now produce side 3–2 to the left a distance $B =$ length of side 1–4, and produce side 1–4 to the right a distance $A =$ length of side 2–3; then connect the ends of the lines 2–3 and 1–4 produced, and the intersection of this line with the line $a\text{-}b$ will give the center of gravity of the trapezoid.

Proof.—To obtain the center of gravity of trapezoid 1–2–3–4 divide it into the triangles 1–2–3 and 1–3–4. Then the area of the triangles 1–2–3 and 1–3–4 may be represented by the lines A and B, respectively.

Now assume that B acts to the left through 5, the center of gravity of triangle 1–2–3, and A acts to the right through 6, the center of gravity of triangle 1–3–4. Then line 7–8 will cut line 5–6 at the center of gravity of the trapezoid 1–2–3–4. Let $\frac{h}{3} + d$ be the distance of the center of gravity above the base. It is required to prove that the dotted line joining 3–2 and 1–4 produced cuts the line a-b at a distance $\frac{h}{3} + d$ above the base. Now in Fig. 72 we have in the similar triangles the bases are to each other as the altitudes, and

$$A + \frac{B}{2} : B + \frac{A}{2} :: x : h - x,$$

where x is the altitude of the lower triangle. Solving

$$h.A + \frac{h.B}{2} - A.x - \frac{B.x}{2} = B.x + \frac{A.x}{2}$$

and

$$x = \frac{(2A + B)h}{3(A + B)} \tag{a}$$

$$= \frac{Ah}{3(A + B)} + \frac{h}{3}\frac{(A + B)}{(A + B)} \tag{b}$$

But in triangles 8–6–CG, and 7–5–CG,

$$A : B :: d : \frac{h}{3} - d$$

and

$$d = \frac{A.h}{3(A + B)} \tag{c}$$

from which we have

$$x = d + \frac{h}{3} \tag{d}$$

which proves the construction.

2. **Hopper Bin, Top Surface Heaped.**—The bin in Fig. 73 is heaped at the angle of repose, $\phi = 30°$. To calculate the pressure on side A-B, proceed as follows: Locate points G and H, and calculate the horizontal pressure $P_1 = 7,680$ lbs., acting on the plane H-K at

$\frac{1}{3}HK$ above H. Pressure P_1 was calculated by the graphic method described in Chapter II, Fig. 23. Produce P_1 until it intersects at O the line of action of the weight of the triangle GHK acting through the center of gravity of the triangle. From O lay off $O1 = W =$

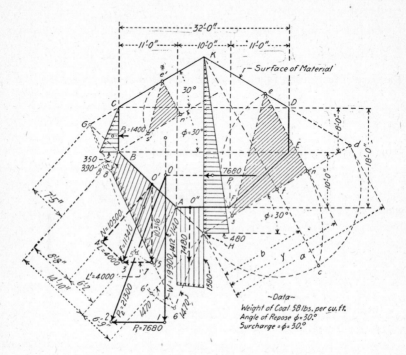

FIG. 73.

19,900 lbs., acting downwards, and from 1 lay off $1-2 = P_1 = 7,680$ lbs., acting to the left. Then $O2 = P_2 = 21,300$ lbs. Now $P_2 =$ area triangle $6'GH.w$, and $E =$ area $8'-B-A-5'.w = 11,340$ lbs. Force E acts through the center of gravity of area $8-B-A-7$. The horizontal pressure on plane $C-B = 1,400$ lbs. $=$ area $s'e'n'.w$. The vertical pressure on the left-hand side of the bottom $A-F$ is 7,480 lbs., acting through the center of gravity of the pressure polygon. The vertical unit pressure at A is 1,412 lbs. per sq. ft.

Calculation of Stresses in Framework.—The stresses in a transverse truss are given in Fig. 74. The stresses are calculated in the same manner as in Fig. 71 b. It will be seen that the stresses in several of the members are very much larger than when the top surface is level as in Fig. 71 a.

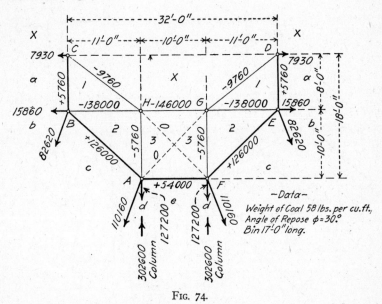

FIG. 74.

3a. Hopper Bin, Top Surface Surcharged.—The bin in Fig. 75 is surcharged from the left to the right side, the surcharge being equal to ϕ, the angle of repose. The pressure on the bin wall C-B was calculated as in Fig. 73, while the presure on bin wall E-D was calculated as on K-H in Fig. 73.

To calculate the presure on bin bottom A-B the pressure on plane H-K was calculated as in Fig. 21, and was found to be $P_1 = 22,060$ lbs. To calculate the pressure on G-H produce P_1 to O, and P_2 is the resultant of P_1 and W, the weight of the triangle HGK, and is $P_2 = 30,000$ lbs. Using the same method as in Case 2, E is found to act through the center of gravity of area 7-B-A-6, and to be equal to 15,500 lbs. To calculate the pressure on bin bottom F-E the pressure on plane H-K was calculated as in Case 2, and was found to be

13

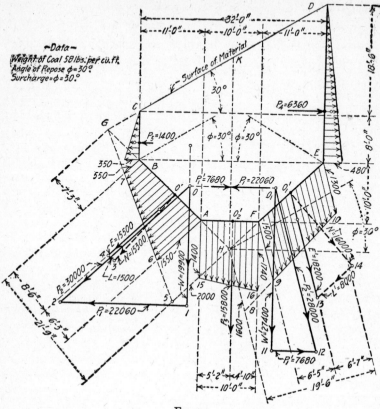

FIG. 75.

$P_1' = 7,680$ lbs.   To calculate the pressure on H-E produce P_1' to O_1, and P_2' is the resultant of P_1' and W', the weight of the area H-K-D-E, and is $P_2' = 28,000$ lbs.   Now P_2' acts through the center of gravity of area 8-H-E-10, and is equal to the area.   By calculation we find $E' = 18,200$ lbs. and acts through the center of gravity of area 9-F-E-10. The stresses in the framework may be calculated as in Case 2.

3b. **Hopper Bin, Top Surface Surcharged and of Indefinite Extent.**—The bin in Fig. 76 is surcharged from the left to the right side, the surcharge being equal to ϕ, the angle of repose, the material extending indefinitely to the right.   (This condition seldom occurs in practice.)

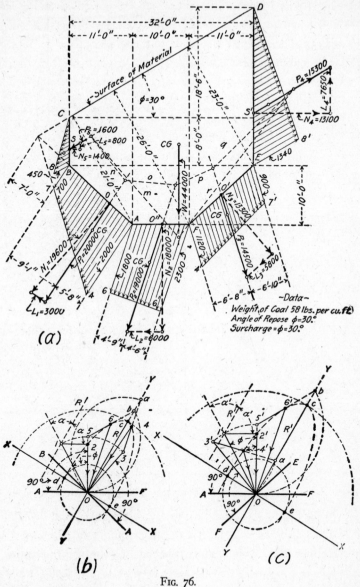

FIG. 76.

The conditions of this problem entirely satisfy Rankine's definition of a granular mass and the stresses may be calculated by the ellipse of stress as given in (b) and (c). The pressures at point A are calculated in (b) as follows: In (b) lay off O1 normal to the plane of repose and equal to $21 \times 58 = 1{,}218$ lbs. Draw O5 vertical and describe arc 15. Then point 2 is a point on the ellipse of stress. Through 1 draw 1R, making angle a = angle a, and through O draw OY parallel to 1R. Then Oc is the semi-major axis and Od the semi-minor axis of the ellipse of stress. To calculate the stress on side A-B, draw $O3 = O1$, normal to A-B and with point 3 as a center and a radius equal O3 describe an arc cutting OY at points O and a. Lay off $34 = 12$, and $O4 = 2{,}000$ lbs. is the pressure per square foot on plane A-B at point A. By proportion the pressure at B is 700 lbs.

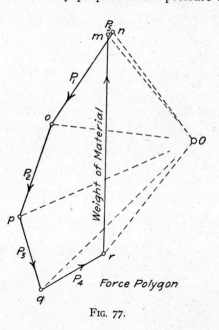

FIG. 77.

per sq. ft., and the total pressure is $P_1 = 20{,}000$ lbs. acting through the center of gravity of 7-B-A-4. To calculate the pressure on bottom A-F at A, draw $O5 = O1$ normal to A-F in (b), with radius O5 and center 5 describe an arc cutting OY at b, lay off $56 = 12$, and $60 = 1{,}800$ lbs. = pressure per square foot at A in (a).

The pressures on F-E and A-F at F are calculated in (c) in the same manner. And $P_2 = 19{,}000$ lbs., and $P_3 = 14{,}500$ lbs. By means of a similar ellipse of stress the pressure at E is found to be 1,340 lbs. per sq. ft., and at B is 450 lbs. per sq. ft., and $P_4 = 15,300$ lbs., and $P_5 = 1,600$ lbs. Pressure P_4 is the passive resistance and is very much in excess of the maximum active pressure. However, if the force polygon for the forces P_1, P_2, P_3, P_4, P_5 and the weight of material be constructed as in Fig. 77 the force polygon will be found to close. The stresses are those that would occur when the bin carries the coal and also takes the thrust from a mass of coal extending up to the right beyond the bin proper. This condition seldom occurs and the problem is of scarcely more than academic interest.

3. **STRESSES IN SUSPENSION BUNKERS.**—The suspension bunker shown in (a) Fig. 78 carries a load which varies from zero at the support to a maximum at the center. If the bunker is level full

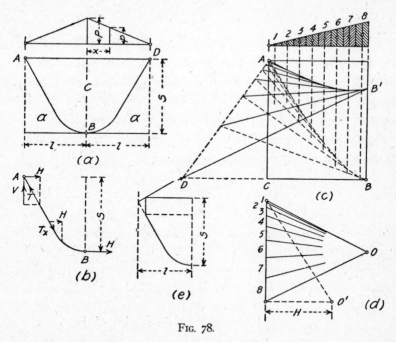

FIG. 78.

the loading from the supports to the center varies nearly as the ordinates to a straight line, while if the bunker is surcharged the straight line assumption for loading is more nearly correct.

We will, therefore, assume that the loading of the bunker in (*a*) is represented by the triangular loading varying from $p=$ zero at each support to a maximum of $p=P$ at the center.

Let $l=$ one-half the span in feet;

$S=$ the sag in feet;

$H=$ the horizontal component of the stress in the plate in lbs. per lineal foot of bin;

$w=$ weight of bin filling in lbs. per cu. ft.;

$T=$ maximum tension in plate in lbs. per lineal foot of bin;

$V=$ reaction of the bunker in lbs. per lineal foot of bin;

$C=$ capacity of bunker in cu. ft. per lineal foot of bin;

$B=$ origin of coördinates.

Now if the right-hand half of the bunker be cut away as in (*b*) and moments be taken about A, the moment will be

$$M = H.S \qquad (88)$$

But if the bunker be assumed as an equilibrium polygon drawn by using a force polygon, the bending moment at the center is equal to the pole distance multiplied by the intercept S. Therefore H must be equal to the pole distance of the force polygon.

Now it has been proved (The Design of Steel Mill Buildings, Chapter XVa) that the differential equation of the elastic curve is

$$\frac{d^2y}{dx^2} = \frac{fx}{H} \qquad (89)$$

where fx is the loading and H is the pole distance of the force polygon as shown in (*d*) Fig. 78.

But

$$fx = p = \frac{l-x}{l} P, \text{ and}$$

$\dfrac{d^2y}{dx^2} = \dfrac{P}{H} - \dfrac{P.x}{l.H}$ is the differential equation of the curve.

Integrating we get

$$\frac{dy}{dx} = \frac{P.x}{H} - \frac{P.x^2}{2l.H} + C_1 \qquad (90)$$

Now $\dfrac{dy}{dx} = 0$ when $x = 0$, and $C_1 = 0$.

Integrating equation (90)

$$y = \frac{P.x^2}{2H} - \frac{P.x^3}{6l.H} + C_2 \qquad (91)$$

Now $y = 0$ when $x = 0$, and $C_2 = 0$.

Therefore we have

$$y = \frac{P.x^2}{2H} - \frac{P.x^3}{6l.H} \qquad (92)$$

When $x = l$, then $y = S$, and

$$S = \frac{P.l^2}{3H}$$

and

$$H = \frac{P.l^2}{3S} \qquad (93)$$

Substituting the value of H given in (93) in (92), we have

$$y = \frac{1}{2}\frac{S}{l^2}\left(3x^2 - \frac{x^3}{l}\right) \qquad (94)$$

which is the final equation of the curve of the bunker. This equation shows that the shape of the curve is independent of the maximum load and depends only on the width and sag. The capacity of a bunker level full is as shown in (a) equal to

$$C = 2l.S - 2a.$$

But

$$a = \int_0^l y.dx = \frac{3}{2}\frac{S}{l^2}\int_0^l x^2.dx - \frac{S}{2l^3}\int_0^l x^3.dx$$

$$= \frac{3}{8}l.S,$$

and

$$C = 2l.S - 2.\frac{3}{8}l.S$$

$$= \frac{5}{4}l.S \qquad (95)$$

In calculating the value of P for any given bunker, since P is the maximum pressure for a triangular loading, we have

$$P.l = C.w, \text{ and}$$

$$P = \frac{C.w}{l} \qquad (96)$$

where $w = $ weight of a unit of the filling. For a bunker level full

$$P = \frac{5}{4}S.w$$

Substituting the value of P in (96) in (93), we have

$$H = \frac{C.w.l}{3S} \qquad (96a)$$

The reaction at A and D in (a), Fig. 78, will be

$$V = \tfrac{1}{2}C.w$$

$$= \tfrac{5}{8}S.l.w \text{ for a bin level full.} \qquad (96b)$$

The tension in the plate at A and D in (a), Fig. 78, will be

$$T = \sqrt{V^2 + H^2}$$

$$= \sqrt{\tfrac{1}{4}C^2.w^2 + \frac{C^2.w^2.l^2}{9S^2}}$$

$$= C.w \sqrt{\tfrac{1}{4} + \frac{l^2}{9S^2}} \qquad (96c)$$

Length of Curve.—The equation for the length of one-half the curve L, is

$$L = \int_0^l \sqrt{dx^2 + dy^2}.$$

Substituting the values of dx and dy from equation (94), we have for the length of one-half the curve

$$L = \frac{1}{2l^3} \int_0^l \sqrt{4l^6 + 9S^2(2x.l - x^2)^2}dx. \qquad (96d)$$

Now for very small values of S equation (96d) may be expanded into a series and integrated directly, but for values of S used for bunkers the series is not converging, and it becomes necessary to integrate by one of the approximate methods. For this purpose Simpson's rule was used with ten divisions. Then the length of curve is

$$L = \frac{1}{2l^3} \times \frac{l}{30} [y_0 + y_{10} + 4(y_1 + y_3 + y_5 + y_7 + y_9) + 2(y_2 + y_4 + y_6 + y_8)] \quad (96e)$$

Where

$$y = \sqrt{4l^6 + 9S^2(2x.l - x^2)^2} \qquad (96f)$$

and $y_0 =$ value of $(96f)$ for $x = 0$; $y_1 =$ value of $(96f)$ for $x = \dfrac{l}{10}$;

$y_2 =$ value of $(96f)$ for $x = \dfrac{2}{10}l$, etc. By substituting different values of S/l the length of the curve can be calculated with considerable precision. Values of L for S/l varying from $\frac{1}{3}$ to $\frac{3}{2}$ have been calculated and are given in Table XXIVa.

TABLE XXIVa.

LENGTH OF ONE HALF CURVE, L.

Sag ratio $= S/l$.	Length, L.
$\frac{1}{3}$	$1.06378l$
$\frac{2}{5}$	$1.13686l$
$\frac{1}{2}$	$1.22992l$
$\frac{3}{5}$	$1.28307l$
$\frac{7}{8}$	$1.36651l$
1	$1.45722l$
$\frac{6}{5}$	$1.61131l$
$\frac{4}{3}$	$1.71906l$
$\frac{3}{2}$	$1.85815l$

As a check the length of the curve with a sag ratio $S/l = 3/2$ was calculated by means of Simpson's rule with 20 divisions, giving $L = 1.85812l$, which differs from the value of L calculated with 10 divisions by $0.00003l$ or less than $\frac{1}{100}$ inch for a bunker 25 feet wide. The difference will be less for smaller values of S/l.

The curve may be constructed graphically as follows: In (c), Fig. 78, it is required to pass the curve through the points A and B. The loads 1, 2, 3, 4, etc., are laid off in the force polygon (d), and a pole O is taken. The equilibrium polygon A-B' is then constructed in (c). Now we know from graphic statics that if two poles be taken for the force polygon in (d), and corresponding equilibrium polygons be drawn through A, the strings meeting on the same load will intersect on a line through A parallel to the line O-O'. Now D is determined by the intersection of rays D-B' and D-B. The true curve is then easily constructed and pole O' is located.

If the bunker is surcharged by vertical walls as shown in (e) the curve is extended until it meets the slope of the material, and the span and sag are to be used as shown.

Diagram for Suspension Bunker.—In Fig. 79 is given a diagram proposed by R. W. Dull, for calculating the stresses, capacity, length of curve, etc., of suspended bunkers. The bunker selected is one that approximates an equilateral triangle. The use of the diagram will be explained by means of an example.

Problem 1. It is required to design a 400-ton bunker 100 feet long. This makes the capacity 4 tons per foot of length. Start on the right side at the 4-ton mark and pass to the left until the area curves are intersected and the width and sag will be found on the lower side. We see that if the bin is to be surcharged at an angle of 35° the width will be 17 feet, with a sag of 10.2 feet, while if the bin is to be level the width will be nearly 21 feet, with a sag of 12.6 feet. Assuming the surcharged bin with a width of 17 feet, we find the length of the curve on the upper side to be 328.7 inches. Passing over to the left on the 4-ton line we find the area of the section 160 square feet; reaction $V = 4{,}000$ lbs.; passing on to the intersection of the 4,000-lb. line with the diagonal line we find the stress per foot of length of plate, $T = 4{,}600$ lbs., and the tension $H = 2{,}300$ lbs. This furnishes the necessary information for the design.

Diagrams for other shapes of bunkers may be constructed in the same manner.

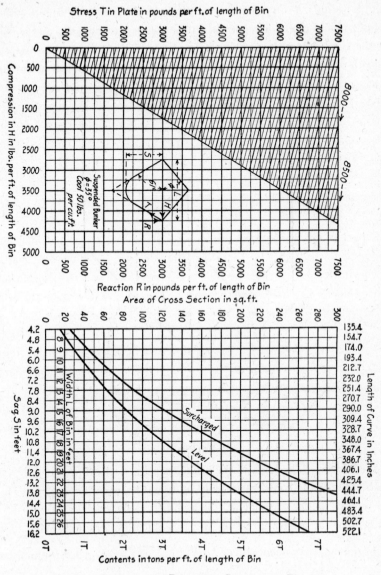

FIG. 79. DIAGRAM FOR DESIGNING SUSPENSION BUNKER.

4. STRESSES IN CONICAL BIN BOTTOMS.—A conical bin

with a radius r is supported by a circular girder, carries a filling with a
weight w and angle of repose ϕ. It is required to calculate the stresses
in the conical bottom and in the girder. If the sides of the bin are
smooth or the depth of the bin is small the entire weight will be carried

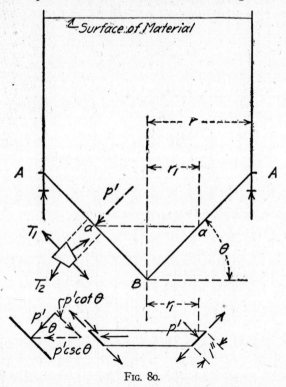

FIG. 80.

on the bottom of the bin. If the bin is deep the vertical pressure, V, on
the bottom of the conical part may be found by equation (144). The
top surface of the material will be assumed to be level.

Let V be the vertical pressure at any point in the granular mass, then
the horizontal component will be $L = V\dfrac{1 - \sin\phi}{1 + \sin\phi}$[*]. Any horizontal joint
in the cone must carry a load W_1 equal to the total vertical pressure
on the circle cut by the section a-a plus the weight of the cone and

[*] More correctly $L = k.V$, where k is determined by experiment, see Chapter
XVIII.

filling below the plane of a-a. To calculate W_1 in a deep bin substitute in formula (144) using r_1 for the radius of the bin and $\phi' = \phi$, because the filling tends to slide on itself.

Now the stress in the cone will be tangential to the shell and

$$T_1 = \frac{W_1 \cdot \csc \theta}{2\pi \cdot r_1} = \tfrac{1}{2} V \cdot r_1 \cdot \csc \theta \tag{97}$$

which varies from zero at B to a maximum at A.

Shallow Bins.—To find the stress in the ring a-a, assume a section of unit slant height cut from the cone. Now the normal pressure p' on the element may be found from the ellipse of stress and is given by the formula

$$p' = V \frac{\sin^2 (\theta + \phi)}{\sin^3 \theta \left(1 + \dfrac{\sin \phi}{\sin \theta} \right)^2}$$

Now substitute for the pressure p' which acts normally to the ring the two components $p' \cdot \cot \theta$ which acts along an element, and $p' \cdot \csc \theta$ which causes tension in the ring. Then

$$T_2 = p' \cdot r_1 \cdot \csc \theta \tag{98}$$

Stress T_2 varies from zero at B to a maximum at A.

Deep Bins.—It may easily be proved that

$$T_2 = L \cdot r_1 \tag{98a}$$

The circular girder which carries the entire weight of the bin and contents is carried at three or more points, so that it is subjected to compression, bending, and torsion. The compression in the ring is $\dfrac{W \cdot \cot \theta}{2\pi}$ where W is the total weight of bin and filling. The bending and torsion are calculated as described under stresses in a circular girder.

5. STRESSES IN SPHERICAL BIN BOTTOMS.—The stress T_1 is calculated in the same manner as for the conical bin and

$$T_1 = \frac{W_1}{2\pi \cdot r' \sin^2 a'} = \tfrac{1}{2} V \cdot r' \tag{99}$$

The tension on any meridian joint a-a is

$$T_2 = \tfrac{1}{2}V . r' = T_1 \qquad\qquad (100)$$

where V is calculated by formula (144) for the cylinder a-a as for the conical bin. The stresses in a spherical bottom are less than in a conical bottom.

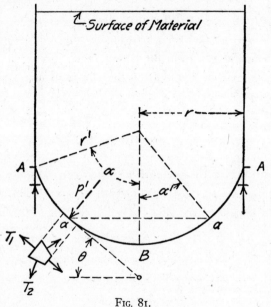

FIG. 81.

6. STRESSES IN A CIRCULAR GIRDER.—The circular girder supports the weight of the bin, the contents of the bin, and its own weight. The load is uniformly distributed along the girder. The girder rests on or is supported by four or more columns, and transmits its load to them.

Let W = total load on girder in pounds,

r = radius of girder in inches,

n = number of posts,

$a = \dfrac{2\pi}{n}$ = angle at center subtended by radii through two con-

secutive posts,

$a' =$ angle subtended at center by any arc,

$M =$ direct bending moment in the girder at any point in in.-lbs.,

$T =$ torsional bending moment in girder at any point in in.-lbs.,

$S =$ shear in girder at any point,

$P_a = P_b$, etc., $=$ reactions of posts.

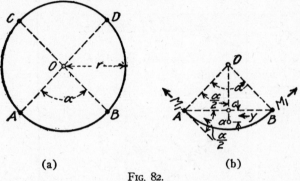

(a)   (b)

FIG. 82.

Now cut away the girder as in (b), Fig. 82, and replace the stresses and moments in the parts cut away by external forces and moments. The shear to the left of A is $S = \dfrac{W}{2n}$. The section of girder A-B tends to drop downward like a cantilever beam producing a moment $= - M_1$ at each post tangent to the circle at A and B. If a is the center of gravity of arc A-B, and y the distance of a from the line A-B, then

$$- 2M_1 \cdot \sin \frac{a}{2} = \frac{W}{n} y, \quad \text{and} \quad - 2M_1 = \frac{W}{n} y \cdot \csc \frac{a}{2}, \quad \text{but}$$

$$Oa = \frac{2r \cdot \sin \dfrac{a}{2}}{a}, \quad \text{and}$$

$$y = 2r \left(\frac{\sin \dfrac{a}{2}}{a} - \tfrac{1}{2} \cos \frac{a}{2} \right) \tag{101}$$

and substituting the value of y, we have

$$-M_1 = \frac{W.r}{n}\left(\frac{\sin\frac{a}{2}}{a} - \tfrac{1}{2}\cos\frac{a}{2}\right) csc\frac{a}{2}$$

$$= \frac{W.r}{n}\left(\frac{1}{a} - \tfrac{1}{2}\cot\frac{a}{2}\right) \tag{102}$$

If $n = 4$, then $a = \dfrac{\pi}{2}$, and

$$M_1 = \frac{W.r}{2}\left(\tfrac{1}{4} - \frac{1}{\pi}\right) \tag{103}$$

$$= -0.03415\,W.r$$

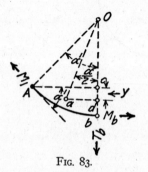

Fig. 83.

At any point in the girder, Fig. 83, we will have a direct moment M_b tangent to the girder and a torsional moment T_b normal to the girder. Taking moments about b-O, we have

$$M_b = M_1.\cos a' + (P_a - S)cA - \frac{W.a'.ad}{2\pi} \tag{104}$$

Now

$$cA = r.\sin a'$$

$$Oa = \frac{2r.\sin\frac{a'}{2}}{a'}, \text{ and } ad = \frac{2r.\sin^2\frac{a'}{2}}{a'},$$

and

$$M_b = M_1\cos a' + \frac{W}{2n}\,r.\sin a' - \frac{W.r.\sin^2\frac{a'}{2}}{\pi} \tag{105}$$

When

$$a' = 0$$

$$M_b = M_1$$

and when $a' = \dfrac{a}{2}$, we have bending moment at a point midway between posts $= M_2$

$$M_2 = M_1 . \cos \frac{a}{2} + \frac{W.r}{2n}\left(\sin \frac{a}{2} - \frac{2 \sin^2 \dfrac{a}{4}}{\dfrac{a}{2}} \right) \qquad (106)$$

If $n = 4$, then $a = \dfrac{\pi}{2}$, and

$$M_2 = M_1 . \cos 45° + \frac{W.r}{8}\left(\sin 45° - \frac{8 \sin^2 22\frac{1}{2}°}{\pi} \right), \text{ and}$$

$$M_2 = 0.01762\ W.r$$

To find the point of contra-flexure place $M_b = 0$, and solve for a'. Assume $n = 4$, and

$$M_b = \frac{W.r}{2}\left(\tfrac{1}{4} - \frac{1}{\pi} \right)\cos a' + \frac{W.r}{8}\sin a' - \frac{W.r}{\pi}\sin^2\frac{a'}{2} = 0 \qquad (107)$$

which after reduction gives

$$\cos a' + \sin a' = \frac{4}{\pi} \qquad (108)$$

and

$$a' = 19° \ 12' \text{ or } 70° \ 48'$$

The torsional moment at any point b is found by taking moments about a tangent at b.

$$T_b = - M_1 \sin a' - (P_a - S)\ cb + \frac{W.a'}{2\pi}\ db \qquad (109)$$

Now

$$cb = r(1 - \cos a'),$$

$$db = r - oa.\cos\frac{a'}{2}$$

$$= r - \frac{2r.\sin\dfrac{a'}{2}\cos\dfrac{a'}{2}}{a'}$$

$$= r\left(1 - \frac{\sin a'}{a'} \right)$$

$$T_b = - M_1.\sin a' - \frac{W}{2n}\ r(1 - \cos a') + \frac{W.a'}{2\pi}\ r\left(1 - \frac{\sin a'}{a'} \right) \qquad (110)$$

14

Now when $a' = 0$, then $T_1 = 0$.

When $a' = \dfrac{a}{2}$, then

$$T_b = - M_1 . \sin \frac{a}{2} - \frac{W.r}{2n}\left(1 - \cos \frac{a}{2}\right) + \frac{W.a.r}{4\pi}\left(1 - \frac{\sin \dfrac{a}{2}}{a}\right) = 0 \quad (111)$$

To find the maximum value of T_b differentiate (110) with reference to a'

$$dT_b = \left(- M_1.\cos a' - \frac{W.r}{2n}\sin a' + \frac{W.r}{2\pi} - \frac{W.r \cos a'}{2\pi}\right) da' = 0 \quad (112)$$

and

$$- M_1.\cos a' - \frac{W.r}{2n}\sin a' + \frac{W.r}{2\pi}(1 - \cos a') = 0 \quad (113)$$

If $n = 4$, then

$$M_1 = \frac{W.r}{2}\left(\tfrac{1}{4} - \frac{1}{\pi}\right),$$

and

$$\cos a' + \sin a' = \frac{4}{\pi}, \quad (114)$$

and

$$a' = 19°\ 12', \text{ or } 70°\ 48'$$

and

$$T_b = 0.0053\ W.r$$

From the preceding discussion we see that the bending moment M_1 has maximum values at the posts and midway between the posts and is zero at the points of contra-flexure; while the torsional moment T_1 has maximum values at the points of contra-flexure, and is zero at points of maximum bending moments.

TABLE XXIVa.

STRESSES IN CIRCULAR GIRDER.*

No. of Posts.	Load on Post, Lbs.	Max. Shear, Lbs.	Bending Moment at Posts. In.-lbs.	Bending Moment Midway Between Posts. In.-lbs.	Angular Distance From Post to Point of Max. Torsion.	Max. Torsional Moment. In.-lbs
4	$W \div 4$	$W \div 8$	$-0.03415\,Wr$	$+0.01762\,Wr$	$19°\ 12'$	$0.0053\ Wr$
6	$W \div 6$	$W \div 12$	$-0.01482\,Wr$	$+0.00751\,Wr$	$12\quad 44$	$0.00151\ Wr$
8	$W \div 8$	$W \div 16$	$-0.00827\,Wr$	$+0.00416\,Wr$	$9\quad 33$	$0.00063\ Wr$
12	$W \div 12$	$W \div 24$	$-0.00365\,Wr$	$+0.00190\,Wr$	$6\quad 21$	$0.000185\,Wr$

* From article by H. J. Burt, M. Am. Soc. C. E., in Technograph No. 16.

The shear, bending moments and torsional moments calculated by the above formulas for circular girders having 4, 6, 8, and 12 posts are given in Table XXIVa.

7. **STRESSES IN COLUMNS.**—The stresses in the columns will be due to the dead load and to the wind moment. The dead load stress will be equal to W divided by the number of columns, where W is the total weight of bin and filling. To calculate the stresses due to wind moment in the columns proceed as follows: Calculate the wind force by multiplying the exposed surface by the wind pressure, and

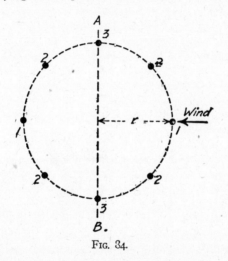

FIG. 84.

assume the wind force as acting through the center of gravity of the exposed surface. The pressure on circular bins may be taken at from 18 to 30 lbs. per sq. ft. of surface at right angles to the direction of the wind, depending upon the location and surroundings. To calculate the stresses in the columns at any point pass a horizontal section through the columns as in Fig. 84. Then the maximum vertical stress in column 1 will occur on the leeward side when the wind is blowing in the direction 1–1. If M is the wind moment about the axis A-B, the moment of the stresses in the column about axis A-B will be equal to M. In a bin with 8 columns as in Fig. 84 we have (stress 1) $\times 2r$ + (stress 2) $\times 4r.\cos 45° = M$.

But stress 1 is to stress 2 as r is to $r.\cos 45°$. From which

$$\text{Stress } 1\,(2r + 2r) = M$$

$$\text{Stress } 1 = \frac{M}{4r}, \text{ and}$$

$$\text{Stress } 2 = \frac{0.7M}{4r}$$

In a 6 column bin the stress in the most remote post is $\dfrac{M}{3r}$, and on each of the others is $\dfrac{1}{2}\dfrac{M}{3r}$. In a 4 column bin the stress in each post is $\dfrac{M}{2r}$. If the columns are vertical the maximum stresses will occur at the foot of the columns; if the columns are inclined the stress should be calculated at both the top and the bottom. The maximum stresses will be the sum of the dead and wind load stresses.

If the upward pull of the columns on the windward side is greater than the dead load when the bin is empty the column must be anchored down. The masonry footing should have a weight equal to at least twice the resultant upward pull.

For the calculation of footings see " Steel Mill Buildings," Chapter XXI.

NOTE 1911.—The foregoing chapter has been translated and used, with proper credit, by Mr. S. Sor in " Handbuch für Eisenbetonbau," Band IV, Teil 2. Mr. Sor has also made numerous other references to " The Design of Walls, Bins and Grain Elevators."

Numerous references to this book have also been made in " Manual of Reinforced Concrete Construction," by Charles F. Marsh and William Dunn.

CHAPTER X.

EXPERIMENTS ON PRESSURE ON BIN WALLS.

Introduction.—Comparatively few experiments have been made on the pressure of coal, ore, ashes, etc., on bin walls. The following are all that have been available to the author:

Portland Cement Materials.* Experiments were made by L. D. Gilbert and S. F. Barth at the Portland Cement Co.'s plant, Portland, Colorado, in January, 1906, to determine data to use in the design of cement bins. The results are given in Table XXV. In making the tests great care was used, each value given being the mean of three independent values.

The materials were weighed in a box holding one cubic foot, the material was packed by tapping the sides and jarring the bottom and was then struck level, the aim being to obtain as nearly as possible the same conditions that exist in a stock bin. The fineness was determined by standard sieves.

In making the tests for lateral pressure a small bin was built of dressed Mexican clear lumber, three feet square inside, and four feet deep, with an opening 12 inches square cut through one side starting at the bottom, the hole being cut with a bevel to allow ample clearance in the opening. A door was hinged on the bottom of the opening with steel butts. The door was hung with the center line of butts flush with the inside face and set inside of bin a scant ⅛ inch. The opening was covered with a light piece of linen duck stretched tight and tacked all around about three or four inches from the hole, forming a diaphragm. An iron bracket was screwed on the outside of the door and the pressure was carried to the scale platform. The scale used was a small platform scale weighing to one-half pound.

*Courtesy of Mr. L. D. Gilbert.

Before putting any material in the bin the scale was tested with a standard 50-lb. weight, and the weight of the lever and door noted. Material to the depth of 12 inches was then put in the bin and the resultant pressure on the scales noted, then another 12 inches of material was added and the pressure noted, and so on. In each case the surface was leveled and brought to the proper height.

In making the three tests on the same material the pressure ran very close, and as the angle of repose decreased the lateral pressure increased.

In all cases, especially with the finer materials, the pressure was greatest at the time the bin was filled, and fell off considerably upon standing an hour or so, indicating that in a large bin requiring a considerable time to fill the pressure would be less than in a small bin.

TABLE XXV.

EXPERIMENTS ON PORTLAND CEMENT MATERIALS.

Material.	Weight per Cu. Ft. in Pounds.	Per Cent Passing.	Angle of Repose φ.	Ratio of Lateral to Vertical Press.
Clinker.	85.3	All passed 1½″ ring.	33°	.30
Cement from Kom's.	97.0	95% through No. 20.	37.5°	.32
Finished cement.	103.0	96% through No. 100.	See Fig. 85 a	.42
Rock from crusher (Shale).	89.7	All passed 2½″ ring.	39°	.28
Raw mat. from Kom's.	79.9	90% through No. 20.	33°	.40
Raw mat. from tube mills.	67.6	89% through No. 100.	See Fig. 85 b	.42
Coal-slack.	53.0	All passed 2″ ring.	37.5°	.31
Coal from Williams mill.	50.6	63% through No. 10.	34.5°	.33
Coal from tube mills.	42.0	98% through No. 100.	16°	.41

The Portland cement assumed a curved surface of repose as shown in Fig. 85 a; while the material from the tube mills assumed the curved surface shown in Fig. 85 b.

Coal and Ashes.—The author can find no records of tests for powdered coal aside from those given by Gilbert and Barth. The values for weight and angle of repose in use by different firms and engineers are given in Table XXVI. It should be remembered that the coarser the material the less the pressure.

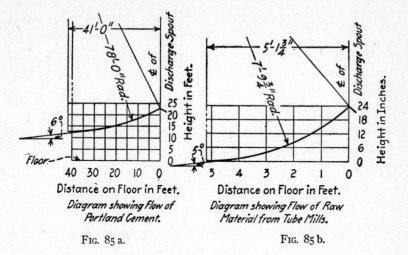

FIG. 85 a.

Diagram showing Flow of Portland Cement.

FIG. 85 b.

Diagram showing Flow of Raw Material from Tube Mills.

TABLE XXVI.

WEIGHT AND ANGLE OF REPOSE OF COAL, COKE, ASHES AND ORE.

Material.	Weight Lbs. per Cu. Ft.	Angle of Repose ϕ in Degrees.	Authority.
Bituminous coal.	50	35	Link Belt Machinery Co.
Bituminous coal.	47	35	Link Belt Engineering Co.
Bituminous coal.	47 to 56		Cambria Steel.
Anthracite coal.	52	27	Link Belt Machinery Co.
Anthracite coal.	52.1	27	Link Belt Engineering Co.
Anthracite coal fine.		27	K. A. Muellenhoff.
Anthracite coal.	52 to 56		Cambria Steel.
Slaked coal.		45	Wellman-Seaver-Morgan Co.
Slaked coal.	53	37½	Gilbert and Barth.
Coke.	23 to 32		Cambria Steel.
Ashes.	40	40	Link Belt Machinery Co.
Ashes, soft coal.	40 to 45		Cambria Steel.
Ore, soft iron.		35	Wellman-Seaver-Morgan Co.

Mr. J. E. A. Moore, engineer, The Wellman-Seaver-Morgan Company, states that coal, ore, etc., in lumps will commonly slide at an angle of 30° if the material is dry, but if the material is wet the angle of repose may increase to nearly 90°. For dry slack coal he uses $\phi = 45°$ and for soft iron ore, comparatively dry, he uses $\phi = 35°$.

Angle of Friction on Bin Walls.—The values differ with materials and with the bin wall. The following values may be used in the absence of more accurate data:

TABLE XXVII.

ANGLE OF FRICTION OF DIFFERENT MATERIALS ON BIN WALLS.

Material.	Steel Plate. ϕ' in Degrees.	Wood Cribbed. ϕ' in Degrees.	Concrete. ϕ' in Degrees.
Bituminous coal.	18	35	35
Anthracite coal.	16	25	27
Ashes.	31	40	40
Coke.	25	40	40
Sand.	18	30	30

Self-Cleaning Hoppers.—In order to have hoppers self-cleaning when the material is moist it is necessary, especially with fine material, to have the hopper bottoms slope at an angle considerably in excess of the angle of repose ϕ' or ϕ.

Ore pockets on the Great Lakes are made with hopper bottoms having an angle with the horizontal of from 38° 40′ to 50° 45′, but the majority are at an angle of 39° to 45°.

Crushed quartz from 1½ in. to ⅛ in. in size was found to readily slide down a steel plate floor at an angle of 40°, while ore finer than ⅛ in. would not move. Experiments showed that bituminous coal would slide down a steel chute at an angle of 40°, and down a wooden chute at 45° to the horizontal. Anthracite will slide down steel at 30° and down wood at 35°.*

Professor Emil Morsch gives the data in Table XXVIIA in "Der Eisenbetonbau."

TABLE XXVIIA.

WEIGHT AND ANGLE OF REPOSE OF MATERIALS.

Material.	Weight, lbs. per Cu. Ft.	ϕ in Degrees.
Gas Coal	50–56	45
Cement	87	40
Small Slag	100–112	45
Malt	33	22
Wheat	51	25
Ore	125	45

* Richard Lamb, in Trans. Am. Soc. C. E., Vol. 53.

CHAPTER XI.

THE DESIGN OF BINS.

Introduction.—The problem of the design of the structural part of steel bins is similar to the design of Steel Mill Buildings, and the reader is referred to the author's book on the Design of Steel Mill Buildings. For the design of reinforced concrete bins the reader is referred to Appendix I and Chapter XVIII, also to the descriptions of actual structures in Chapters XII and XIX. The design of circular bins is taken up in Chapter XIX. In this chapter only the details of design that are fundamental or are peculiar to bins are treated.

Flat Plates.—The analysis of the stresses in flat plates supported or fixed at their edges is extremely difficult. The following formulas by Grashof may be used: The coefficient of lateral contraction is taken as $\frac{1}{4}$. For a full discussion of these formulas based on Grashof's "Theorie Der Elasticitat und Festigkeit" see Lanza's Applied Mechanics.

1. *Circular plate of radius r and thickness t, supported around its perimeter and loaded with w per square inch.*—Let $f =$ maximum fiber stress, $v =$ maximum deflection, and $E =$ modulus of elasticity.

$$f = \frac{117}{128} \frac{w.r^2}{t^2} \tag{115}$$

$$v = \frac{189}{256} \frac{w.r^4}{E.t^3} \tag{116}$$

2. *Circular plate built in or fixed at the perimeter.*

$$f = \frac{45}{64} \frac{w.r^2}{t^2} \tag{117}$$

$$v = \frac{45}{256} \frac{w.r^4}{E.t^3} \tag{118}$$

3. *Rectangular plate of length a, breadth b, and thickness t, built in or fixed at the edges and carrying a uniform load w per square inch.*—

217

Let f_a be the unit stress parallel to a, f_b be the unit stress parallel to b, and $a > b$.

$$f_a = \frac{b^4.w.a^2}{2(a^4 + b^4)t^2} \; ; \; f_b = \frac{a^4.w.b^2}{2(a^4 + b^4)t^2} \tag{119}$$

$$v = \frac{a^4.b^4.w}{(a^4 + b^4)32 E.t^3} \tag{120}$$

For a square plate $a = b$,

$$f = \frac{w.a^2}{4t^2} \tag{121}$$

$$v = \frac{w.a^4}{64E.t^3} \tag{122}$$

The strength of plates simply supported on the edges is about $\frac{2}{3}$ the strength of plates fixed. Plates riveted or bolted around the edges may be considered as fixed.

Diagram for Square Plates.—The safe loads on square plates for a fiber stress of 10,000 pounds per square inch may be obtained from the diagram in Fig. 86. As an example, required the safe load for a $\frac{1}{4}$-in. plate 3 feet square. Begin at 3 on the bottom of the diagram, follow upward to the line marked $\frac{1}{4}$-in. plate, from the intersection follow to the left edge and find 280 lbs. per sq. ft. For any other fiber stress multiply the safe load found from the diagram by the ratio of the fiber stresses. To use the diagram for a rectangular plate take a square plate having the same area.

Buckle Plates.—Buckle plates are made by "dishing" flat plates as in Table XXVIIIa. The width of the buckle W or length L, varies from 2' 6" to 5' 6". The buckles may be turned with the greater dimension in either direction of the plate. Several buckles may be put in one plate, all of which must be the same size and symmetrically placed. Buckle plates are made $\frac{1}{4}''$, $\frac{5}{16}''$, $\frac{3}{8}''$ and $\frac{7}{16}''$ in thickness. The common standard sizes are given in Table XXVIIIa.

Buckle plates should be firmly bolted or riveted around the edges with a maximum spacing of 6 inches, and should be supported transversely between the buckles. The process of buckling distorts the

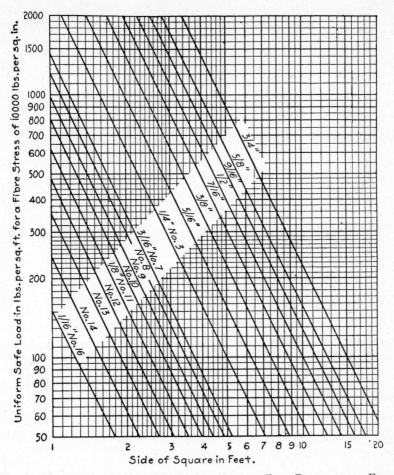

FIG. 86. SAFE UNIFORM LOAD PER SQUARE FOOT ON FLAT PLATES FOR A FIBER STRESS OF 10,000 LBS. PER SQUARE INCH.

plate and an extra width should be ordered and the plate should be trimmed after the process is complete.

Strength of Buckle Plates.—The safe load for a buckle plate with buckles placed up, is approximately given by the formula

$$W = 4f.R.t \qquad (123)$$

where W = total safe uniform load,

f = safe unit stress in pounds per square inch,

$R =$ depth of buckle in inches,

$t =$ thickness of plate in inches.

Where buckle plates are riveted and the buckle placed down the safe load is from 3 to 4 times that given above.

TABLE XXVIIIa.

AMERICAN BRIDGE CO.'S STANDARD BUCKLE PLATES.

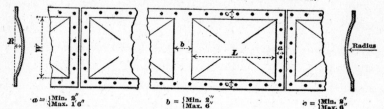

$a = \begin{cases} \text{Min. } 2'' \\ \text{Max. } 1' 6'' \end{cases}$　　　$b = \begin{cases} \text{Min. } 2'' \\ \text{Max. } 6'' \end{cases}$　　　$a = \begin{cases} \text{Min. } 2'' \\ \text{Max. } 6'' \end{cases}$

No. of Plate.	Size of Buckle in Feet and Inches.		Rise in Inches. R	Rad. of Buckle in Feet and Inches.		Maximum No. of Buckles.	No. of Plate.	Size of Buckle in Feet and Inches.		Rise in Inches. R	Rad. of Buckle in Feet and Inches.		Maximum No. of Buckles.
	Length. L	Width W		Length. L	Width. W			Length. L	Width. W		Length. L	Width. W	
1	3–11	4–6	3½	6–8	8–9	7	20	2–9	2–6	2½	4–7	3–10	10
2	4–6	3–11	3½	8–9	6–8	6	21	2–6	2–6	2½	3–10	3 10	10
3	3–11	3–6	3	7–9	6–3	7	22	3–5	3–6	3	5–11	6–3	8
4	3–6	3–11	3	6–3	7–9	8	23	3–6	3–5	3	6–3	5–11	8
5	3–9	3–9	3	7–1	7–1	8	24	3 6	3–9	3	6–3	7–1	8
6	3–1	3–9	3	4–10	7–1	9	25	3–9	3–6	3	7–1	6–3	8
7	3–9	3–1	3	7–1	4–10	8	26	3–1	3–2	3	4–10	5–1	9
8	3–8	3–8	2	10–2	10–2	8	27	3–2	3–1	3	5–1	4–10	9
9	2–8	3–8	2	5–5	10–2	10	28	3–1	3–0	3	4–10	4–7	9
10	3–8	2–8	2	10–2	5–5	8	29	3–0	3–1	3	4–7	4–10	9
11	2–2	3–8	2	3–7	10–2	10	30	2–0	2–6	2½	2–6	3–10	10
12	3–8	2–2	2	10–2	3–7	8	31	2–6	2–0	2½	3–10	2–6	15
13	3–0	3–0	2	6–10	6–10	9	32	3–6	5–6	3½	5 4	13–1	5
14	2–9	2–9	3	3–10	3–10	10	33	5–6	3–6	3½	13 1	5–4	1
19	2–6	2 9	2½	3–10	4–7	10	34	4–0	4 0	3	8–1	8–1	7

Plates are made $\frac{1}{4}''$, $\frac{5}{16}''$, $\frac{3}{8}''$ or $\frac{7}{16}''$ thick.

Buckles of different sizes should not be used in the same plate.

Rivets generally $\frac{5}{8}''$ or $\frac{3}{4}''$ diameter.

Rivets and Riveted Joints.—Plates are fastened together with rivets in several different ways. If the plates are lapped over each other the joint is a *lap* joint, the joint being called a *single lap,* Fig. 87 a; *double lap,* Fig. 87 b; *triple lap,* etc., depending upon the number of rows of rivets. If the plates are fastened together with one splice plate as in Fig. 88 a, the joint is called a *single strap butt* joint; while if two plates are used, as in Fig. 88 b, the joint is called a *double strap butt* joint. Butt joints may have single, double, etc., riveting on each side of the joint. Where more than one row of rivets is used on one side of a joint the rivets in one row are placed opposite the middle of the rivets in the other row, *i. e.*, the rivets are *staggered*. When joints are designed to be water tight the edges of the plates are beveled and the joint is calked after riveting by driving the metal of the beveled edge back into the joint with a chisel, called a *calking tool*.

Investigation of Riveted Joints.—*Lap joint single riveting.* In Fig. 87 a let P be the tensile stress transmitted from one plate to another by a single rivet, t be the thickness of the plate, p be the pitch of the

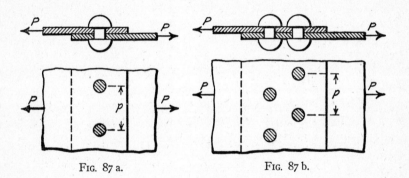

FIG. 87 a.   FIG. 87 b.

rivets, and d be the diameter of a rivet. Let S_t be the tensile unit-stress which occurs in the plate between the rivets, S_s the unit shearing stress in the rivet, and S_c the unit compression on the vertical projection of the rivet at right angles to the line of stress.

Then the equations between the stresses and force P are

$$t(p-d)S_t = P \text{ for tension on plate,} \tag{124}$$

$$t.d.S_c = P \text{ for compression on rivet,} \tag{125}$$

$$\tfrac{1}{4}\pi.d^2.S_s = P \text{ for shear on rivet.} \tag{126}$$

For a lap joint with double riveting, let P be the tension on a width p. Then the equations between the stresses and the force P are

$$t(p-d)S_t = P \qquad (127)$$

$$2t.d.S_c = P \qquad (128)$$

$$2\frac{\pi}{4}.d^2.S_s = P \qquad (129)$$

For a butt joint with a single strap and a single row of rivets, as in Fig. 88 a, the joint becomes two single riveted lap joints and the same equations may be used. For a butt joint with double strap plates and a single row of rivets on each side the following equations are used in designing the joint, t being the thickness of the main plate:

$$t(p-d)S_t = P \qquad (130)$$

$$t.d.S_c = P \qquad (131)$$

$$2\frac{\pi}{4}.d^2.S_s = P \qquad (132)$$

The strap plates should never be less than one-half the thickness of the main plate.

While for a butt joint with double strap plates and double riveting on each side, as in Fig. 88 b, the following equations are used in designing the joint, t being the thickness of the main plate:

$$t(p-d)S_t = P \qquad (133)$$

$$2t.d.S_c = P \qquad (134)$$

$$4\frac{\pi}{4}.d^2.S_s = P \qquad (135)$$

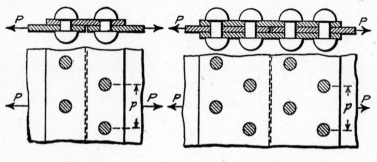

FIG. 88 a.   FIG. 88 b.

The investigation of a joint consists in calculating the values of S_t, S_c, and S_s, and comparing them with the allowable values. The allowable values for S_t, S_c, and S_s are not usually the same. In the author's specifications for Steel Frame Buildings as given in the Design of Steel Mill Buildings, the following allowable stresses are given: $S_t = 16{,}000$ lbs., $S_c = 22{,}000$, and $S_s = 11{,}000$ lbs. per sq. in.

The "efficiency" of a joint is the ratio of its allowable stress to the allowable stress on the unriveted plate. For a riveted joint three efficiencies may be obtained by dividing the three values of P for tension, compression and shear by $p.t.S_t$, the strength of the unriveted plate. For example, let $S_t = 16{,}000$, $S_c = 22{,}000$, and $S_s = 11{,}000$ lbs. per sq. in., and let $p = 2\frac{1}{2}''$, $d = \frac{7}{8}''$, and $t = \frac{3}{8}''$, for a lap joint with double riveting. Then the efficiency for tension is $(p-d)t.S_t/p.t.S_t$ $= \dfrac{(p-d)}{p} = 0.65$; the efficiency for compression is $2t.d.S_c/p.t.S_t =$ $2d.S_c/p.S_t = 0.96$; and the efficiency for shear is $\frac{1}{2}\pi.d^2.S_s/p.t.S_t = 0.88$. The efficiency of this joint is therefore 65 per cent of the unriveted plate.

For bins subjected to severe usage the usual values for the allowable stresses are $S_t = 10{,}000$, $S_c = 15{,}000$, and $S_s = 7{,}500$ lbs. per sq. in. For these values the efficiencies of the above joint are, tension $= 0.65$, compression $= 1.00$, and shear $= 0.96$. By equating the three expressions for efficiency, values of t, d, and p can be calculated. Using $S_t = 10{,}000$, $S_c = 15{,}000$, and $S_s = 7{,}500$ lbs. per sq. in., and solving as above we have for a riveted lap joint with single riveting

$$d = 2.55\,t$$

$$p = 6.37\,t$$

$$\text{Efficiency} = 0.60$$

For a lap joint with double riveting

$$d = 2.55\,t$$

$$p = 10.2\,t$$

TABLE XXIX.
SHEARING AND BEARING VALUE OF RIVETS.

Values Above or to Right of Upper Zigzag Lines are Greater Than Double Shear. Values Below or to Left of Lower Zigzag Lines are Less Than Single Shear.

| Diam. of Rivet. | | Area in Sq. Ins | Single Shear at 6,000 Pounds | Bearing Value for Different Thickness of Plate at 12,000 Pounds per Square Inch. | | | | | | | | | | | | |
Frac.	Dec'l.			1/4	5/16	3/8	7/16	1/2	9/16	5/8	11/16	3/4	13/16	7/8	15/16	1
3/8	.375	.1104	660	1,130	1,410	1,690										
1/2	.500	.1963	1,180	1,500	1,880	2,250	2,630	3,000								
5/8	.625	.3068	1,840	1,880	2,340	2,810	3,280	3,750	4,220	4,690						
3/4	.750	.4418	2,650	2,250	2,810	3,380	3,940	4,500	5,160	5,630	6,190	6,750				
7/8	.875	.6013	3,610	2,630	3,280	3,940	4,590	5,250	5,910	6,560	7,220	7,880	8,530	9,190	9,840	
1	1.000	.7854	4,710	3,000	3,750	4,500	5,250	6,000	6,750	7,500	8,250	9,000	9,750	10,500	11,250	12,000

| Diam. of Rivet. | | Area in Sq. Ins | Single Shear at 7,500 Pounds | Bearing Value for Different Thickness of Plate at 15,000 Pounds per Square Inch. | | | | | | | | | | | | |
Frac.	Dec'l.			1/4	5/16	3/8	7/16	1/2	9/16	5/8	11/16	3/4	13/16	7/8	15/16	1
3/8	.375	.1104	830	1,410	1,760	2,110										
1/2	.500	.1963	1,470	1,880	2,340	2,810	3,280	3,750								
5/8	.625	.3068	2,300	2,340	2,930	3,520	4,100	4,690	5,280	5,860						
3/4	.750	.4418	3,310	2,810	3,520	4,220	4,920	5,630	6,330	7,030	7,720	8,440				
7/8	.875	.6013	4,510	3,280	4,100	4,920	5,740	6,560	7,380	8,200	9,030	9,850	10,670	11,480	12,300	
1	1.000	.7854	5,890	3,750	4,690	5,620	6,560	7,500	8,440	9,380	10,310	11,250	12,190	13,130	14,060	15,000

TABLE XXIX.—*Continued.*
SHEARING AND BEARING VALUE OF RIVETS.

Values Above or to Right of Upper Zigzag Lines are Greater Than Double Shear. Values Below or to Left of Lower Zigzag Lines are Less Than Single Shear.

Bearing Value for Different Thickness of Plate at 22,000 Pounds per Square Inch.

Diam. of Rivet. Frac.	Dec'l.	Area in Sq. Ins.	Single Shear at 11,000 Pounds	$\frac{1}{4}$	$\frac{5}{16}$	$\frac{3}{8}$	$\frac{7}{16}$	$\frac{1}{2}$	$\frac{9}{16}$	$\frac{5}{8}$	$\frac{11}{16}$	$\frac{3}{4}$	$\frac{13}{16}$	$\frac{7}{8}$	$\frac{15}{16}$	1
⅜	.375	.1104	1,210	2,060	2,580	3,090										
½	.500	.1963	2,160	2,750	3,440	4,130	4,820	5,500								
⅝	.625	.3068	3,370	3,440	4,300	5,160	6,020	6,880	7,740	8,600						
¾	.750	.4418	4,860	4,130	5,160	6,190	7,220	8,250	9,280	10,320	11,340	12,380				
⅞	.875	.6013	6,610	4,810	6,020	7,220	8,430	9,630	10,840	12,040	13,240	14,440	15,640	16,840	18,050	
1	1.000	.7854	8,640	5,500	6,880	8,250	9,630	11,000	12,380	13,750	15,130	16,500	17,880	19,520	20,630	22,000

Bearing Value for Different Thickness of Plate at 24,000 Pounds per Square Inch.

Diam. of Rivet. Frac.	Dec'l.	Area in Sq. Ins.	Single Shear at 12,000 Pounds	$\frac{1}{4}$	$\frac{5}{16}$	$\frac{3}{8}$	$\frac{7}{16}$	$\frac{1}{2}$	$\frac{9}{16}$	$\frac{5}{8}$	$\frac{11}{16}$	$\frac{3}{4}$	$\frac{13}{16}$	$\frac{7}{8}$	$\frac{15}{16}$	1
⅜	.375	.1104	1,320	2,250	2,810	3,380										
½	.500	.1963	2,360	3,000	3,750	4,500	5,250	6,000								
⅝	.625	.3068	3,680	3,750	4,690	5,620	6,560	7,500	8,440	9,370						
¾	.750	.4418	5,300	4,500	5,620	6,750	7,870	9,000	10,120	11,250	12,370	13,500				
⅞	.875	.6013	7,220	5,250	6,560	7,870	9,190	10,500	11,810	13,120	14,440	15,750	17,060	18,370		
1	1.000	.7854	9,430	6,000	7,500	9,000	10,500	12,000	13,500	15,000	16,500	18,000	19,500	21,000	22,500	24,000

15

$$\text{Efficiency} = 0.75$$

This shows the advantage of double riveting.

Where the rivet holes in the plates are made by punching specifications require that the diameter of the rivet before driving be used in calculating the strength of the rivet, and that the rivet hole be taken $\frac{1}{8}$ inch larger than the undriven rivet.

To obtain a tight joint the rivets should be spaced close together and as near the edge as practicable to make it possible to thoroughly calk the joint; while for strength the rivets should be spaced far apart and placed well back from the edge.

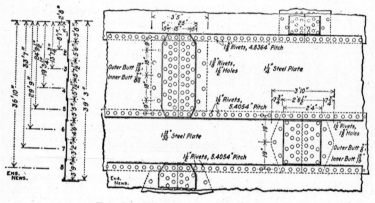

FIG. 89.   RIVETING ON GAS HOLDER.

The arrangement of plates and the rivet details for the vertical butt joints and horizontal lap joints for a gas holder are shown in Fig. 89.

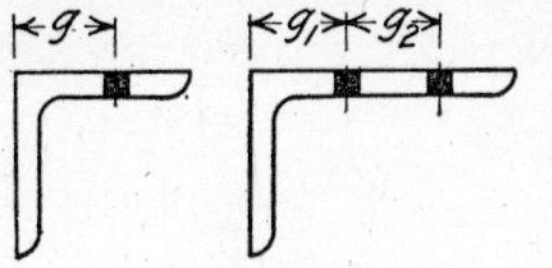

GAGES
in inches

Leg	Gage g	Max. Rivet	Leg	Gage g_1	Gage g_2	Max. Rivet
8	$4\frac{1}{2}$	$\frac{7}{8}$	8	3	3	$\frac{7}{8}$
7	4	$\frac{7}{8}$	7	$2\frac{1}{2}$	3	$\frac{7}{8}$
6	$3\frac{1}{2}$	$\frac{7}{8}$	6	$2\frac{1}{4}$	$2\frac{1}{4}$	$\frac{7}{8}$
5	3	$\frac{7}{8}$	5	2	$1\frac{3}{4}$	$\frac{7}{8}$
4	$2\frac{1}{2}$	$\frac{7}{8}$	When 6" L exceeds $\frac{3}{4}$"			
$3\frac{1}{2}$	2	$\frac{7}{8}$	6	$2\frac{1}{2}$	2	$\frac{7}{8}$
3	$1\frac{3}{4}$	$\frac{7}{8}$				
$2\frac{3}{4}$	$1\frac{5}{8}$	$\frac{3}{4}$				
$2\frac{1}{2}$	$1\frac{3}{8}$	$\frac{3}{4}$				
$2\frac{1}{4}$	$1\frac{1}{4}$	$\frac{5}{8}$				
2	$1\frac{1}{8}$	$\frac{5}{8}$				
$1\frac{3}{4}$	1	$\frac{1}{2}$				
$1\frac{1}{2}$	$\frac{7}{8}$	$\frac{3}{8}$				
$1\frac{3}{8}$	$\frac{7}{8}$	$\frac{3}{8}$				
$1\frac{1}{4}$	$\frac{3}{4}$	$\frac{3}{8}$				
1	$\frac{5}{8}$	$\frac{1}{4}$				

MINIMUM RIVET SPACING

Size of Rivet inches	Min. Distance inches
1	3
$\frac{7}{8}$	$2\frac{5}{8}$
$\frac{3}{4}$	$2\frac{1}{4}$
$\frac{5}{8}$	2
$\frac{1}{2}$	$1\frac{3}{4}$
$\frac{3}{8}$	$1\frac{1}{4}$
$\frac{1}{4}$	1

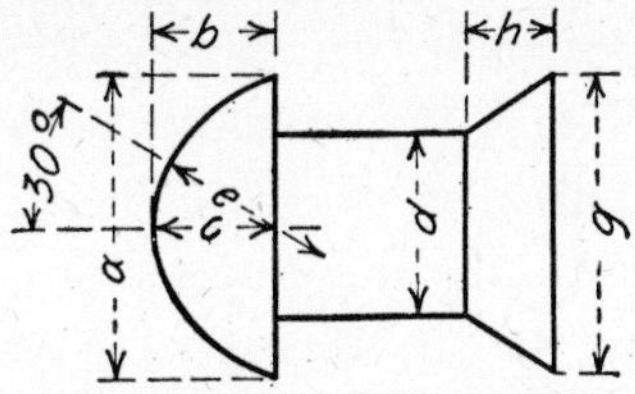

PROPORTIONS OF RIVETS
in inches

Diameter of Shank d	Full Head: Diameter a	Full Head: Height b	Full Head: Radii c	Full Head: Radii e	Countersunk: Diameter g	Countersunk: Depth h
1	$1\frac{5}{8}$	$\frac{11}{16}$	$\frac{11}{16}$	$1\frac{1}{32}$	$1\frac{9}{16}$	$\frac{1}{2}$
$\frac{7}{8}$	$1\frac{7}{16}$	$\frac{39}{64}$	$\frac{39}{64}$	$\frac{59}{64}$	$1\frac{3}{8}$	$\frac{7}{16}$
$\frac{3}{4}$	$1\frac{1}{4}$	$\frac{17}{32}$	$\frac{17}{32}$	$\frac{51}{64}$	$1\frac{3}{16}$	$\frac{3}{8}$
$\frac{5}{8}$	$1\frac{1}{16}$	$\frac{29}{64}$	$\frac{29}{64}$	$\frac{43}{64}$	1	$\frac{5}{16}$
$\frac{1}{2}$	$\frac{7}{8}$	$\frac{3}{8}$	$\frac{3}{8}$	$\frac{9}{16}$	$\frac{25}{32}$	$\frac{1}{4}$
$\frac{3}{8}$	$\frac{11}{16}$	$\frac{19}{64}$	$\frac{19}{64}$	$\frac{7}{16}$	$\frac{19}{32}$	$\frac{3}{16}$

MINIMUM STAGGER FOR RIVETS

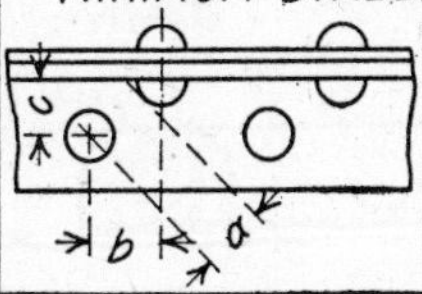

c inches	b in inches, For $\frac{3}{4}$" Rivet $a=1\frac{1}{8}$"	b in inches, For $\frac{7}{8}$" Rivet $a=1\frac{1}{4}$"
$1\frac{1}{8}$	$1\frac{1}{4}$	$1\frac{1}{2}$
$1\frac{3}{16}$	$1\frac{3}{16}$	$1\frac{7}{16}$
$1\frac{1}{4}$	$1\frac{1}{8}$	$1\frac{3}{8}$

c inches	b in inches, For $\frac{3}{4}$" Rivet $a=1\frac{1}{8}$"	b in inches, For $\frac{7}{8}$" Rivet $a=1\frac{1}{4}$"
$1\frac{5}{16}$	$1\frac{1}{16}$	$1\frac{5}{16}$
$1\frac{3}{8}$	$\frac{15}{16}$	$1\frac{1}{4}$
$1\frac{7}{16}$	$\frac{7}{8}$	$1\frac{3}{16}$
$1\frac{1}{2}$	$\frac{3}{4}$	$1\frac{1}{8}$
$1\frac{9}{16}$	$\frac{9}{16}$	1
$1\frac{5}{8}$	$\frac{3}{8}$	$\frac{15}{16}$
$1\frac{11}{16}$	0	$\frac{13}{16}$
$1\frac{3}{4}$		$\frac{5}{8}$
$1\frac{13}{16}$		$\frac{7}{16}$
$1\frac{7}{8}$		0

MINIMUM BUTTON SETS

For $\frac{3}{4}$" and $\frac{7}{8}$" Rivets $2\frac{1}{4}$"

For Rivets less than $\frac{3}{4}$" 2"

STANDARD CLEARANCE FOR RIVETING

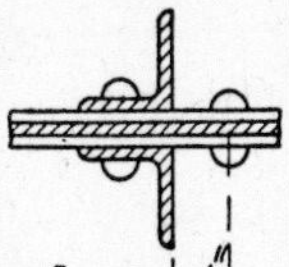

For $\frac{7}{8}$" Rivets $1\frac{1}{4}$"

For $\frac{3}{4}$" Rivets $1\frac{1}{8}$"

RIVETS IN CRIMPED Ls

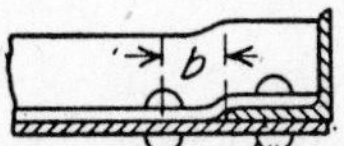

Distance b should = $1\frac{1}{2}$" + 2 × thickness chord Ls, but never less than 2"

FIG. 90. AMERICAN BRIDGE CO.'S STANDARDS FOR RIVETS AND RIVETING.

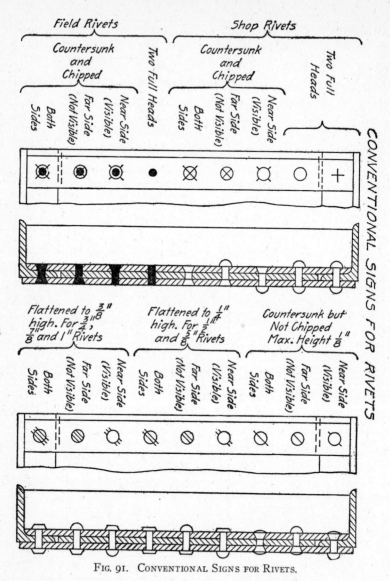

FIG. 91. CONVENTIONAL SIGNS FOR RIVETS.

The shearing and bearing value of rivets for different unit stresses are given in Table XXIX.

The proportions of rivets and standards for riveting structural steel as adopted by the American Bridge Company are given in Fig. 90.

In structural drawing it is necessary to use conventional methods to indicate the different kinds of riveting. The conventional signs for riveting in use by the American Bridge Co. are given in Fig. 91.

The standard rivet spacing for calking as used by the Gillette-Herzog Manufacturing Co. is given in Table XXX.

TABLE XXX.

STANDARD SPACING AND EDGE DISTANCE IN INCHES OF RIVETED JOINTS FOR CALKING.

Thickness of Plate.	3/8″ Rivets.			1/2″ Rivets.			5/8″ Rivets.			3/4″ Rivets.			7/8″ Rivets.		
	p	p'	E	p	p'	E	p	p'	E	p	p'	E	p	p'	E
1/8″	1 1/4	2	5/8												
3/16	1 1/2	2 1/4	3/4	1 1/2	2 1/4	3/4									
1/4	1 1/4	2 1/4	3/4	1 3/4	2 1/2	7/8	1 7/8	2 5/8	1	2	2 3/4	1 1/8			
5/16				1 3/4	2 1/2	7/8	2	2 3/4	1	2 1/8	2 7/8	1 1/8			
3/8				1 7/8	2 5/8	1	2	2 3/4	1	2 1/4	3	1 1/8	2 3/8	3 1/8	1 1/4
7/16							2 1/8	2 7/8	1	2 1/4	3	1 1/8	2 3/8	3 1/4	1 3/8
1/2							2 1/4	3	1 1/8	2 3/8	3 1/8	1 1/4	2 1/2	3 1/4	1 1/2
5/8										2 1/2	3 1/4	1 1/4	2 5/8	3 3/8	1 1/2

p = pitch for single riveting, p' = pitch for double riveting, and E = edge distance.

Design of Stiffeners.—Stiffeners are riveted to the sides of bin plates to carry part of the flexural stress and also to transmit the shear as in plate girders. In designing the stiffener to take flexural stress

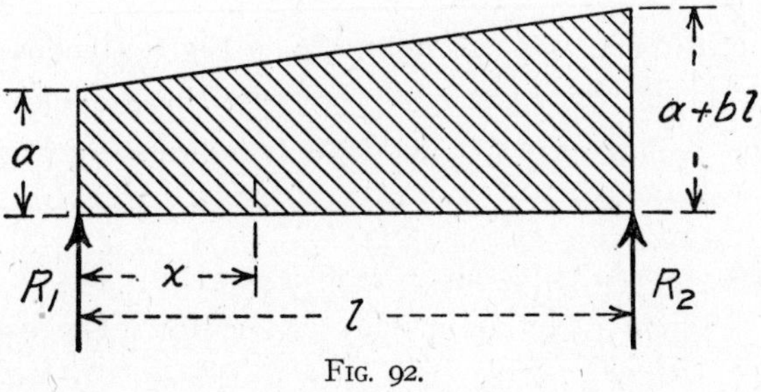

FIG. 92.

it is usual to assume that the stiffener acts as a beam and carries the load on one-half the area on either side. This makes the stiffener a beam carrying a wedge-shaped mass as in Fig. 92.

$$R_1 = \frac{a.l}{2} + \tfrac{1}{6}b.l^2$$

$$R_2 = \frac{a.l}{2} + \tfrac{1}{3}b.l^2$$

The bending moment at any point x, is

$$M = R_1.x - \left(\frac{a.x^2}{2} + \frac{b.x^3}{6}\right) \qquad (136)$$

Solving for a maximum

$$dM = R_1.dx - a.x.dx - \frac{b.x^2.dx}{2} = 0, \text{ and}$$

$$x = -\frac{a}{b} + \sqrt{\frac{a^2}{b^2} + \frac{a.l}{b} + \tfrac{1}{3}l^2} \qquad (137)$$

and the maximum bending moment will be found by substituting the value of x in (136). *

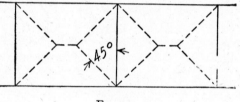

FIG. 93.

Where the stiffener supports an area as in Fig. 93 the loading will be unsymmetrical, and can most easily be found by graphics. The stiffener may be assumed to carry the load as indicated in Fig. 93 by the dotted lines.

Bin Gates.—Many gates have been devised to make it possible to handle the different materials quickly and easily. The gates in Fig. 94 have been designed by the Link Belt Machinery Co., and are especially adapted to coal and similar materials. Gate (f) is an ordinary slide gate, while the other gates are of the under-cut type.

Gate (a) in Fig. 95 operates very easily, while (b) is the type of gravity gate commonly used in ore bins. A detailed description of gate (b) is given on page 183. Gate (c) is often used in grain bins.

* The maximum bending moment is very closely $M = \tfrac{1}{8} W.l$, where $W =$ total load on beam; $= a.l + \tfrac{1}{2} b.l^2$.

The gate in Fig. 96 is of the under-cut type and was used on an ore bin.

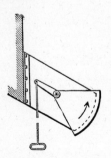

(a)

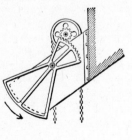

(b)

(c)

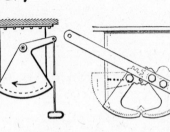

(d)   (e)

(f)

FIG. 94.

(a)   (b)   (c)

FIG. 95.

The gate shown in Fig. 97 a was designed by the Link Belt Engineering Co., and was used on the bin in Fig. 105.

The gate shown in Fig. 97 b was used on the circular ore bins shown in Fig. 58.

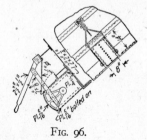

FIG. 96.

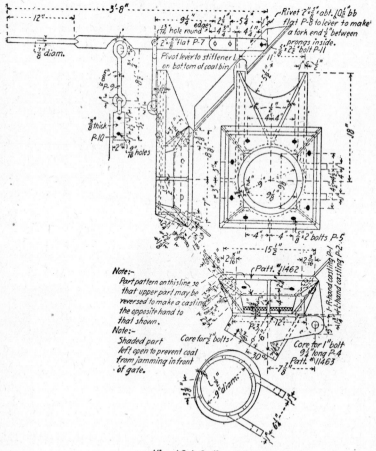

Hinged Gate Casting—Left hand as shown.

FIG. 97 a.

For additional details of gates see Fig. 56, Fig. 98, Fig. 111, and Fig. 117.

Specifications.—The allowable stresses in bin plates and the structural framework supporting the bins will depend upon the use that is to be made of the bin. The factor of safety should vary from 4 for

FIG. 97 b. GATE FOR CIRCULAR ORE BIN, ARIZONA. (SEE BIN IN FIG. 58 AND FIG. 118.)

quiescent loads to 6 for bins that are to be subjected to hard usage. All steel should be made by the open hearth process, structural or tank steel plates being used for flat plates and flange steel being used for all bent or flanged plates.

The specifications for materials and workmanship for steel structures adopted by the American Railway Engineering and Maintenance of Way Association, and the American Society for Testing Materials are standard and are given in Appendix IV. For ordinary conditions in bin design use the allowable stresses given, while for bins to receive severe treatment use ⅔ of the allowable stresses.

For specifications for Steel Frame Mill Buildings, see the author's specifications in "The Design of Steel Mill Buildings."

Painting.—Paints used on structural work may be divided into oil paints, asphalt paints, coal tar paints, etc. The oil paints are made by grinding or mixing a pigment with linseed oil. The common pigments are red lead, white lead, oxide of iron, zinc and graphite. For a description of the different kinds of oil paints see Chapter XXVII in the author's "The Design of Steel Mill Buildings."

Asphalt paint is made by mixing asphalt with a bitumen, the mixture being applied hot. Many so-called asphalt paints are only coal tar mixtures.

Coal tar paint is occasionally used for painting gas tanks and similar structures that receive rough usage. Coal tar paint mixed as described below has been used by the U. S. Navy Department for painting the hulls of ships. It should give satisfactory service where the metal is subject to corrosion. The coal tar paint is mixed as follows: The proportions of the mixture are slightly variable according to the original consistency of the tar, the use for which it is intended and the climate in which it is used. The proportions will vary between the following proportions in volume.

	Coal Tar.	Portland Cement.	Kerosene Oil.
New Orleans Mixture..................	8	1	1
Annapolis Mixture	16	4	3

The Portland cement should first be stirred into the kerosene, forming a creamy mixture, the mixture is then stirred into the coal tar. The paint should be freshly mixed and kept well stirred. This paint sticks well, does not run when exposed to the sun's rays and is a very satisfactory paint for rough work. The cost of the paint will vary from 10 to 20 cents per gallon. The kerosene oil acts as a dryer, while the Portland cement neutralizes the coal tar.

Carbon and graphite paints are much used for painting structural and bin work. While the cost per gallon of these paints is usually rather high, $1.00 to $1.50 per gallon, the paints cover so much surface that the actual cost of the paint is not high.

The Wellman-Seaver-Morgan Co. recommends American graphite mixed with boiled linseed oil for painting the structural framework and outside of the bin plates. This company recommends that steel bins be lined with a layer of concrete about $1\frac{1}{2}''$ thick, the concrete being reinforced with expanded metal or wire fabric. This concrete lining has been found to protect the surface of the steel both from wear and corrosion.

The American Bridge Co. uses linseed oil mixed with $\frac{3}{4}$ lb. of lamp-black per gallon as a priming coat with very satisfactory results. For further information on paint see " The Design of Steel Mill Buildings," Chapter XXVII. For the cost of painting see Chapter XIII.

Freezing in Bins.—Where a wet ore is stored in bins with steel bottoms or with thin and exposed bottoms of other materials the stored material is liable to freeze and stick in the bin. The Colorado Fuel and Iron Co. has solved this problem in the steel bins at its Minnequa plant by building a false timber bottom about a foot below the steel bottom, and connecting the air space thus formed with specially constructed stoves.

CHAPTER XII.

EXAMPLES AND DETAILS OF BINS.

Introduction.—Examples of bins built for different purposes will be given in this chapter, and details of the different structures will be briefly discussed. The examples have been grouped under the following heads: (1) Suspension Bunkers; (2) Hopper Bins; (3) Circular Bins. For a brief description of these different types see Chapter VIII.

1. SUSPENSION BUNKERS. Lackawanna Steel Co.'s Plant. —In Fig. 98 and Fig. 99 are shown the details of a panel of the ore and limestone bins at the Lackawanna Steel Co.'s plant, Buffalo, N. Y., built by Wellman-Seaver-Morgan Company, Cleveland, Ohio. The bin is of the suspension bunker type with $\frac{3}{8}''$ hopper plates. The tracks on the top of the bin are for the traveling gantry bins and dump cars. The material is discharged from the bins through spouts onto larrys running on the track beneath the spouts. The hopper plates are $\frac{3}{8}''$ thick. It will be seen in Fig. 99 that openings are provided in the hopper just above the spouts to enable the material inside the bin to be loosened up. The details and construction are fully shown in Fig. 98 and Fig. 99.

The details of a 1,500 ton coal bin built by the Wellman-Seaver-Morgan Company for the above company are shown in Fig. 100. This bin is of the suspension type with a double discharge spout, under which is a Seaver ore gate. The coal stored in this bin is crushed and is quite wet. It is delivered into the top of the bin by a belt conveyor. The $12'' \times 14''$ hole in the spout is to allow bars to be inserted to loosen the material in the bins. Details of the bin are fully shown in the drawing.

The bin is lined with a concrete lining reinforced with expanded metal and finished with a coating of one to one Portland cement mortar. The bin plates are $\frac{3}{8}''$ thick. The bin is covered with corrugated steel supported on a steel framework. The entire structure was painted

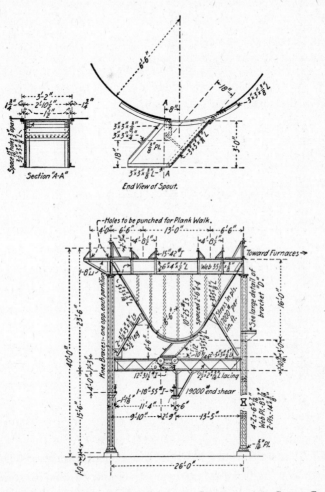

FIG. 98. ORE AND LIMESTONE BUNKERS, LACKAWANNA STEEL CO.

one coat of graphite paint in the shop and one coat after erection. The load was taken as 23 tons per lineal foot of bin. The stresses in the framework and the plates and other details are given in Fig. 100.

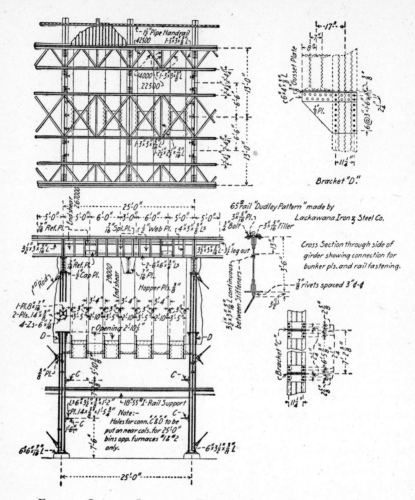

FIG. 99. ORE AND LIMESTONE BUNKERS, LACKAWANNA STEEL CO.

Rapid Transit Subway Power House Coal Bunkers.—The 1,000 ton suspension coal bunker at the Fifty-eighth St. and Eleventh Ave. power house of the Rapid Transit Subway is shown in Fig. 101 and Fig. 102.

The bunker is supported on braced posts and is covered with a steel frame house carrying the Robins belt conveyor. The bin is lined with $3\frac{1}{2}$ inches of concrete reinforced with expanded metal. The loads and

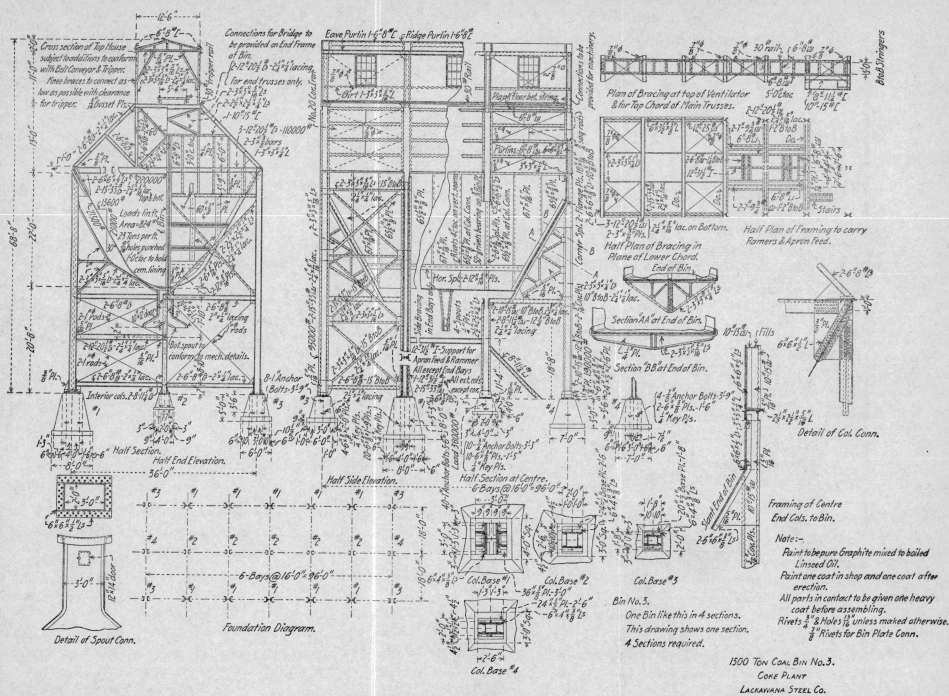

Fig. 100.

1500 Ton Coal Bin No. 3.
Coke Plant
Lackawana Steel Co.

stresses in frame work and plates are given in Fig. 101. The bunker
has $2\frac{1}{2}'' \times 2'' \times \frac{1}{2}''$ angles placed horizontally 4' 0'' apart and riveted
to the bunker plates. The bunker is covered with galvanized corru-
gated steel supported on a steel framework. The details of construction are clearly shown in the drawings. This bunker was designed
and constructed by the American Bridge Co.

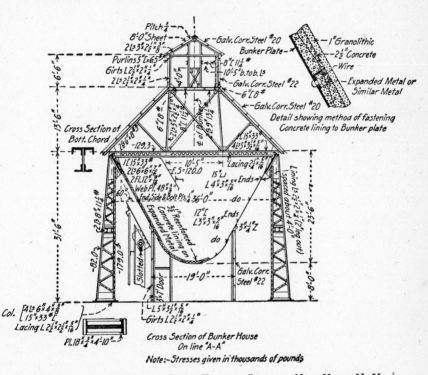

FIG. 101. COAL BUNKERS, RAPID TRANSIT SUBWAY, NEW YORK, N. Y.

2. HOPPER BINS. Cananea Consolidated Copper Co.—The

hopper ore bin shown in Fig. 103 was built by the Minneapolis Steel
& Machinery Co. for the Cananea Consolidated Copper Co., Cananea,
Mexico.

The ore is coarse and heavy and is dumped from cars on the track
on top of the bins. The ore is drawn off through gates in the bottom,
operated by rack and pinion and is carried away on a conveyor. The

side plates are $\frac{1}{4}''$ thick and have $7''$ [stiffeners spaced about 4 feet apart. The hopper plates are $\frac{3}{8}''$ thick and are stiffened with $10''$ [s. A cut of this bin is given in Chapter VIII. The details are clearly shown in Fig. 55 and Fig. 103.

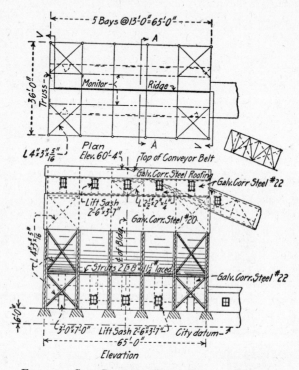

FIG. 102. COAL BUNKERS, RAPID TRANSIT SUBWAY.

Details of Hopper Coal Bins.—Detail drawings of a hopper coal bin designed by the Link Belt Engineering Co., Nicetown, Pa., are shown in Figs. 104 to 106. The plan of the hopper and detail drawings of the side plates are shown in Fig. 104; the detail drawings of the end plates are given in Fig. 105; and the details of supporting columns, the spouts, and miscellaneous details are shown in Fig. 106. This bin is designed to supply two furnaces having automatic stokers. The details are well worked out and are excellent examples of bin design. It will be seen that each plate, angle, etc., is completely detailed and is given a distinct erection mark. The stiffeners are placed on the outside of the bin only, and have fillers to avoid crimping the

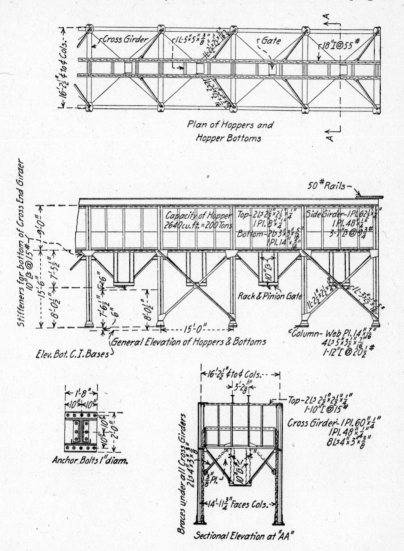

FIG. 103. HOPPER BIN CANANEA CONSOLIDATED COPPER CO., CANANEA, MEXICO.

angles. The side and hopper plates are $\frac{1}{4}''$ thick. The bin is braced as shown in Fig. 104. The gate for this bin is shown in Fig. 97 a.

16

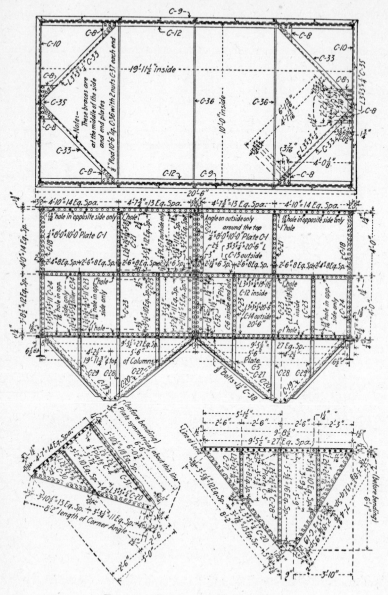

FIG. 104.   DETAILS OF HOPPER BIN.

Coal Storage Plant, Cincinnati Water Works.—The coal storage house, Fig. 107, consists of a steel bin 225 × 69 feet × 17 feet deep, supported on columns which rest on concrete pedestals. Between the columns are hopper bottoms which are provided with valves for discharging the coal into cars which are pushed by hand into the boiler house. The bins are filled from cars which are pushed in on the

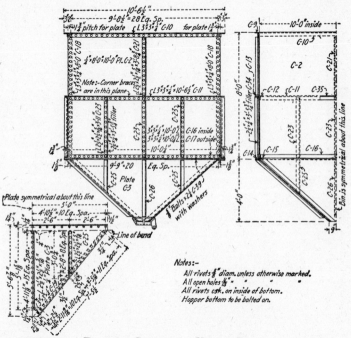

FIG. 105. DETAILS OF HOPPER BIN.

suspended floor. The outside columns are braced to take the thrust due to the coal. The sides of the bin are lined with $\frac{5}{16}''$ plates, while the hopper bottoms are made of $\frac{3}{8}''$ plates. The details are shown in Fig. 107.

For design of a steel hopper bin for coke and stone see Fig. 56.

Reinforced Concrete Coal and Coke Bins for Key City Gas Co.—The coal and coke bins built for the Key City Gas Co., Dubuque, Iowa, by the Expanded Metal and Corrugated Bar Co., St. Louis, Mo., are excellent examples of reinforced concrete bin construction. The structure is 33′ 8″ wide, 148′ 0″ long, and 38′ 3″ high.

A half plan of the bins showing the arrangement and the size of the bins is given in Fig. 109. A cross section and a longitudinal section

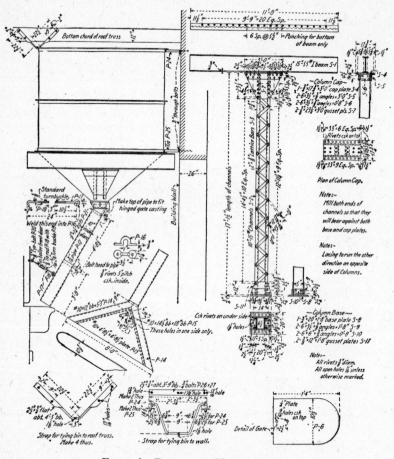

FIG. 106. DETAILS OF HOPPER BIN.

of the bins showing the details of the bins and the thickness of the concrete and the reinforcement are given in Fig. 108. The concrete was 1–2–5 Portland cement concrete, for which the modulus of elasticity was taken equal to 2,800,000, and the ultimate compressive stress

equal to 2,700 lbs. per sq. in. The ultimate tensile strength of the
steel was assumed as 55,000 lbs. per sq. in. The beams were designed

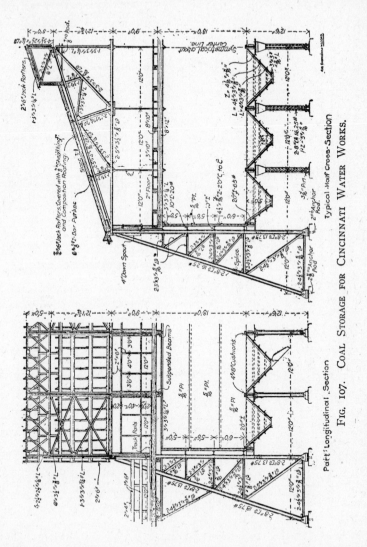

FIG. 107. COAL STORAGE FOR CINCINNATI WATER WORKS.

for a factor of safety of 4 in both concrete and steel, A. L. Johnson's
formula being used. Coal was assumed to weigh 50 lbs. per sq. ft.,
and coke to weigh 32 lbs. per sq. ft.

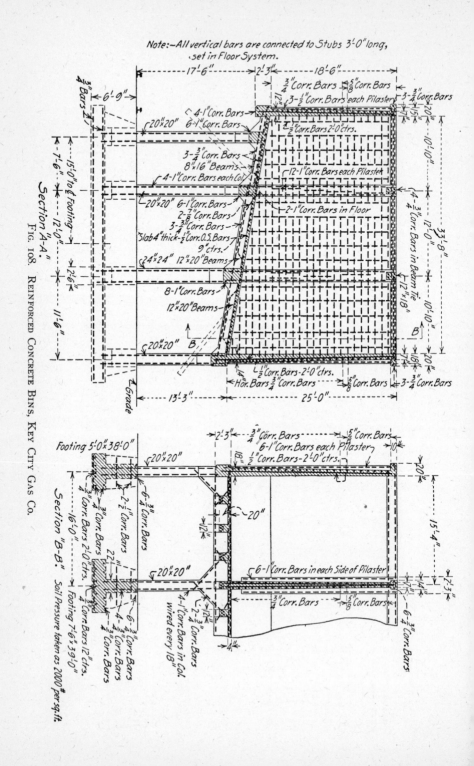

Note:—All vertical bars are connected to Stubs 3'-0" long, set in Floor System.

Section "A-A."

Fig. 108. Reinforced Concrete Bins, Key City Gas Co.

Section "B-B." Soil Pressure taken as 2000# per sq.ft.

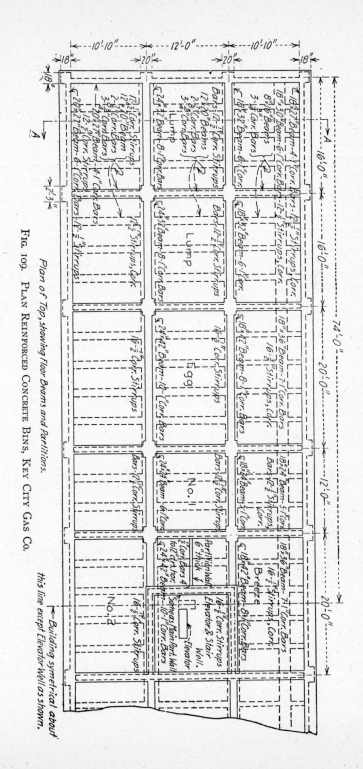

Plan of Top, showing Floor Beams and Partitions.

Fig. 109. Plan Reinforced Concrete Bins, Key City Gas Co.

Steel and Concrete Coal Storage Plant.*—The coal storage plant of the Lowell Gas Light Company, Lowell, Mass., is 500 feet long and 65 feet wide and has a storage capacity of 25,000 tons. The steel transverse bents are spaced 25′ 0″ centers. A cross section is shown in Fig. 110. The plant is a steel frame with concrete filled walls, concrete foundations and floor, and a tile roof supported on steel purlins. The side columns are braced frameworks and carry the pressure of the coal and the wind pressure. The roof is covered with non-glazed Ludowici tile laid on angle sub-purlins. Light is obtained through skylights in the roof made by substituting glass tile for the ordinary tile; ventilation is obtained through the opening between the roof and the wall. The steel work that would be exposed to coal is completely imbedded in concrete.

The conveyor is of the gravity bucket type with buckets 18 inches wide by 24 inches long, pivoted in the chain in such a manner that

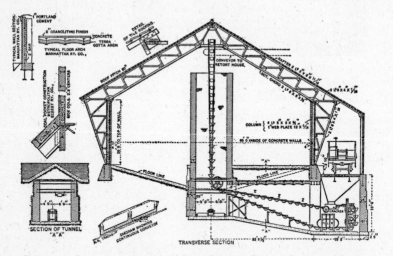

FIG. 110. STEEL AND CONCRETE COAL STORAGE PLANT, LOWELL, MASS.

while they maintain themselves normally in an upright position, they can turn through a complete revolution. The chain is composed of double flat links of steel, and the conveyor moves about 40 feet per

* *Trans. Am. Soc. M. E.,* May 1902.

minute. The machinery receives the coal from the railroad cars, cracks the lumps to a uniform size and carries them to any part of the building without transfer.

In removing the coal from storage it is drawn into the conveyor through a filler which is movable and which is placed under valves placed between columns 25′ 0″ apart. The openings are through buckle plates 10 feet square which may be removed to facilitate rapid

FIG. III. COALING STATION, MORRISVILLE, PA.

emptying in case of fire from spontaneous combustion. Wrought iron pipes run through the coal to facilitate the determination of the temperature of the coal.

Coaling Station at Morrisville, Pa.—The coaling station of the P. R. R. Co. at Morrisville, Pa., is made of a steel framework with reinforced concrete sides and lining. The coaling station is 204′ 0″ long, 14′ 0″ wide and 19′ 0″ above the top of the concrete foundations, the top of the foundations being 12′ 6″ above the base of rail and 16′ 6″ above the footing. The bins are 14′ 0″ wide and 12′ 0″ long, with a double hoppered bottom. The details of the steel framework are shown in Fig. 112. The finished coaling station is shown in Fig. 111. The specifications for the reinforced concrete were as follows:

Reinforced Concrete.—Reinforced concrete to include the sides and bottom of bins. All exposed sides and bottoms of bins, including

columns shall be inclosed in concrete covered at least $1\frac{1}{2}''$, the concrete
to be composed of Portland cement 1 part, clean, sharp sand $2\frac{1}{2}$ parts,
and broken stone not larger than $\frac{3}{4}''$ in diameter 5 parts. The concrete
to be well mixed and thoroughly rammed. The slabs for the bottom
to be $5\frac{1}{2}''$ thick, not including the finish (which shall be 1'' thick), and

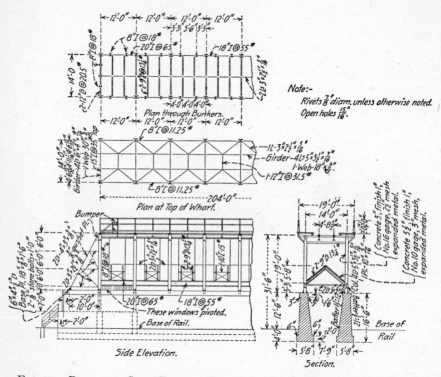

FIG. 112. DETAILS OF STEEL FRAMEWORK FOR COALING STATION, MORRISVILLE, PA.

to be reinforced with No. 10 gage 3'' mesh expanded metal; the slabs
for the sides to be 3'' thick, not including the finish (which shall be 1''
thick), and to be reinforced with No. 16 gage $2\frac{1}{2}''$ expanded metal.
The inside of the bunkers to be finished with a granolithic top coat 1''
thick composed of Portland cement 1 part, clean, sharp sand 1 part,
and fine crushed granite 1 part. The outside surface to be finished by
making a perfectly smooth surface by finishing the same with a thin
coat of cement.

Gates.—The gates were manufactured by the Link Belt Engineering Co. The Link Belt coaling chute is a patented device consisting of an under-cut gate and a swinging apron. The gate sides project upward in the form of a toothed segment and mesh with spur pinions mounted on a through shaft to which is keyed a combination hand and chain wheel. This combination facilitates operation and prevents the straining and bending to which gates of large capacity are subject. The gate is opened by a rotary downward swing and is closed instantly by an upward, or cutting off movement that is not retarded by the flowing coal, the chute being open at the top prevents danger from jamming. The flow being cut off permits the apron to be raised out of the way

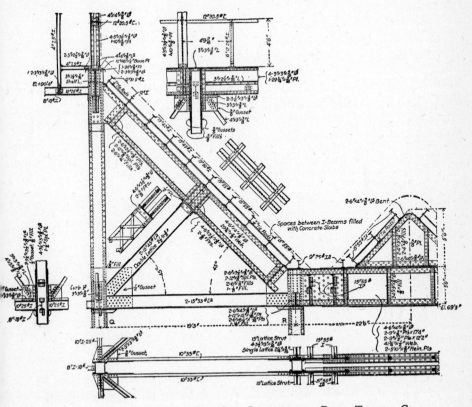

Fig. 113. Transverse Bent Coal Bin, Interborough Rapid Transit Co.

of passing locomotives and trains. It is held in position by counter weights. A hand chain permits control from the ground.

For a timber coaling station, see Fig. 132.

Coal Bin, Power House, Interborough Rapid Transit Co.—The coal bins are 61′ 0″ wide and extend nearly the full length of the power station. The bins have a W cross section as shown in Fig. 113. The transverse trusses are spaced 4′ 11″ and 15′ 6½″, and are supported

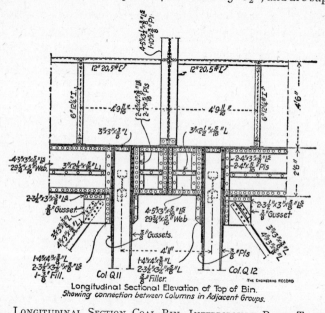

Longitudinal Sectional Elevation of Top of Bin.
Showing connection between Columns in Adjacent Groups.

FIG. 114. LONGITUDINAL SECTION COAL BIN, INTERBOROUGH RAPID TRANSIT CO.

on four rows of columns. The transverse trusses carry 15-in. I-beams spaced 3′ 0″ centers. These beams are connected by tie rods and have concrete arches with expanded metal reinforcement. The concrete arches are filled to a depth of 1½″ above the tops of the flanges and a finish coat of one to one Portland cement mortar 2″ thick is put on top of the arch filling. The concrete sides are carried up 4′ 6″ above the sloping sides. The bins are designed for a load of 45 tons per lineal foot of bin. The dead load was taken at 150 lbs. per sq. ft. for the sloping sides and 200 lbs. per sq. ft. for the bottom. A transverse section is shown in Fig. 113, and a view of the end framing of

a bin is shown in Fig. 115. The girders and beams are made massive
and amply strong.

The stresses in this bin were calculated as for the coal bins of the
Ninety-sixth St. Station (see *Engineering Record,* September 1, 1900).

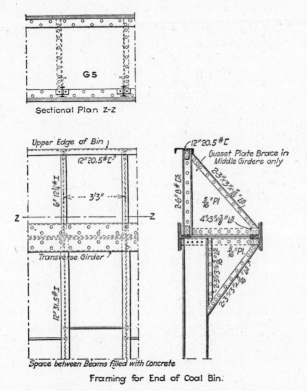

FIG. 115. END FRAMING COAL BIN, INTERBOROUGH RAPID TRANSIT CO.

Ore Docks, Chicago & Northwestern Ry., Escanaba, Mich.—
The ore dock is a timber structure 1,920 feet long, 50 feet 2 inches
wide, 70 feet high from the water to the dock. It has 320 pockets
with a storage capacity of 58,000 tons. The construction is shown
very clearly in Fig. 116 and Fig. 117. Rows of piles 30 to 46 feet
long were driven in 20 feet of water, the bents being 6 feet apart, with
18 and 20 piles in alternate bents. Just above the water surface these

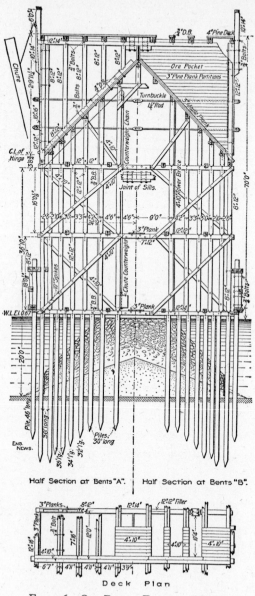

Half Section at Bents "A". | Half Section at Bents "B".

Deck Plan

FIG. 116. ORE DOCKS, ECANABA, MICH.

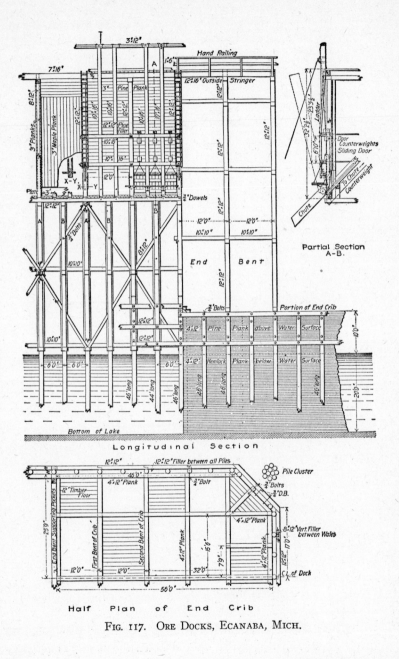

FIG. 117. ORE DOCKS, ECANABA, MICH.

piles are capped with timbers 12 × 14 in., forming the sills for the framed bents of the dock. The posts and caps are largely of timber 12 × 12 in., and 8 × 12 in., with longitudinal diagonals 8 × 12 in., and transverse diagonals or sway braces 4 × 10 in. These timbers are

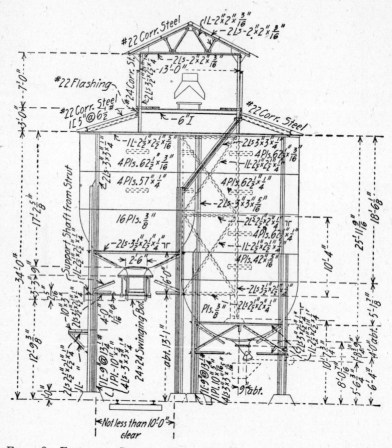

FIG. 118. ELEVATION CIRCULAR STEEL ORE BIN FOR OLD DOMINION COPPER MINING CO.

bolted and drift bolted together. Two rows of 1¼-in. transverse bars, set up by turn-buckles, pass through the pockets and resist the bursting pressure of the ore upon the face of the dock.

The pockets have sloping bottoms at an angle of 45° sheathed with 3-in. maple plank laid lengthwise up and down the slope. The parti-

tions in front of the pockets are of 3-in. pine plank. Vertical sliding
doors cover the openings, through which the ore flows to the chutes.
These doors are counterweighted. The chutes are also balanced, the
chain from the end of the chute passing up to a pulley above the dock,

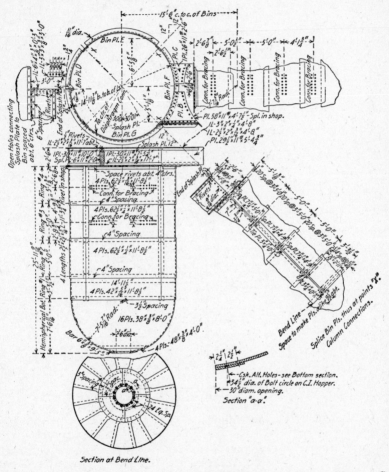

FIG. 119. DETAILS FOR CIRCULAR BINS FOR OLD DOMINION COPPER MINING CO.

down to a pulley below the pocket, up under the pocket to another
pulley, then down to a circular weight which hangs near the water line.

3. CIRCULAR BINS. Ore Bin for Old Dominion Copper Mining and Smelting Co.—

The circular ore bin shown in Fig. 118, Fig. 119,

17

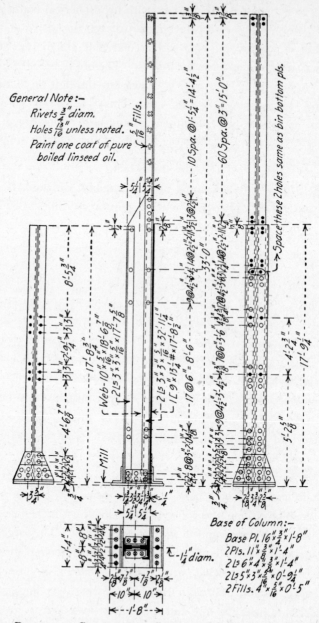

General Note:—
Rivets $\frac{3}{4}$" diam.
Holes $\frac{13}{16}$" unless noted.
Paint one coat of pure
boiled linseed oil.

Base of Column:—
Base Pl. 16"×$\frac{3}{4}$"×1'-8"
2 Pls. 11$\frac{1}{4}$"×$\frac{3}{4}$"×1'-4"
2 Ls 6"×4"×$\frac{3}{4}$"×1'-4"
2 Ls 5"×3$\frac{1}{2}$"×$\frac{5}{16}$"×0'-9$\frac{1}{4}$"
2 Fills. 4"×$\frac{5}{16}$"×0'-5"

FIG. 120.   DETAILS OF COLUMNS FOR CIRCULAR ORE BINS FOR OLD DOMINION
COPPER MINING CO.

and Fig. 120 is one of 8 circular bins with hemispherical bottoms built by the Minneapolis Steel & Machinery Co. for the above company. In Fig. 118 it will be seen that the circular bins are of two heights, there being two large and six small ones. The ore is brought into the bin shed on side dump cars, and is drawn out through the bottom by means of gates as shown in Fig. 118. This type of gate is a very satisfactory one. Detail plans of one of the larger bins are given in Fig. 119, and are self-explanatory. Details of the columns supporting the bins are given in Fig. 120.

Cement Storage Bins, Illinois Steel Company, Chicago, Ill.—The storage plant consists of four cylindrical reinforced concrete bins, constructed on the Monier System.* Details are given in Fig. 121, Fig. 122, and Fig. 123. The total capacity including the space between the bins is 25,000 barrels. The bins are 25 feet in diameter and are spaced 29 feet center to center, the space between each pair of adjacent walls being closed by a cylindrical shaft 30 inches in diameter, the entire structure being monolithic. The foundation is a continuous floor or bed of concrete 3 feet thick, 66×66 feet, with corners of 18 ft. 6 in. radius. About 5 inches above the base of the foundation is imbedded a netting of 9-in. mesh formed by $\frac{5}{8}$-in. round steel rods, tied together at their intersections by No. 18 wire. Upon this concrete bed is a series of piers 12 ft. 6 in. high, and 1 ft. 10 in. thick. Those near the outer surface of the tank are mainly 3 ft. 5 in. long, but others near the central portion are from 6 ft. 8 in. to 7 ft. 10 in. long. All the smaller piers have four steel rails imbedded in the concrete, the rails being connected by spacing bars riveted to them, and resting on $\frac{1}{2}$-in. steel plates imbedded in the concrete floor about 15 inches below the surface. The piers are capped with similar plates. The larger piers have six or eight rails. Upon the piers rest concrete-steel girders 15 inches deep and 4 feet wide, with vertical openings at intervals for the discharge spouts. Through each girder run four lines of horizontal steel bars near the top, and four other lines bent to form truss rods, with sheets of wire netting on each side of each set of bars.

* Designed by E. Lee Heidenreich.

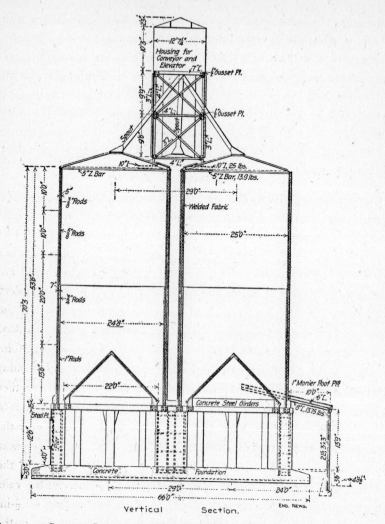

Vertical   Section.

FIG. 121. CEMENT STORAGE BINS OF REINFORCED CONCRETE, MONIER CONSTRUC-
TION, ILLINOIS STEEL COMPANY, CHICAGO, ILL.

The cylindrical tanks, 53 ft. 6 in. high, rest upon this system of
girders, the base being 13 feet 9 in. above the level of the concrete
floor. The walls are 7 inches thick in the lower part and 5 inches
thick in the upper part, the thickness being increased where they unite
with the circular walls which close the spaces between the tanks.

Within the concrete walls is imbedded a continuous sheet of netting of No. 9 wires electrically welded at their intersections and forming rectangular meshes 1 × 4 inches. Around this (and alternately inside and outside of it) are horizontal rings of rods 4 inches apart, tied to

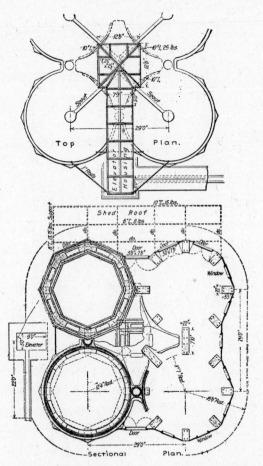

FIG. 122. PLAN OF REINFORCED CONCRETE CEMENT STORAGE BINS.

the netting by wire. These rods vary from 1 inch in diameter near the base to ⅜ inch in diameter near the top, while the top is finished with a ring formed by a 5-in. Z-bar. The roof is conical, 2 inches thick, with a manhole near the edge and an opening at the top for the spout. It was thought that with a hopper bottom and central discharge, material such as cement would give trouble by bridging, and the bottom is, therefore, made conical with eight discharge openings in the circular space between the base of the cone and the side of the

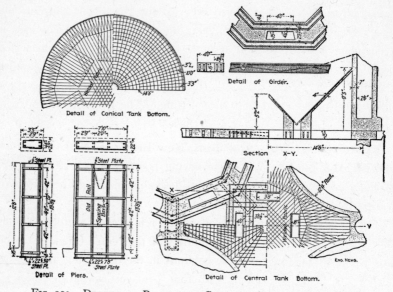

FIG. 123. DETAILS OF REINFORCED CONCRETE CEMENT STORAGE BINS.

tank. These are about 15 × 18 inches, and each serves two spouts leading to conveyors which carry the cement to the packing and shipping department. The conical bottom is 4 inches thick, reinforced with bars and wire netting, and its diameter at the base is 22 feet.

The concrete in the foundation floor and piers is composed of 1 part Portland cement, 3 parts coarse sand, and 4 parts broken stone. That of the bins is composed of 1 part Portland cement, to 3½ parts sand, no broken stone being used. It was mixed moderately wet and lightly rammed in wooden forms. These forms were constructed of 3-inch plank 3 feet long, kept together by three horizontal angle irons supported by three vertical angle irons clamped together above the wall. The concrete was poured in and tamped inside the forms, which were raised in 45° sections 28 inches high, every 24 hours. The work was carried on by day and night so as to prevent any setting between the layers of concrete.

The cement is brought from the mill by a horizontal screw conveyor and delivered into the boot of a vertical bucket elevator, which again delivers it to a horizontal screw conveyor above the bins, by which it is carried to the spout of one or other of the bins. The elevator runs in a rectangular shaft 12 × 14 feet, and the distributing conveyor in a chamber or housing 10 ft. 3 in. × 12 ft. 4 in. supported on a steel bent. The shaft and housing are built of a framing of steel angles, sheathed with Monier concrete steel plates 2 × 5 feet × ⅜ in. thick, made of cement mortar and wire netting. The floor of the conveyor housing is of similar plates 1 inch thick.

Reinforced Concrete Sand Bins, New Brighton, N. J.—The plant consists of a reinforced concrete drying house 34 ft. × 52 ft. and 87 ft. high, and two sand bins 30 ft. inside diameter and 50 ft. high, with a capacity of 1140 tons of dry sand each.

The two bins are supported on fifteen reinforced concrete columns. The center column and the six columns of the center ring of each bin are 22 inches square, while the columns in the outer ring are 18 × 22 inches, and all are reinforced with four ¾-in. vertical bars.

The side walls are 10 inches thick and are reinforced with horizontal bars with ends overlapping 24 inches, and of sizes as shown in Fig. 124. The walls are also reinforced by two sets of vertical bars; the lower set of ½-in. bars are 11 feet long and are spaced 2 ft. 6 in. apart, while the upper set of ⅜-in. bars are 14 ft. 6 in. long spaced 2 ft. 6 in. apart. The bars overlap 6 inches. The walls were built in 5-foot courses, which were bonded together by an additional set of ⅜-in. bars, 2 ft. long and spaced 2 ft. 6 in. The bottom is 13 inches thick and is reinforced with circular and inclined radial bars as noted in the drawing. The molds for the circular bins were made with planed vertical staves 1⅛ inches thick, forming panels 5 feet high, and about 8 feet long. The staves were nailed to 2 × 10-inch horizontal segmental ribs, one at the upper edge, one at the lower edge, and one at the center of each panel. The ribs were arranged so as to lap with the ribs of the adjacent panels to which they were bolted. The ribs were braced by inside and outside vertical standards 4 feet apart on centers, each made

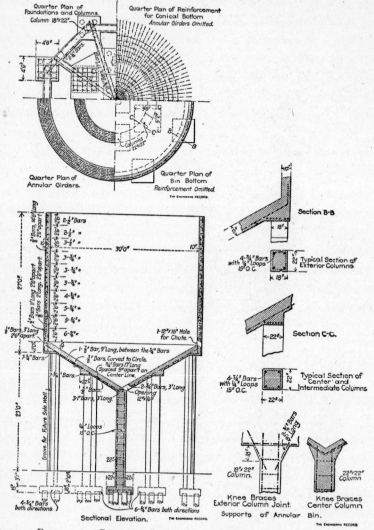

FIG. 124. REINFORCED CONCRETE SAND BIN, J. B. KING & CO., NEW BRIGHTON, STATEN ISLAND.

with a pair of 2 × 6-inch strips 6 feet long, fillered 1 inch apart and tied together by temporary radial bolts through the molds. These bolts passed through sleeves of No. 16 gage black sheet iron bent cold, permanently imbedded in the concrete and finally filled with mortar. Enough molds were made for one complete course for one bin and were therefore used ten times in constructing the two bins.

After the concrete was 24 hours old, the tie bolts were removed from the molds and they were lifted by a small hoist until the lower edges engaged the top of the concrete for about 2 inches and the vertical standards engaged it for about 1 foot. The molds were supported on blocks bolted to the wall through the sleeves in which the mold bolts had passed. The interior of the molds was thoroughly covered with soft soap to prevent adhesion of the concrete. Each 5-foot course was made monolithic by continuous concreting in one day's work. The bin bottom was made without an inside mold.

In calculating the bottom and walls of the bins, fluid pressure for dry sand weighing 100 lbs. per cu. ft. was assumed, and a working stress of 30,000 lbs. per square inch allowed on steel bars.

Reinforced Concrete Coal Pocket, Atlantic City Water Works.— The coal bin is 30 feet in diameter with conical bottom and pyramidal roof as shown in Fig. 125. The capacity of the bin is 400 tons.

The concrete was made of 1 part Alpha Portland cement, $2\frac{1}{2}$ parts bank sand, and 5 parts gravel. The sand and gravel both had 38 per cent voids. The gravel was cleaned and screened so as to be $\frac{1}{4}$ to $\frac{3}{4}$ in. in size for the shell of the coal bin, and $\frac{1}{4}$ to 2 in. in size for the other work. The concrete weighed exactly 150 lbs. per cu. ft.

The steel reinforcement was mild steel and was required to pass standard tests. Plain bars were used.

The molds for all parts above the foundation were of matched lumber, surfaced one side only. The rough side was placed on the side in contact with the concrete on interior surfaces, but on all other surfaces the planed side was placed next to the concrete. Concrete ingredients were added by actual measurements. The cement and sand were mixed dry, water was added and the whole mixed. The gravel was wet and thoroughly mixed with the mortar, and water added to make a wet mixture.

All surfaces above the foundation except the interior of the bin and the roof were given a coat of neat cement grout mixed with lampblack, applied with a brush. The roof was finished on top with 1 inch of 1 to 2 cement plaster applied while the cement was green.

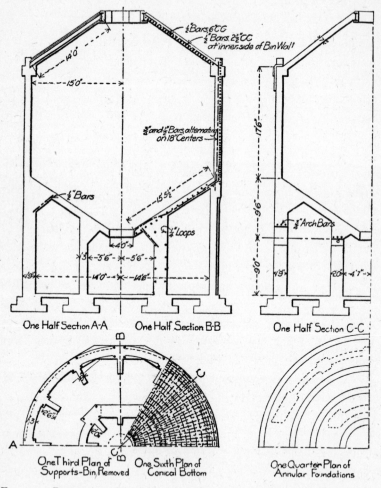

FIG. 125. REINFORCED CONCRETE COAL BIN, ATLANTIC CITY WATER WORKS.

The following are the approximate quantities in the work: Excavation, 233 cu. yds.; concrete, 317 cu. yds.; steel for reinforcement,

13,700 lbs.; steel beams, plates, etc., 3,250 lbs.; 3-in. down-spouts, 210 lin. ft.

The contract price of the coal bin was $3,795; of the elevating machinery $2,650; which, together with $37.50 for extra work, makes a total cost of $6,482.50.

The bin was designed by Kenneth Allen, city engineer.

Reinforced Concrete Sand Bins, Peerless Brick Co.—The reinforced concrete sand bins shown in Fig. 126 have a capacity of 2,200 cubic yards, and were built in 1905 for the Peerless Brick Co., New York, N. Y. The bin walls are 8 inches in thickness and are reinforced with vertical and horizontal Ransome bars. The vertical bars are $\frac{2}{8}$ inch square and are spaced 18 inches centers. The horizontal bars vary from $\frac{2}{8} \times 1\frac{1}{2}$ inch bars, spaced 8 to 12 inches centers, to $\frac{2}{8}$ inch square bars, spaced 18 inches centers, as shown in Fig. 126. The vertical rods are in lengths of about 14 feet, lap 18 inches at the joints and are wired together. The horizontal bars are set just inside the vertical bars and are $1\frac{1}{2}$ inches clear of outer surface. Their ends lap from 12 to 16 inches, and are separated by a $\frac{1}{2}$-inch washer and connected by a $\frac{1}{2}$-inch bolt at the center of each joint. The ends of the bars are bent outward 90°, and project 1 inch to secure additional grip in the concrete.

The lower part of the walls and the floor are waterproofed with 4-ply tar and felt. The roof is covered with tar and gravel. Other details are clearly shown in Fig. 126.

The concrete was composed of 1 part Lehigh Portland cement, 3 parts sand, and 5 parts gravel, mixed very wet in a Ransome mixer.

The forms for the cylindrical walls were made in segments about 9 feet long. They were 7 feet in height, the entire ring holding 42 cubic yards, which was filled in one day. The joints between the different fills were bonded by vertical $\frac{2}{8}$-in. bars 3 feet long and 2 feet apart on centers. The inner and outer molds were each stiffened with three horizontal circular ribs, one in the center, one at the top and one at the bottom. The inside and outside molds were tied together by horizontal bolts. Radial knee-brace timbers about 10 feet apart

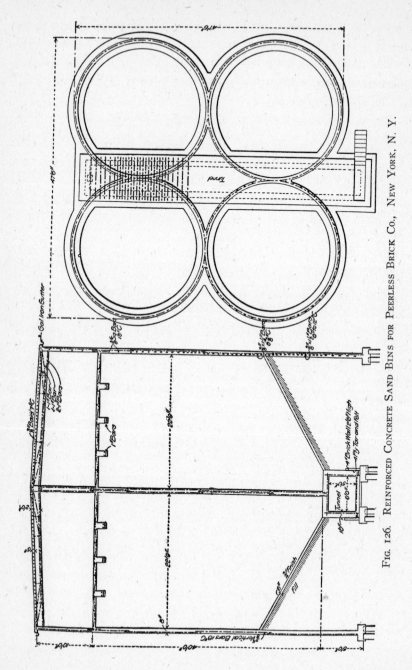

FIG. 126. REINFORCED CONCRETE SAND BINS FOR PEERLESS BRICK CO., NEW YORK, N. Y.

were bolted to the walls just below the top of the molds, and projected 4 feet beyond it, both inside and outside to carry the working platforms. After the completion of the wall these braces were removed and the holes left were carefully filled and pointed with mortar.

The bins were designed according to Janssen's formula (144).

The bins contain in all 680 cubic yards of concrete, and 4,510 lbs. of steel. They were built in about 60 working days with an average force of 11 carpenters and 14 laborers.

A Railway Coaling Station.—A railway coaling station recently installed at Waukegan, Illinois, for the Elgin, Joliet & Eastern Ry. is shown in Fig. 126a. The coal is delivered in hopper bottom railway dump cars and is charged into a concrete receiving hopper beneath the track. The outlet from the track hopper is fitted with a rotary charging gate or feeder which is operated automatically. The gate holds a full charge for a one and one-half ton Holmen dumping bucket, and when the bucket is in place at the bottom of the loading pit the gate revolves so that its open side is over the bucket while its other side closes the hopper outlet. As the bucket rises, the gate revolves so that its open side is opposite the outlet, allowing another charge to flow into the gate. The bucket works in a steel tower 85 ft. high, and is operated by an electric hoist in a cabin on one side of the tower. On reaching the top of its travel the bucket is dumped into the conical head of a cylindrical steel bin having a capacity of 300 tons of coal. The bottom of the bin is conical, being arranged so that the apex comes between the two coaling tracks. Two pivoted or counterweight chutes, each with an undercut gate project on opposite sides of the apex. The capacity of the plant is 60 tons per hour.

The coaling station was designed by the Roberts-Schaeffer Company under the direction of Mr. A. Montzheimer, Chief Engineer of the Joliet & Illinois Ry.

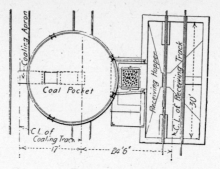

Plan.

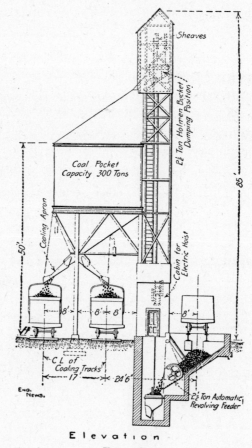

Elevation

FIG. 126 a.

CHAPTER XIII.

COST OF BINS.

Introduction.—The cost of bins depends so much upon the design and upon local conditions that it is possible to give only average conditions that may be used as a guide to the experienced estimator. For methods of estimating the weight of steel in structures and for additional data on costs see the author's "The Design of Steel Mill Buildings."

COST OF STEEL BINS.—The cost of steel bins may be divided into (1) cost of material; (2) cost of fabrication; (3) cost of erection; and (4) cost of transportation.

1. **Cost of Material.**—The price of structural steel is quoted in cents per pound delivered free on board cars (f. o. b.) at the point at which quotation is made. Current prices may be obtained from the Engineering News, Iron Age, or other technical papers. Present prices (1906) f. o. b. Pittsburg, Pa., are as follows:

TABLE XXXI.
PRICES OF STRUCTURAL STEEL (1906), F. O. B. PITTSBURG, PA., IN CENTS PER POUND.

Material.	Price in Cents per Lb.
I beams 18″ and over	1.70
I beams and channels 3″ to 15″	1.60
Angles 3″ to 6″ inclusive	1.70
Angles over 6″	1.80
Tees 3″ and over	1.80
Zees 3″ and over	1.70
Channels, angles, Ts and Zs under 3″	1.60
Plates, structural, base	1.60
Plates, flange, base	1.70
Bars and rivet rods	1.60

Material.	Price in Cents per Lb.
Deck beams and bulb angles	1.90
Checkered plates	2.25
Forged rounds 5″ to 11″ diameter	2.75
Eye bar flats 8″ to 12″ inclusive	2.10
Eye bars over 6″ and under 8″	1.90
Eye bars 6″ and under	1.60

Eye bars over 12″ wide subject to special arrangement.

Rolled rounds over 3″ diameter, 18″ long or over, 0.35 cents per lb. extra.

Rolled rounds over 3″ diameter, under 18″ long, 0.65 cents per lb. extra.

The prices above are net with the exception of those for plates and bars which are subject to standard extras as follows:

Extras.—*Shapes, Plates and Bars:*

(Cutting to length)

Under 3′ to 2′, inclusive	0.25 cts. per lb.	
Under 2′ to 1′, inclusive	0.50	" "
Under 1′	1.55	" "

Extras—Plates (*Card of January 7, 1902*):

Base ¼″ thick, 100″ wide and under, rectangular (see sketches).

Weights—see Mfgr's. Standard Specifications, Carnegie or Cambria Hand-Books, or Appendix II.

	Per 100 Lbs.
Widths—100″ to 110″	$ .05
110″ to 115″	.10
115″ to 120″	.15
120″ to 125″	.25
125″ to 130″	.50
Over 130″	1.00
Gages under ¼″ to and including ⅛″	.10
Gages under ⅛″ to and including No. 8	.15
Gages under No. 8 to and including No. 9	.25
Gages under No. 9 to and including No. 10	.30
Gages under No. 10 to and including No. 12	.40
Complete circles	.20
Boiler and flange steel	.10
Marine and fire box	.20
Ordinary sketches	.10

(Except straight taper plates, varying not more than 4″ in width at ends, narrowest end not less than 30″, which can be supplied at base prices.)

TABLE XXXII.

STANDARD CLASSIFICATION OF EXTRAS ON IRON AND STEEL BARS.*
Rounds and Squares.

Squares up to 4¼ inches only.   Intermediate sizes take the next higher extra.

Per 100 lbs.

¾ to 3 inches	....	Rates.
⅝ to 1 1⁄16 "	....	\$0.10 extra.
½ to 9⁄16 "	....	.20 "
7⁄16 "	....	.40 "
⅜ "	....	.50 "
5⁄16 "	....	.60 "
¼ and 9⁄32 "	....	.70 "
7⁄32 "	....	1.00 "
3⁄16 "	....	2.00 "
3 1⁄16 to 3½ "	....	.15 "
3 9⁄16 to 4 "	....	.25 "
4 1⁄16 to 4½ "	....	.30 "
4 9⁄16 to 5 "	....	.40 "
5⅛ to 5½ "	....	.50 "
5⅝ to 6 "	....	.75 "
6⅛ to 6½ "	....	1.00 "
6⅝ to 7¼ "	....	1.25 "

Flat Bars and Heavy Bands.

Per 100 lbs.

1 to 6 inches x ⅜ to 1 inch	....	Rates.
1 to 6 " x ¼ and 5⁄16 "	....	\$0.20 extra.
1 1⁄16 to 1 5⁄16 " x ⅜ to ¾ "	....	.40 "
1 1⁄16 to 1 5⁄16 " x ¼ and 5⁄16 "	....	.50 "
9⁄16 and ⅝ " x ⅜ to ½ "	....	.50 "
9⁄16 and ⅝ " x ¼ and 5⁄16 "	....	.70 "
½ " x ⅜ and 7⁄16 "	....	.90 "
½ " x ¼ and 5⁄16 "	....	1.10 "
7⁄16 " x ⅜ "	....	1.00 "
7⁄16 " x ¼ and 5⁄16 "	....	1.20 "
⅜ " x ¼ and 5⁄16 "	....	1.50 "

* Adopted August, 1902.

18

Per 100 lbs.

$1\frac{1}{8}$	to	6	inches x $1\frac{1}{16}$ to	$1\frac{3}{16}$ inch	....	.10	"
$1\frac{1}{8}$	to	6	" x $1\frac{1}{4}$ to	$1\frac{1}{2}$ "	....	.20	"
$1\frac{3}{4}$	to	6	" x $1\frac{5}{8}$ to	$2\frac{3}{4}$ "	....	.30	"
$3\frac{1}{8}$	to	6	" x 3 to	4 "	....	.40	"

Light Bars and Bands.

Per 100 lbs.

$1\frac{1}{2}$ to	6	in. x Nos. 7, 8, 9 and $\frac{3}{16}$	....	$0.40 extra.
$1\frac{1}{2}$ to	6	in. x Nos. 10, 11, 12 and $\frac{1}{8}$ in	....	.60	"
1 to	$1\frac{7}{16}$	in. x Nos. 7, 8, 9 and $\frac{3}{16}$ in	....	.50	"
1 to	$1\frac{7}{16}$	in. x Nos. 10, 11, 12 and $\frac{1}{8}$ in	....	.70	"
$1\frac{3}{16}$ to	$1\frac{5}{8}$	in. x Nos. 7, 8, 9 and $\frac{3}{16}$ in	....	.70	"
$1\frac{3}{16}$ and	$1\frac{5}{8}$	in x Nos. 10, 11, 12 and $\frac{1}{8}$ in	....	.80	"
$1\frac{1}{16}$ and	$\frac{3}{4}$	in. x Nos. 7, 8, 9 and $\frac{3}{16}$ in	....	1.00	"
$1\frac{1}{16}$ and	$\frac{3}{4}$	in. x Nos. 10, 11, 12 and $\frac{1}{8}$ in	....	1.20	"
$\frac{9}{16}$ and	$\frac{5}{8}$	in. x Nos. 7, 8, 9 and $\frac{3}{16}$ in	....	1.20	"
$\frac{9}{16}$ and	$\frac{5}{8}$	in. x Nos. 10, 11, 12 and $\frac{1}{8}$ in	....	1.30	"
$\frac{1}{2}$		x Nos. 7, 8, 9, and $\frac{3}{16}$ in	....	1.30	"
$\frac{1}{2}$		x Nos. 10, 11, 12 and $\frac{1}{8}$ in	....	1.50	"
$\frac{7}{16}$		x Nos. 7, 8, 9 and $\frac{3}{16}$ in	....	1.80	"
$\frac{7}{16}$		x Nos. 10, 11, 12 and $\frac{1}{8}$ in	....	2.10	"
$\frac{3}{8}$		x Nos. 7, 8, 9 and $\frac{3}{16}$ in	....	1.90	"
$\frac{3}{8}$		x Nos. 10, 11, 12 and $\frac{1}{8}$ in	....	2.40	"

2. Cost of Fabrication.—The cost of fabrication of structural steel work may be divided into (1) cost of drafting; (2) cost of mill details; and (3) cost of shop labor.

Cost of Drafting.—The cost of drafting varies with the character of the work, and the tonnage to be made from one detail, so that costs per ton may mean but little. The amount of work on a standard sheet 24 in. × 36 in. is also a variable quantity. As a rough estimate the cost of standard sheets may be placed at from $10.00 to $15.00 per sheet.

Details of circular grain or ore bins cost from $1.50 to $3.00 per ton; details of conical or hopper bottoms cost from $4.00 to $6.00 per ton. Details of rectangular hoppered bins cost from $2.00 to $4.00 per ton, including columns and bracing.

Actual Cost of Drafting.—The cost for detailing 8 steel grain tanks, weight 700 tons, was $1.20 per ton, not including distribution for operating, which was estimated at $0.80 per ton, making total actual cost $2.00 per ton.

The cost for detailing 8 cylindrical tanks with spherical bottoms, including columns and bracing and weighing 100 tons, was $3.00 per ton, not including distribution for operating expenses, which was estimated at $2.00 per ton, making total actual cost $5.00 per ton.

For additional costs of detailing see " The Design of Steel Mill Buildings," Chapter XXVIII.

Cost of Mill Details.—The American Bridge's Co.'s card for cost of mill details differs somewhat from the standard card of cost of mill details given in the author's book on " The Design of Steel Mill Buildings," Chapter XXVIII.

American Bridge Co.'s card of cost of mill details:
Mill Rates:
" *a* " — 0.15 cts. per lb.
This covers:
Plain punching 1 size hole in web only,
Plain punching 1 size hole in one or both flanges,
" *b* " — 0.25 cts. per lb.
This covers plain punching one size hole in either web and one flange or web and both flanges. (The holes in the web and flange must be of the same size.)
" *c* " — 0.30 cts. per lb.
This covers:
Punching of 2 size holes in the web only,
Punching of 2 size holes in one or both flanges.
" *d* " — 0.35 cts. per lb.
This covers punching and assembling into girders. Coping, ordinary beveling, including riveting and bolting of standard connection angles (this class includes beams shipped with connection angles bolted).
" *e* " — 0.40 cts. per lb.
This covers the punching of one size hole in the web and another size hole in the flanges.
" *f* " — 0.15 cts. per lb.
This covers cutting to length with less variation than plus or minus $\frac{3}{8}$".

"*r*" — 0.50 cts. per lb.

This covers beams with cover plates, shelf angles and ordinary riveted beam work, unless they are charged under class "*d*."

If this work consists of bending or any unusual work, the beams should not be included in the beam classification but estimated the same as riveted work. On all material estimated for cost at mill rates, 10 cts. per 100 lbs. is to be allowed for painting and 5 cts. per 100 lbs. is to be allowed for drawings.

Fittings.—All fittings, whether loose or attached, such as angle connections, bolts, separators, tie rods, etc., whenever they are estimated on in connection with beams or channels, to be charged at 1.55 cts. per lb. over and above the base price. The extra charge for painting is to be added to the price for fittings also. The base price on which fittings are based is not the base price of the beams to which they are attached, but is in all cases the base price of beams 15″ and under. The above rates will not include painting or oiling, which should be charged at the rate of 0.10 cts. per lb. for one coat, over and above the base price plus the extra specified above. For plain punched beams, where holes of more than two sizes are used, 0.15 cts. per lb, should be added for each additional size hole; for example—Plain punched beams, where three size holes occur, would be indicated as "*e*" plus 0.15 cts.; four size holes as "*e*" plus 0.30 cts.; for example—A beam with ⅝″ and ¾″ holes in the flanges and ⅝″ and ¾″ holes in the web should be included in class "*e*."

Cutting to length can be combined with any of the other rates except "*d*" and would have to be indicated, for example—Plain punching one size hole in either web and one flange, or web and both flanges, and cutting to length would be marked "*bf*," which would establish a total charge of 0.40 cts. per lb.

Note to class "*d*":

No extra charge can be rendered to this class for punching various size holes or cutting to length; in other words, if a beam is coped, or has connection angles riveted or bolted to it, it makes no difference how many size holes are punched in this beam—the extra will always be the same, namely, 0.35 cts.

Beams with shelf angles, short seat angles or cover plates are strictly not covered by card rates. They can be charged either under class "*d*," this rate covering only the beam proper, in which case all other material ought to be rated as fittings with the charge of 1.55 cts. per lb. over and above the base price, or they can be classified under a special shop rate, "r," — 0.50 cts. per lb. This rate applies to all material forming the piece. It is the intention to charge whatever figures are the lowest, in order to give the customer the benefit of the doubt. In preparing the estimate, beam material should be marked with the letter "b" and to this should be added the letter giving the classification, thus: A beam punched with one size hole in one or both flanges will be marked "$b\ a$," etc.

In ordering material from the mill the following items should be borne in mind. Where beams butt at each end against some other member, order the beams $\frac{1}{2}$ inch shorter than the figured lengths; this will allow a clearance of $\frac{1}{4}$ inch if all beams come $\frac{3}{8}$ of an inch too long. Where beams are to be built into the wall, order them in full lengths making no allowance for clearance. Order small plates in multiple lengths. Irregular plates on which there will be considerable waste should be ordered cut to templet. Mills will not make reentrant cuts in plates. Allow $\frac{1}{4}$ of an inch for each milling for members that have to be faced. Order web plates for girders $\frac{1}{4}$ to $\frac{1}{2}$ inch narrower than the distance back to back of angles. Order as nearly as possible every thing cut to required length, except where there is liable to be changes made, in which case order long lengths.

It is often possible to reduce the cost of mill details by having the mills do only part of the work, the rest being done in the field, or by sending out from the shop to be riveted on in the field connection angles and other small details that would cause the work to take a very much higher price. Standard connections should be used wherever possible, and special work should be avoided.

The classification of iron and steel bars is given in Table XXXII. The full extra charges for sizes other than those taking the base rate are seldom enforced; one-half card extras being very common.

In estimating the cost of plain material in a finished structure the shipping weight from the structural shop is wanted. The cost of material f. o. b. the shop must therefore include the cost of waste, paint material, and the freight from the mill to the shop. The waste is variable but as an average may be taken at 4 per cent. Paint material

may be taken as one dollar per ton.   The cost of plain material at the
shop would be

Average cost per pound f. o. b. mill say .... 1.75   cts.
Add 4 per cent for waste .... .07   "
Add $1.00 per ton for paint material....................... .05   "
Add freight from mill to shop (Pittsburg to St. Louis)...... .225   "

Total cost per pound f. o. b. shop..................... 2.095   "

To obtain the average cost of steel per pound multiply the pound
price of each kind of material by the percentage that this kind of
material is of the whole weight, the sum of the products will be the
average pound price.

Shop Cost.—The following estimated shop costs include the cost of
detailing and shop labor.   The costs include an allowance of 25 per
cent to cover distribution for contracting and administration.   To
obtain base costs subtract 20 per cent from the values given.

TABLE XXXIIa.

SHOP COST OF CIRCULAR AND RECTANGULAR BINS NOT INCLUDING HOPPERS OR
BOTTOMS.

Thickness of Metal.	Shop Cost in Cents per Lb.
$\frac{1}{4}''$	0.80
$1\frac{5}{16}$	0.75
$\frac{3}{8}$	0.70
$\frac{1}{2}$	0.65

TABLE XXXIIb.

SHOP COST OF BOTTOMS FOR CIRCULAR AND RECTANGULAR BINS.

Thickness of Material.	Flat Bottom Cents per Lb.	Spherical Bottom Cents per Lb.	Conical Bottom Cents per Lb.	Hopper Bottom Cents per Lb
$\frac{1}{4}''$	1.50	4.00	3.50	2.50
$1\frac{5}{16}$	1.45	4.15	3.00	2.40
$\frac{3}{8}$	1.40	4.40	2.75	2.25
$\frac{1}{2}$	1.25	4.50	2.50	2.00

For the shop cost of bracing, columns and trusses see " The Design of Steel Mill Buildings," Chapter XXVIII.   (The cost of shop
work has increased from 20 to 25 per cent since the shop costs in
" Steel Mill Buildings " were prepared.)

3. **Cost of Erection.**—In estimating the cost of erection of bins it is best to divide the cost into (*a*) cost of placing and bolting the steel, and (*b*) cost of riveting. The cost will be based on labor at $3.00 per day of 8 hours.

(*a*) *Cost of Placing and Bolting.*—The cost of placing and bolting up plain grain tanks may be estimated at from $10.00 to $15.00 per ton. The cost of placing and bolting up circular or rectangular ore or coal bins with hopper bottoms may be estimated at from $12.00 to $18.00 per ton.

(*b*) *Cost of Riveting.*—It will cost from 6 to 10 cents per rivet to drive $\frac{5}{8}$ or $\frac{3}{4}$ inch rivets by hand in structural framework where a few rivets are found in one place. A fair average is 7 cents per rivet. The same size rivets can be driven in tank work for from 4 to 7 cents per rivet, with 5 cents per rivet as a fair average.

The cost of riveting by hand is distributed about as follows:

3 men, 2 driving and 1 bucking up, at $3.50 per day of 8 hours..$10.50
1 rivet heater at $3.00 per day of 8 hours.................... 3.00
Coal, tools, superintendence................................. 1.50

    Total per day.......................................$15.00

On structural work a fair day's work driving $\frac{3}{4}''$ or $\frac{5}{8}''$ rivets will be from 150 to 250, depending upon the amount of scaffolding required. This makes the total cost from 6 to 10 cents per rivet.

On bin work when the rivets are close together and little staging is required the gang above will drive from 200 to 400 rivets per day. This makes the total cost from about 4 to 7 cents per rivet.

Rivets can be driven by power riveters for one-half the above or less, not counting the cost of installation.

Soft iron rivets $\frac{1}{2}$ inch and under can be driven cold for about one-half what the rivet can be driven hot, or even less.

Actual Erection Costs.—A steel grain elevator, including steel working house and 8 steel tanks and weighing 700 tons, cost $20.00 per ton to erect complete. This is a fair average for steel elevators.

A steel ore bin having 8 circular tanks with spherical bottoms and framework, weighing 100 tons, cost $20.00 per ton to erect and rivet complete. For additional costs of erecting grain elevators, see Chapter XX.

COST OF REINFORCED CONCRETE BINS.—The plans and details of reinforced concrete bins differ so much that it is difficult to give a general analysis. For the cost of concrete, forms, etc., see Chapter VII. The costs of several reinforced concrete bins are given in Chapter XII. For the cost of reinforced concrete grain bins, see Chapter XX. Detail costs for three coal bins are given in Table XXXIIIA.

Relative Costs of Bins.—Suspension bunkers are cheaper than other types of bins, costing only 50 to 70 per cent of the cost of rectangular bins. Circular bins are slightly cheaper than rectangular bins. Reinforced concrete bins cost approximately the same as steel bins of the same type. Wooden bins cost about one-half as much as concrete or steel bins.

For the cost of grain bins see Chapter XX. For the cost of miscellaneous material and methods of calculating same see " The Design of Steel Mill Buildings," Chapter XXVIII.

Cost of Painting.—The amount of materials to make a gallon of paint and the surface covered by one gallon are given in Table XXXIII.

TABLE XXXIII.

AVERAGE SURFACE COVERED PER GALLON OF PAINT.

Paint.	Volume of Oil.	Pounds of Pigment	Volume and Weight of Paint.	Square Feet.	
				1 Coat.	2 Coats.
			Gals. Lbs.		
Iron oxide (powdered)......	1 gal.	8.00	1.2 = 16.00	600	350
Iron oxide (ground in oil)..	1 "	24.75	2.6 = 32.75	630	375
Read lead (powdered)......	1 "	22.40	1.4 = 30.40	630	375
White lead (ground in oil)..	1 "	25.00	1.7 = 33.00	500	300
Graphite (ground in oil).....	1 "	12.50	2.0 = 20.50	630	350
Black asphalt.....	1 " (turp.)	17.25	4.0 = 30.00	515	310
Linseed oil (no pigment) ...	1 "	......	....	875	......

Light structural work will average about 250 square feet, and heavy structural work about 150 square feet of surface per net ton of metal, while No. 20 corrugated steel has 2,400 square feet of surface.

It is the common practice to estimate ½ gallon of paint for the first coat and ⅜ gallon for the second coat per ton of structural steel, for average conditions.

The price of paint materials in small quantities in Chicago are (1906) about as follows: Linseed oil, 50 to 60 cents per gal.; iron oxide, 1 to 2 cents per lb.; red lead, 7 to 8 cents per lb.; white lead, 6 to 7 cents per lb.; graphite, 6 to 10 cents per lb.

A good painter should paint 1200 to 1500 square feet of plate surface or corrugated steel or 300 to 500 square feet of structural steel work in a day of 8 hours; the amount covered depending upon the amount of staging and the paint. A thick red lead mixed with 30 lbs. of lead to the gallon of oil will take fully twice as long to apply as a graphite paint or linseed oil.

For additional information on paints and painting see Chapter XI, also see " The Design of Steel Mill Buildings, Chapter XXVII.

Actual Costs of Reinforced Concrete Bins.—The detail costs of three reinforced concrete coal bins are given in Table XXXIIIA. The bins were constructed with stationary forms.

TABLE XXXIIIA.

COST OF REINFORCED CONCRETE COAL BINS.*

Coal Pocket		Cost of Forms, per Sq. Ft.		Cost of Concrete, per Cu. Ft.		Cost of Handling Steel, per ton.
		Materials.	Labor.	Materials.	Labor.	Labor.
1. Lawrence, Mass.	Concrete Columns....	$0.025	$0.057	$0.114	$0.193	28 tons @ $16.47 per ton.
	Beam Floors...........	0.041	0.072	0.114	0.088	
	Walls above Grade...	0.058	0.118	0.116	0.074	
2. Hartford, Conn.	Concrete Columns....	0.049	0.098	0.124	0.162	195 tons @ $11.88 per ton.
	Beam Floors...........	0.034	0.06	0.136	0.100	
	Walls above Grade...	0.049	0.096	0.152	0.198	
3. Providence, R. I.	Reinforced Concrete..	0.021	0.087	0.192	0.082	
4. Dalton, Mass.						8½ tons @ $7.26 per ton.

*Leonard C. Wason, President Aberthaw Construction Co.

The cost per cubic yard for an 8 inch wall reinforced with one per cent of steel on the same basis as the Hartford, Connecticut, bin is as follows.

Concrete,	27 cu. ft. @ $0. 35	=	$ 9.45
Forms,	81 sq. ft. @ 0.145	=	11.75
Steel,	132 lbs. @ 0.02	=	2.64
Placing steel 132 lbs.	@ 0.000	=	.79
	Total cost per cu. yd.		$24.63

With moving forms the cost of forms would be very much less than the value above.

CHAPTER XIV.

METHODS OF HANDLING MATERIALS.

Introduction.—The problem of handling material by mechanical means is a large and important one and it will be possible only to outline a few of the more common methods of handling coal, ashes, ore, grain, etc. Material is handled (*a*) continuously, or (*b*) intermittently. Material is handled continuously by means of elevators, steel screw conveyors, belt conveyors, push plate conveyors, traveling trough conveyors, and pneumatic conveyors. Material is handled intermittently by means of cable conveyors, and cars with rope haulage.

Elevators.—An appliance for lifting material from one level to another is called an elevator. Elevators for handling different materials necessarily have different details. The elevators shown in Figs. 127 to 129 are for handling grain. In Fig. 127 is shown an elevator leg with the boot for receiving the grain at the bottom and the elevator head for discharging the grain at the top. The buckets carrying the grain are commonly made of steel and are carried either on a chain or a flat belt usually of rubber.

Elevators for handling coal, ore, ashes, etc., are arranged in a somewhat different manner from those for handling grain. The elevator and conveyor shown in Fig. 130 was designed by the Link Belt Machinery Co. to convey and elevate coal. The coal is fed onto the conveyor by an automatic feeder. This type of elevator is much used in coaling plants.

A chain belt elevator for elevating coal into a circular steel storage bin placed outside the power house is shown in Fig. 131.

A railway coaling station is shown in Fig. 132. In this station the coal is dumped or shoveled from cars and is elevated by chain belt elevators to the coal pockets.

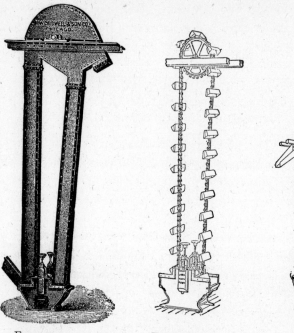

FIG. 127.   FIG. 128.   FIG. 129.
ELEVATOR LEG.   CHAIN ELEVATOR.   BELT ELEVATOR.

A typical arrangement of elevators, bins and spouts for a power plant, as designed by the Jeffrey Manufacturing Co., for the Cleveland Arcade Building, Cleveland, Ohio, is shown in Fig. 133.   This eleva-

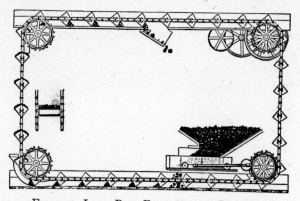

FIG. 130.   LINK BELT ELEVATOR AND CONVEYOR.

tor handles 30 tons of coal per hour. Ashes and coal should not be handled by the same elevator for the reason that while coal protects the metal, ashes corrode the parts and choke the elevator.

Fig. 131.

Steel Screw Conveyors.—Steel screw or worm conveyors have been extensively used for conveying grain, flour, and similar materials for comparatively short distances. The continuous spiral conveyor is most often used, although conveyors with paddles are used for mixing and

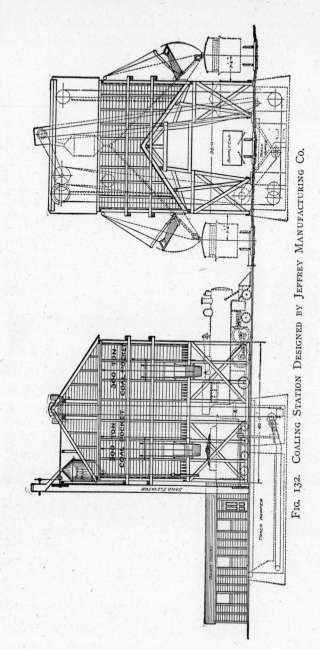

FIG. 132. COALING STATION DESIGNED BY JEFFREY MANUFACTURING CO.

conveying materials. The conveyor hangers require care to insure clear action. The conveyor should not be driven too fast or the material will be carried around without being advanced. Details of screw conveyors are shown in Fig. 134.

FIG. 133. TYPICAL COAL AND ASH HANDLING PLANT.

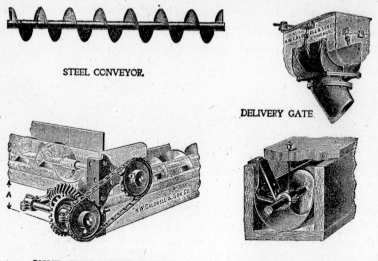

STEEL CONVEYOR.

DELIVERY GATE.

RIGHT-ANGLE CONVEYOR DRIVE.   CONVEYOR HANGER

FIG. 134.

The following experiments on a conveyor 6 inches in diameter, with 2 inches pitch and a one-inch shaft are recorded in Zimmer's "Mechanical Handling of Materials."

Revolutions per Minute.	Material Delivered in Cu. Ft. per Minute.
60	28
80	36
100	30
140	Delivery ceased altogether.

The principal advantages of screw conveyors are their simplicity and low first cost. Screw conveyors are extensively used in country grain elevators, while belt conveyors are commonly used for large grain elevators.

Belt Conveyors.—Belt conveyors are used chiefly for conveying grain and other material in a finely divided state, although coarse coal and ore may be handled very satisfactorily if the conveyors are properly designed. The belts may be run flat as in Fig. 135, or trough-shaped as in Fig. 136. It has been found that grain will be carried on flat belts if the material is properly delivered to the belt at the same speed as the belt. Where flat belts are used the belt is usually hollowed at the point where the material is fed onto the conveyor. To deliver the material at any point the direction of the belt is suddenly changed downward by passing over a pulley on the throw-off carriage. The

FIG. 135.   FIG. 136.

grain leaves the belt by its own momentum and falls into a hopper. Belts are kept properly tightened by an automatic belt tightener. Belt conveyors for handling coal, coke, etc., are always run on grooved

FIG. 137.   CONVEYOR GALLERY—ALBERT DICKINSON CO.'S ELEVATOR, MINNEAPOLIS, MINN.

rollers as shown in Fig. 136. Conveyor belts for handling grain are commonly made of rubber reinforced with cotton warp. Canvas belts are also used for grain conveyors. A conveyor gallery of a grain eleva-

19

tor is shown in Fig. 137. This conveyor gallery contains two belt conveyors that carry grain from the working house to the steel grain storage bins.

Conveyor belts for handling coal, coke, etc., are made stronger than for grain and are sometimes made of woven wire for handling washed coal, etc.

Belt conveyors may be operated on a maximum slope of 17 to 24°, depending upon the material and the belt. The maximum limit of 17° is commonly used. The maximum speed of belt conveyors for handling oats and other light grains should not exceed 400 feet per minute, while for wheat the belt may be run at a speed of 600 feet per minute.

Belt conveyors carrying large pieces of coal, coke, etc., should be run slowly, 150 to 250 feet per minute, while for finer materials the belt may be run as high as for wheat.

Belt conveyors are expensive to install and require careful supervision. The use of belt conveyors in large grain elevators is almost universal. A belt conveyor is used for handling coal in the power plant in Fig. 138.

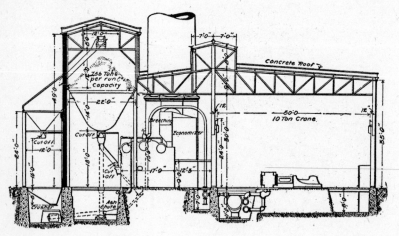

FIG. 138. TYPICAL ARRANGEMENT OF A COAL AND ASH HANDLING PLANT.

Push Plate Conveyors.—Conveyors in which the material is pushed along in metal or wooden troughs are used for handling coal, coke, etc.

Conveyors of this type should never be used for gritting materials, but sticking material can be handled in this manner much more satisfactorily than by means of the screw conveyor. The Link Belt elevator

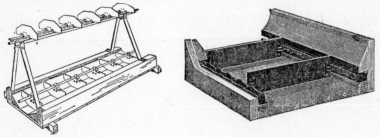

FIG. 139 a.   FIG. 139 b.

shown in Fig. 130 is a push plate conveyor and a chain elevator combined.

A push plate conveyor with metal plates and a bar chain is shown in Fig. 139 a, and a push plate conveyor with wooden plates and a chain is shown in Fig. 139 b.

Traveling Trough Conveyors.—The traveling trough conveyor is simply a metal band conveyor with channel sides. The operation is

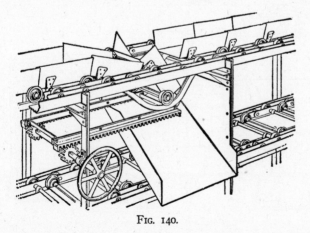

FIG. 140.

clearly shown in Fig. 140. This conveyor has a movable unloader which makes it possible to dump at any point. This type of conveyor is much used in handling coal.

Pneumatic Conveyors.—Pneumatic conveyors are used for conveying and elevating grain.   Pneumatic conveyors are of three types: (1)
the blast system; (2) the suction system; and (3) the combined blast
and suction system.

The pneumatic system will be illustrated by describing the operation
of the system, Fig. 141, in use by the Steel Storage and Elevator
Construction Co., Buffalo, N. Y., which is of the combined blast and
suction type.

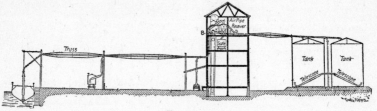

FIG. 141.

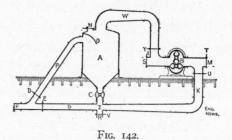

FIG. 142.

Fig. 142 shows the main operating device located in the elevator
house   In this device *A* is an air-tight receiver with a hopper bottom,
and openings as shown.   Underneath the receiver is a continuous
feed device, *C,* which is operated by means of a belt from a pulley on
the line shaft.   The blast pipe *K,* leading to the point of discharge
under the receiver, is made tapering to increase the current of air
created by the blower *B,* which always runs in the same direction.

To convey grain from the elevator to the storage tanks, grain is
admitted into the receiver through valve *N.*   Valves *X, U,* and *E* are
opened, and valves *T, V, Y* and *D* are closed.   The grain passes
through the feed device *C,* comes in contact with the blast and is

forced through the pipes G and F to the storage tanks, as shown in Fig. 141.

To transfer grain from the storage tanks, valves D, T, V, Y and M are opened, and valves E, I, U and X are closed, which changes the air

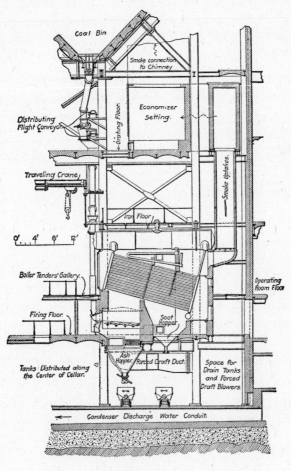

FIG. 143.

blast to suction. Grain is drawn from the bins by suction entering receiver A through pipe P, and can be drawn off through opening R to stock bins, etc.

The principal objection to the pneumatic system for handling grain is the large initial cost and large power cost for operation.

Cable Conveyors.—In cable conveyors the buckets conveying the material are attached to a trolley which is carried on a fixed rope and is moved along by a runner, or the buckets are attached directly to a moving cable or runner which is carried on pulleys. Cable conveyors are much used where it is difficult to erect and operate a car system and for coaling at sea.

Car with Rope Haulage.—This method is used where the material is to be moved a considerable distance, or where an intermittent system is preferred. Cars are made self dumping, and may have a capacity of from $\frac{1}{4}$ to 3 or 4 tons.

An example of the use of this system for handling ashes is given in Fig. 143.

Miscellaneous Methods.—Coal is taken from vessels by means of clam shell buckets, which are lowered into the vessel, are lifted, carried into the storage shed by means of a trolley and dumped. There are many variations of this method in use by different companies. Coal, ashes, etc., are sometimes elevated in cars on a cage or in a skip as in mines.

Coal is sometimes loaded on cars from stock piles by means of steam shovels. Coal and ore may be unloaded by dumping through the bottom in dump cars, or box cars are lifted and turned upside down.

PART III.

THE DESIGN OF GRAIN BINS AND ELEVATORS.

Introduction.—The grain elevator plays a very important part in the handling of grain in America. The grain (wheat, corn, oats, rye, etc.) is hauled in wagons to the country elevator at the railroad station. The wagon is weighed and driven up an incline onto the dump; here the back end of the wagon is dropped and the front end raised so that the grain runs into the dump hopper, the empty wagon is then weighed and the amount of grain determined. From the dump the grain runs by gravity into the boot of the elevator leg. The elevator leg consists essentially of two pulleys, one in the boot, and the other at the head, over which runs a belt, either a rubber or a chain belt; at intervals along the belt are metal buckets attached, which scoop up the grain from the boot and carry it to the head, where it is discharged into spouts, which deliver the grain onto conveyor belts which in turn carry the grain to other points, or discharge directly into bins. The grain in the country elevator is elevated by the elevator leg and conveyed or spouted into bins. If it is to be stored for some time, it may be conveyed to storage bins outside the main elevator or working house by a steel screw or belt conveyor. Usually it will be run through a cleaner where the dust and defective grains are removed, then it is elevated into the shipping scale hopper, where it is weighed and run directly into the cars by gravity.

When the cars loaded with grain arrive at a terminal elevator, where the grain is to be reshipped by rail or water, they are delivered to the elevator, and are placed alongside hoppers near the receiving legs by means of a car puller. These hoppers are either in the working house or in a shed annex alongside. The cars are unloaded by two power car shovels, each shovel being operated by one man, who carries a large scoop at the end of the shovel rope back into the car. When he stops and allows the rope to slack, the mechanism of the spool pulls the scoop loaded with grain to the car door where it stops automatically. The grain falls into the hopper and runs by gravity, or is conveyed by belt conveyors to the boot of the receiving elevator leg, where it is carried by the elevator buckets to the top of the leg, and discharged into garner hoppers mounted on scales, where it is weighed. It is then conveyed by conveyor belts to the bin it is to occupy, or is run into the cleaner bin and through the cleaner, and then is conveyed to the proper bin.

Bins are emptied through spouts in the bottom directly into cars, or the grain is conveyed to the boot of the shipping elevator leg, which elevates it to the shipping hopper bins mounted on scales, from which it is spouted directly into cars or is conveyed to other bins.

In many elevators the grain is cleaned, polished, dried, and graded to improve its quality.

When grain is received directly into the elevator from vessels a " marine " leg is used. This is equipped with a mechanism for raising or lowering, so that the grain may be elevated from the hold of the vessel into the building.

In filling vessels, the grain may be spouted directly from the bins, as is done on the Great Lakes, or, as is common for ocean vessels, may be conveyed by conveyor belts through shipping galleries, from which it is spouted into the vessel. This makes it possible to load several vessels at the same time. In this connection it should be remembered that lake vessels carry full cargoes of grain, while sea-going vessels usually carry mixed cargoes.

The foregoing description will give an idea of the function of the grain elevator. Grain elevators are of several different types, which will now be described.

CHAPTER XV.

TYPES OF GRAIN ELEVATORS.

Introduction.—Grain elevators, or "silos," as they are called in Europe, may be divided into two classes according to the arrangement of the bins and elevating machinery: (*a*) elevators which are self contained, with all the storage bins in the main elevator or working house, as for example, the Great Northern Ry. steel elevator, West Superior, Wis.; and (*b*) elevators having a working house containing the elevating machinery, while the storage is in bins connected with the working house by conveyors, as for example, the Independent Elevator, Omaha, Neb. The working house is usually rectangular in shape, with square or circular bins; while the independent storage bins are usually circular.

With reference to the materials of which they are constructed, elevators may be divided into (1) timber; (2) steel; (3) concrete; (4) tile; and (5) brick.

1. Timber.—Timber was formerly the principal material used in building grain elevators, and is at present used very extensively for small country elevators. For large bins, the "crib" construction is most used. In this construction, pieces of $2'' \times 4''$, $2'' \times 6''$, or $2'' \times 8''$ are laid flatwise, so as to break joints and bind the structure together, and are spiked firmly. This makes a strong form of construction, and one very cheap with the former low price of lumber. Care must be used in filling elevators of this type for the first time, to fill all bins uniformly to prevent unequal settlement caused by the compression of the timber and the closing up of the horizontal joints. Cribbed timber bins have been known to settle 18 inches in a height of 70 feet. Timber elevators are liable to be destroyed by fire, and call for a very high rate of insurance. A view of a timber grain elevator during erection

297

is shown in Fig. 144. This elevator was designed and built by the
John S. Metcalf Co., Chicago, Ill.

FIG. 144. TIMBER CRIBBED BIN, MANCHESTER SHIP CANAL CO.'S ELEVATOR NO. 7,
MANCHESTER, ENGLAND.

FIG. 145. L. S. AND M. S. RY. STEEL ELEVATOR, BUFFALO, N. Y.

2. **Steel.**—Steel has come rapidly into use in the last ten years for fire-proof elevator construction. The first steel elevator in the United States was the Washington Avenue elevator of the Grand Point Storage Company, Philadelphia, started in 1859 and completed in

FIG. 146. THE WINONA MALTING CO.'S ELEVATOR UNDER CONSTRUCTION.

1866. The 88 iron grain bins were 11 feet in diameter, and 45 feet high. After 37 years the iron was in an excellent state of preservation, the outside of the bins having been painted once in 7 years, and the inside not at all. Steel elevators are built (*a*) of the working house type with square bins, as in the Great Northern Ry. elevator, West

Superior, Wis., or the Windmill Point Elevator, Figs. 192 and 193, or with circular bins, as in the Buffalo Steel Elevator, or the L. S. & M. S. Ry. Steel Elevator in Fig. 145; or (*b*) of the working house and storage bin type, as in the Independent Elevator, Omaha, Neb., Chapter XIX, or the Winona Malting Co.'s steel elevator, Figs. 146 and 147.

FIG. 147. STEEL GRAIN ELEVATOR FOR THE WINONA MALTING CO. OF WINONA, MINN.

(*a*) *Working House Steel Elevator.*—The "Great Northern" Steel Elevator, designed by Max Tolz, for the Great Northern Elevator Co., Buffalo, N. Y., in 1897, was one of the first notable examples of this type of elevator, while the Great Northern Elevator at West Superior, Wis., designed by Mr. Tolz, is an excellent example of a modern steel elevator of the working house type. These elevators are described in Chapter XVIII and Chapter XIX, respectively.

The L. S. & M. S. Steel Elevator shown in Fig. 145, constructed on the McDonald system, as described in Chapter XVIII; and the Windmill Point Steel Elevator, constructed on the Metcalf system, shown in Figs. 192 and 193, and described in Chapter XVIII, are excellent examples of this type of construction.

(*b*) *Working House and Steel Storage Bins.*—The Independent Elevator at Omaha, described in Chapter XIX, is an excellent example of an elevator of this type. The elevator shown in Fig. 146 and Fig. 147 is an excellent example of a small elevator of this type. The working house is 32′ 0″ × 32′ 0″ × 150′ 0″ high; and the bins are 20′ 0″ × 80′ 0″. The capacity of the working house is 55,000 bushels,

FIG. 147a. STEEL STORAGE BIN WITH ELEVATOR LEG.

of the bins 295,000 bushels, or a total capacity of 350,000 bushels. The working house cost about $1.00, and the bins about 14 cents per bushel of storage capacity. This elevator was designed and erected by the Minneapolis Steel & Machinery Co., Minneapolis, Minn. This type of elevator costs more per bushel for the working house, but very much less per bushel of storage, than grain elevators of the working house type (*a*).

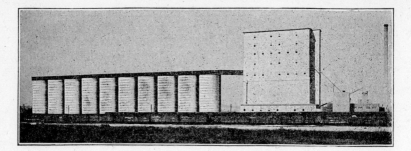

FIG. 148. CONCRETE GRAIN BINS, MISSOURI PACIFIC RY., KANSAS CITY, MO.

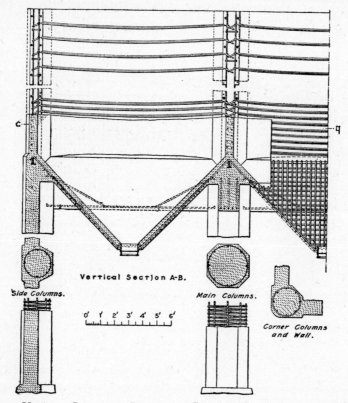

Vertical Section A-B.

Side Columns.

Main Columns.

Corner Columns and Wall.

0' 1' 2' 3' 4' 5' 6'

FIG. 149. VERTICAL SECTION OF REINFORCED CONCRETE GRAIN ELEVATOR DESIGNED
BY J. A. JAMIESON.

A steel grain storage bin with a steel elevator leg outside of the
bin is shown in Fig. 147 a. The elevator leg is arranged to fill the

bin, or to raise the grain so that it can be spouted into a car or into other bins.

3. **Concrete.**—Reinforced concrete elevators are commonly built of type (*b*) with working house and storage bins. The working house is usually built of steel or timber, and the bins of reinforced concrete. The Missouri Pacific Ry. Co.'s reinforced concrete elevator is shown in Fig. 148. Specifications and a detailed description of this elevator

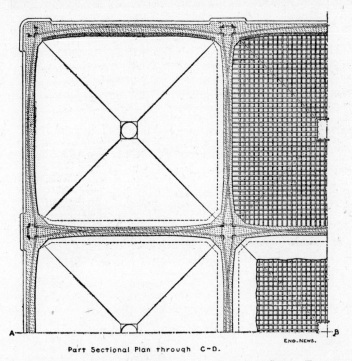

Part Sectional Plan through C–D.

FIG. 150. HORIZONTAL SECTION OF REINFORCED CONCRETE GRAIN ELEVATOR DESIGNED BY J. A. JAMIESON.

are given in Chapter XVIII. The Santa Fe Elevator, Chicago, Ill., and the Canadian Pacific Elevator, Port Arthur, Ontario, are excellent examples of the use of reinforced concrete for storage bins, and are described in Chapter XIX.

The grain elevator shown in Fig. 149 and Fig. 150 was designed by Mr. J. A. Jamieson, Montreal, Canada. The bins are rectangular, and are carried on reinforced concrete columns, which continue up through the bin corners. In this design the interior reinforced concrete walls may be replaced by steel trough plate construction.

4. **Tile.**—Bins for storing grain are frequently made of tile construction reinforced with steel. There are two systems, both patented, one by the Barnett-Record Co., Minneapolis, Minn., and the other by the Witherspoon-Englar Co., Chicago, Ill. A bin in process of con-

Fig. 151. Tile Grain Bins During Construction.

struction is shown in Fig. 151. The specifications for the construction of these bins are given in Chapter XVIII, and details of construction are given in Fig. 201.

The Canadian Northern Ry. elevator, described in Chapter XIX, is an excellent example of tile bin construction, and was built by the Barnett-Record Co.

In Fig. 202 is shown the system patented by the Witherspoon-Englar Co., Chicago, Ill. This system is very much like the Barnett-Record system and is constructed in the same manner.

5. **Brick.**—*Circular storage bins* are constructed of brick in a manner similar to the tile construction described above. The following

description of a circular brick bin, 31' 6" in diameter and 80' 0" high, built by the Cleveland Elevator Building Co., Minneapolis, Minn., will illustrate the construction.

The bin wall is a three-course wall, the two inner courses being laid solid, a space of 3 inches being left between the two inner courses and the outer course, making a wall 16 inches thick. The outer course is bonded to the two inner courses by wire bonds, passing through the air space. A channel is formed every 12 inches in height in the inner wall by splitting a course of brick, making the channel about $2\frac{1}{2}$ inches wide and a brick high, and a brick from the inner surface. The steel reinforcement is placed in this channel, and is grouted with one to two Portland cement grout, as in the construction of the tile bins.

Rectangular bins are made of brick as follows: The bins are made rectangular in sets, with brick pilasters at the outside corners, and columns at the interior corners of the bins. Bars passing through the pilasters and columns are then placed in the planes of the walls, and the walls are made of brick arches, with the concave side of the arch outside. This system works very well for fire-proof country elevators.

Comparison of Different Types.—The different types of fire-proof grain bins appear to fill all the requirements, and the question of local cost or preference will usually determine the type to select. The grain keeps well and is protected from weevil in all types. It has been claimed by some that steel bins sweat or heat the grain, but this is now an exploded theory. It is, however, a well known fact that green or damaged grain will heat and go through a sweat, whether contained in a timber or other type of bin. When heated the grain is changed from one bin to another and aired in transit. This makes it necessary to have an efficient conveyor system and an ample number of bins.

The cost of the different types of fire-proof bins is a matter of local conditions, the cost usually being about the same, although steel probably has a slight advantage over the other materials. For a detailed discussion of the cost of grain bins and elevators, see Chapter XX.

The working house in fire-proof elevators is generally made of steel

20

frame construction, the working house of the Independent Elevator, described in Chapter XIX, being an excellent example.

The price of timber is advancing very rapidly, and this, together with the high insurance rates on timber elevators, will tend to limit the use of timber grain elevators.

Note in 1911.—Since the above was written the use of reinforced concrete for grain bins and elevators has increased and the methods of construction have been improved, so that the present (1911) cost of reinforced concrete bins is generally less than the cost of steel bins. It has also been proved by experience with diastrous fires that reinforced concrete bins are more nearly fireproof than any other type of bin.

Several reinforced concrete grain elevators have recently been constructed on the working house plan.   See Chapter XIX for the description of the F. C. Ayres Mercantile Co.'s Grain Elevator.

CHAPTER XVI.

Introduction.—The problem of calculating the pressure of grain on bin walls is somewhat similar to the problem of the retaining wall, but is not so simple. The theory of Rankine will apply in the case of shallow bins with smooth walls where the plane of rupture cuts the grain surface, but will not apply to deeper bins or bins with rough walls. (It should be remembered that Rankine assumes a granular mass of unlimited extent.)

Two solutions of the problem of the calculation of the pressure in grain bins have been proposed: (1) Janssen's Solution, and (2) Airy's Solution. The results by the two methods agree very closely with experiments.

Nomenclature: The following nomenclature will be used:

$\phi =$ the angle of repose of the grain;

$\phi' =$ the angle of friction of the grain on the bin walls;

$\mu = \tan \phi =$ coefficient of friction of grain on grain;

$\mu' = \tan \phi' =$ coefficient of friction of grain on the bin walls;

$x =$ angle of rupture;

$w =$ weight of grain in lbs. per cu. ft.;

$V =$ vertical pressure of the grain in lbs. per sq. ft.;

$L =$ lateral pressure of the grain in lbs. per sq. ft.;

$A =$ area of bin in sq. ft.;

$U =$ circumference of bin in feet;

$R = A/U =$ hydraulic radius of bin.

JANSSEN'S SOLUTION.—The bin in (*a*) Fig. 152, has a uniform area A, a constant circumference U, and is filled with grain weighing w per unit of volume, and having an angle of repose ϕ. Let V be the vertical pressure, and L be the lateral pressure at any point, both V and L being assumed as constant for all points on the horizontal plane. (More correctly V and L will be constant on the surface of a dome as in (*b*).)

The weight of the grain between the sections of y and $y+dy=A.w.dy$; the total frictional force acting upwards at the circumference will be $=L.U.\tan\phi'.dy$; the total perpendicular pressure on the upper

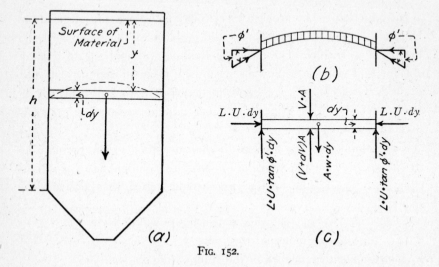

(b)

$L.U.dy$ $V.A$ dy $L.U.dy$

$L.U.\tan\phi'.dy$ $(V+dV)A$ $A.w.dy$ $L.U.\tan\phi'.dy$

(a)   (c)

FIG. 152.

surface will be $=V.A$; and the total pressure on the lower surface will be $=(V+dV)A$.

Now these vertical pressures are in equilibrium, and

$$V.A-(V+dV)A+A.w.dy-L.U.\tan\phi'.dy=0,$$
and
$$dV=(w-L.\tan\phi'\frac{U}{A})dy \qquad (138)$$

Now in a granular mass, the lateral pressure at any point is equal to the vertical pressure times k, a constant for the particular grain, and

$$L=k.V$$

Also let $\frac{A}{U}=R$ (the hydraulic radius), and $\tan\phi'=\mu'$.

Substituting the above in (138) we have

$$dV=(w-\frac{k.V}{R}\mu')dy$$

Now let

$$\frac{k \cdot \mu'}{R} = n \qquad (139)$$

and

$$\frac{dV}{w - n.V} = dy \qquad (140)$$

Integrating (140) we have

$$\log (w - n.V) = -n.y + C = -ny + \log w \qquad (141)$$

Now if $y = 0$, then $V = 0$, and $C = \log w$, and (141) reduces to

$$\log \left(\frac{w - n.V}{w} \right) = -n.y,$$

and

$$\frac{w - n.V}{w} = \frac{1}{e^{n.y}} = e^{-n.y},$$

where e is the base of the Naperian system of logarithms. Solving for V. we have

$$V = \frac{w}{n} (1 - e^{-n.y}) \qquad (142)$$

Substituting the value of n from (139), we have

$$V = \frac{w.R}{k.\mu'} \left(1 - e^{-\frac{k.\mu'.y}{R}} \right) \qquad (143)$$

Now if h be taken as the depth of the grain at any point, we will have

$$V = \frac{w.R}{k.\mu'} \left(1 - e^{-\frac{k.\mu'.h}{R}} \right) \qquad (144)$$

Also since

$$L = k.V,$$

$$L = \frac{w.R}{\mu'} \left(1 - e^{-\frac{k.\mu'.h}{R}} \right) \qquad (145)$$

Now if w is taken in lbs. per cu. ft.. and R in feet, the pressure will be given in lbs. per square foot.

Now both μ' and k can only be determined by experiment on the particular grain and kind of bin. For wheat and a wooden bin, Janssen found $\mu' = 0.3$ and $k = 0.67$, making $k.\mu' = 0.20$.

Jamieson found by experiment that for wheat $k = 0.6$, and he found the following values for μ' with wheat weighing 50 lbs. per cu. ft. and having $\phi = 28°$, $\mu = 0.532$:

Wheat on steel trough plate bin, $\qquad$ $\mu' = 0.468$

Wheat on steel flat plate, riveted and tie bars, $\quad \mu' = 0.375$ to 0.400

Wheat on steel cylinder, riveted, $\qquad$ $\mu' = 0.365$ to 0.375

Wheat on cement-concrete, smooth to rough, $\quad \mu' = 0.400$ to 0.425

Wheat on tile or brick, smooth to rough, $\qquad \mu' = 0.400$ to 0.425

Wheat on cribbed wooden bin, $\qquad$ $\mu' = 0.420$ to 0.450

For additional values of μ' for different grains and different bin walls see tests by Airy and Pleissner in Tables XXXV and XXXVII, Chapter XVII.

Experiments by Bovey, Lufft and the author would appear to prove that k may be very much less than the values given by Janssen and

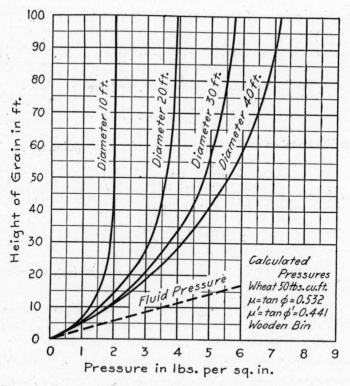

Fig. 153. Lateral Pressure in Wooden Grain Bins Calculated by Janssen's Formula.

Jamieson, and that for wheat k varies from 0.3 to 0.6. Pleissner found that k varies with the grain and the bin walls (see Chapter XVII). However, it will be seen in (145) that the maximum lateral pressure in a bin which must be used in design of deep bins, is independent of k, and that therefore an exact determination of k is not very important. In calculating the values of V and L in (144) and (145), it is neces-

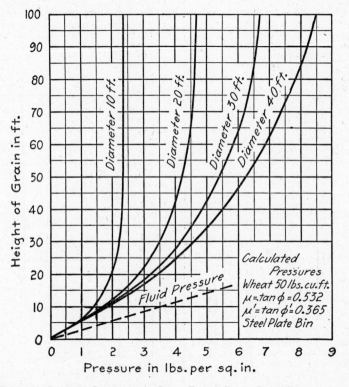

FIG. 154. LATERAL PRESSURE IN STEEL PLATE GRAIN BINS CALCULATED BY JANSSEN'S FORMULA.

sary to use a table of natural or hyperbolic logarithms. A brief table of hyperbolic logarithms is given in Table XXXIV. To find the hyperbolic logarithm of any number, use the relation: *The hyperbolic or Naperian logarithm of any number = common or Brigg's logarithm* $\times 2.30259$.

TABLE XXXIV.

HYPERBOLIC OR NAPERIAN LOGARITHMS.

N.	Log.	N.	Log.	N.	Log.
1.00	0.0000	3.65	1.2947	6.60	1.8871
1.05	0.0488	3.70	1.3083	6.70	1.9021
1.10	0.0953	3.75	1.3218	6.80	1.9169
1.15	0.1398	3.80	1.3350	6.90	1.9315
1.20	0.1823	3.85	1.3481	7.00	1.9459
1.25	0.2231	3.90	1.3610	7.20	1.9741
1.30	0.2624	3.95	1.3737	7.40	2.0015
1.35	0.3001	4.00	1.3863	7.60	2.0281
1.40	0.3365	4.05	1.3987	7.80	2.0541
1.45	0.3716	4.10	1.4110	8.00	2.0794
1.50	0.4055	4.15	1.4231	8.25	2.1102
1.55	0.4383	4.20	1.4351	8.50	2.1401
1.60	0.4700	4.25	1.4469	8.75	2.1691
1.65	0.5008	4.30	1.4586	9.00	2.1972
1.70	0.5306	4.35	1.4701	9.25	2.2246
1.75	0.5596	4.40	1.4816	9.50	2.2513
1.80	0.5878	4.45	1.4929	9.75	2.2773
1.85	0 6152	4.50	1.5041	10.00	2.3026
1.90	0.6419	4.55	1.5151	11.00	2.3979
1.95	0.6678	4.60	1.5261	12.00	2.4849
2.00	0.6931	4.65	1.5369	13.00	2.5649
2.05	0.7178	4.70	1.5476	14.00	2.6391
2.10	0.7419	4.75	1.5581	15.00	2.7081
2.15	0.7655	4.80	1.5686	16.00	2.7726
2.20	0.7885	4.85	1.5790	17.00	2.8332
2.25	0.8109	4.90	1.5892	18.00	2.8904
2.30	0.8329	4.95	1.5994	19.00	2.9444
2.35	0.8544	5.00	1.6094	20.00	2.9957
2.40	0 8755	5.05	1.6194	21.00	3.0445
2.45	0.8961	5.10	1.6292	22.00	3.0910
2.50	0.9163	5.15	1.6390	23.00	3.1355
2.55	0.9361	5.20	1.6487	24.00	3.1781
2.60	0.9555	5.25	1.6582	25.00	3.2189
2.65	0.9746	5.30	1.6677	26.00	3.2581
2.70	0.9933	5.35	1.6771	27.00	3.2958
2.75	1.0116	5.40	1.6864	28.00	3.3322
2.80	1.0296	5.45	1.6956	29.00	3.3673
2.85	1.0473	5.50	1.7047	30.00	3.4012
2.90	1.0647	5.55	1.7138	31.00	3.4340
2.95	1.0818	5.60	1.7228	32.00	3.4657
3.00	1.0986	5.65	1.7317	33.00	3.4965
3.05	1.1154	5.70	1.7405	34.00	3.5264
3.10	1.1314	5.75	1.7492	35.00	3.5553
3.15	1.1474	5.80	1.7579	40.00	3.6889
3.20	1.1632	5.85	1.7664	45.00	3.8066
3.25	1.1787	5.90	1.7750	50.00	3.9120
3.30	1.1939	5.95	1.7834	60.00	4.0943
3.35	1.2090	6.00	1.7918	70.00	4.2485
3.40	1.2238	6.10	1.8083	80.00	4.3820
3.45	1.2384	6.20	1.8245	90.00	4.4998
3.50	1.2528	6.30	1.8405	100.00	4.6052
3.55	1.2669	6.40	1.8563		
3.60	1.2809	6.50	1.8718		

The author has calculated the lateral pressures on wooden and steel plate bins having diameters or sides of 10, 20, 30, and 40 feet. The lateral pressures on round and square wooden bins are given in Fig. 153, and on round and square steel plate bins in Fig. 154.

To use Fig. 153 and Fig. 154 to calculate the pressures in rectangular bins, calculate the pressure in a circular or square bin which has the same hydraulic radius, R ($R =$ area of bin $\div$ perimeter of bin), as the rectangular bin.

It will be seen in Fig. 153 that the pressure varies as the diameters, where the height divided by the diameter is a constant. By using this principle the pressure for any other diameter, within the limits of the diagram, may be directly interpolated.

Problem 1. Required the lateral pressure at the bottom of a cement lined bin, 10 feet in diameter and 20 feet high, containing wheat weighing 50 lbs. per cu. ft. Assume $\mu' = 0.416$, and $k = 0.6$; also R will $= 2\frac{1}{2}$ feet, $w = 50$ lbs., $h = 20$ feet, and $k.\mu' = 0.25$. Now from (145)

$$L = \frac{50 \times 2.5}{0.416}\left(1 - e^{-\frac{0.25 \times 20}{2.5}}\right)$$

$$= 300\left(1 - e^{-2}\right)$$

Now the number whose hyperbolic logarithm is 2.00 is 7.40, and

$$L = 300\left(1 - \frac{1}{7.40}\right),$$

$$= 260 \text{ lbs. per square foot,}$$

$$= 1.8 \text{ lbs. per square inch.}$$

German Practice.—Janssen's formula is given in Hütte Des Ingenieurs Taschenbuch, as the standard formula for the design of grain bins. For wheat Janssen found that $\mu' = 0.3$, and $k = 0.67$, so that $\mu'.k = 0.20$. Using these values and changing to English units, we have for wheat,

$$V = \frac{w.R}{0.2}\left(1 - e^{-0.2\frac{h}{E}}\right)$$

or if $d =$ the diameter or side of bin, then

$$V = \frac{5}{4} w.d \left(1 - e^{-0.8 \frac{h}{d}} \right) \tag{146}$$

$$L = k.V, \quad \text{See P. 119.} \tag{146a}$$

which is the German practice.

LOAD ON BIN WALLS.—The walls of a deep bin carry the greater part of the weight of the contents of the bin. The total weight carried by the bin walls is equal to the total pressure, P, of the grain on the bin walls, multiplied by the coefficient of friction μ' of the grain on the bin walls.

From formula (145) the unit pressure on a unit at a depth y will be

$$L = \frac{w \cdot R}{\mu'} (1 - e^{-k \cdot \mu' \cdot y / R}) \tag{145a}$$

and the total lateral pressure for a depth y, per unit of length of the perimeter of the bin, will be

$$P = \int_0^y L \cdot dy = \int_0^y \frac{w \cdot R}{\mu'} (1 - e^{-k \cdot \mu' \cdot y / R}) dy$$

$$= \frac{w \cdot R}{\mu'} \left[y - \frac{R}{k \cdot \mu'} + \frac{R}{k \cdot \mu'} \cdot e^{-k \cdot \mu' \cdot y / R} \right] \tag{145b}$$

Now the last term in (145b) is very small and may be neglected for depths of more than two diameters, and

$$P = \frac{w \cdot R}{\mu'} \left[y - \frac{R}{k \cdot \mu'} \right] \text{ (approx.)} \tag{145c}$$

The total load per lineal foot carried by the side walls of the bin will be

$$P \cdot \mu' = w \cdot R \left[y - \frac{R}{k \cdot \mu'} \right] \text{ (approx.)} \tag{145d}$$

For the total weight of grain carried by the side walls multiply (145d) by the length of the circumference of the bin.

Formulas (145c) and (145d) may be deduced as follows: The grain carried by the sides of the bin will be equal to the total weight of grain in the bin minus the pressure on the bottom of the bin. If P is the total side pressure on a section of the bin one unit long, then

$$P \cdot U \cdot \mu' = w \cdot A \cdot y - A \cdot V \tag{a}$$

$$= w \cdot A \cdot y - \frac{w \cdot A \cdot R}{k \cdot \mu'} (1 - e^{-k \cdot \mu' \cdot y / R}) \tag{b}$$

and solving (b)

$$P = \frac{w \cdot A}{\mu' \cdot U}\left[y - \frac{R}{k \cdot \mu'}(1 - e^{-k \cdot \mu' \cdot y /R}) \right] \qquad (c)$$

$$= \frac{w \cdot R}{\mu'}\left[y - \frac{R}{k \cdot \mu'}(1 - e^{-k \cdot \mu' \cdot y /R}) \right] \qquad (145b)$$

$$= \frac{w \cdot R}{\mu'}\left[y - \frac{R}{k \cdot \mu'} \right] \text{ (approx.)} \qquad (145c)$$

and the total load carried on a section of the bin one unit long will be found by multiplying P in (145b) by μ', and

$$P \cdot \mu' = w \cdot R\left[y - \frac{R}{k \cdot \mu'}(1 - e^{-k \cdot \mu' \cdot y /R}) \right]$$

$$= w \cdot R\left[y - \frac{R}{k \cdot \mu'} \right] \text{ (approx.)} \qquad (145d)$$

For example take a steel bin 10 ft. in diameter and 100 ft. deep; weight of wheat, $w = 50$ lb. per cu. ft.; angle of friction of wheat on steel, $\mu' = 0.375$; angle of repose of grain on grain, $\mu = \tan 28° = 0.532$ (μ does not occur in formula (145d) but may be used in calculating an approximate value of $k = (1 - \sin 28°)/(1 + \sin 28°) = 0.37$ which is a close approximation to $k = 0.4$ which will be used). Then the load carried by the side walls per lineal foot will be from (145d)

$$P \cdot \mu' = 50 \times 2.5\left[100 - \frac{2.5}{0.4 \times 0.375} \right] = 10,416 \text{ lb.}$$

The total load on the entire bin walls will be

$$P \cdot \mu' \times 31.416 = 327,635 \text{ lb.}$$

The total weight of wheat in the bin is

$$50 \times 78.5 \times 100 = 392,700 \text{ lb.}$$

and the total load carried by the bottom of the bin is

$$392,700 - 327,635 = 65,065 \text{ lb.}$$

and the pressure on the bottom $= V = 65,065/78.54 = 830$ lb. per sq. ft. From formula (144) we find that $V = 830$ lb. per sq. ft.

AIRY'S SOLUTION.—In a paper presented before the Institute of Civil Engineers, and published in Proceedings, Vol. CXXXI, 1897, Wilfred Airy proposed a method for calculating the pressure of grain on bins. The grain is treated as a semi-fluid according to Weisbach, who assumes the pressure on the wall as due to a wedge of grain between the wall and the plane of rupture. There is friction of grain on the bin wall, and on the plane of rupture. There are two cases depending upon the ratio of width or diameter of the bin to depth of grain: Case I, Shallow Bins, where the plane of rupture cuts the surface of the grain within the bin; and Case II, Deep Bins, where the plane of rupture intersects the side of the bin wall.

Case I. Shallow Bins.—To find the pressure on the sides and bottom of a bin, when the depth of grain in the bin is such that the plane

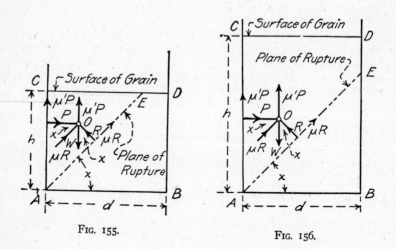

FIG. 155.   FIG. 156.

of rupture passes out of the grain before it meets the opposite side of the bin. Let *CABD* be a vertical section of a bin, Fig. 155, and *CD* the surface of the grain. Let *AE* be the plane of rupture. Then *ACE* is the wedge-shaped mass of grain which causes maximum pressure against the side AC, and O its center of gravity. Let W be the weight of ACE, 1 foot thick, P the pressure against the side AC, $\mu'.P$ the friction between the grain and the side AC, acting in the direction AC, μ' being the coefficient of friction, R the pressure of the mass ACE on the plane of separation AE, $V.\mu.R$ the friction between the grain along the plane of separation AE, μ being the coefficient of friction, h the depth of grain AC in feet, x the angle EAB which the plane of rupture makes with the horizontal, and w the weight of one cubic foot of the grain in pounds.

For convenience, the forces are all drawn as if acting at O in their proper directions; and resolving the forces that support the mass ACE parallel and perpendicular to AE,

$$\mu.R + P.\cos x = (W - \mu'.P) \sin x$$

$$R - P.\sin x = (W - \mu'.P) \cos x$$

whence

$$\mu = \frac{(W - \mu'.P) \sin x - P.\cos x}{(W - \mu'.P) \cos x + P.\sin x}$$

and from this by reduction,

$$P = W \frac{\tan x - \mu}{1 - \mu.\mu' + (\mu + \mu') \tan x}$$

But

$$W = w \times \tfrac{1}{2}AC \times CE = w \times \tfrac{1}{2}h \times \frac{h}{\tan x} = w \times \frac{h^2}{2 \tan x}$$

$$P = w \times \frac{h^2}{2 \tan x} \times \frac{\tan x - \mu}{1 - \mu'.\mu + (\mu + \mu') \tan x}$$

$$= w \times \frac{h^2}{2} \cdot \frac{\tan x - \mu}{(1 - \mu.\mu') \tan x + (\mu + \mu') \tan^2 x}$$

To find the value of x that causes P to be a maximum, place

$$\frac{dP}{dx} = 0$$

Now

$$\frac{dP}{dx} = w \times \frac{h^2}{2} \left\{ \frac{1}{\cos^2 x} [(1 - \mu.\mu') \tan x + (\mu + \mu') \tan^2 x] - (\tan x - \mu) \right.$$

$$\times \left[\frac{1}{\cos^2 x}(1 - \mu.\mu') + 2 \tan x \times \frac{1}{\cos^2 x} \times (\mu + \mu') \right] \Big\}$$

all divided by

$$\{(1 - \mu.\mu') \tan x + (\mu + \mu') \tan^2 x\}^2,$$

therefore

$$(1 - \mu.\mu') \tan x + (\mu + \mu') \tan^2 x - (1 - \mu.\mu')(\tan x - \mu)$$

$$- 2 \tan x (\tan x - \mu)(\mu + \mu') = 0;$$

whence by reduction,

$$\tan x = \mu + \sqrt{\mu \times \frac{1 + \mu^2}{\mu + \mu'}}$$

since the part under the radical is greater than μ. If this value of $\tan x$ is substituted in the expression for P, the lateral pressure of the wedge ACE, 1 foot thick, will be obtained; and this result multiplied by the horizontal circumference of the bin in feet, gives the total pressure on the sides of the bin. This, multiplied by μ', gives the vertical sustaining force of the side friction; and the pressure on the bottom is the total weight of the grain less the vertical sustaining force of the friction. Thus the fundamental equations for Case I are:

$$\tan x = \mu + \sqrt{\mu \times \frac{1 + \mu^2}{\mu + \mu'}} \tag{147}$$

$$P = w \times \frac{h^2}{2 \tan x} \times \frac{\tan x - \mu}{1 - \mu.\mu' + (\mu + \mu') \tan x} \tag{148}$$

Substituting $\tan x$ in (147) in (148)

$$P = \tfrac{1}{2}w \cdot h^2 \left[\frac{1}{\sqrt{\mu(\mu + \mu')} + \sqrt{1 + \mu^2}} \right]^2 \tag{148a}$$

To calculate the unit pressure, L, at any depth, $h = y$, differentiate P in (148a) with respect to the depth, $h = y$

$$L = w \cdot y \left[\frac{1}{\sqrt{\mu(\mu + \mu')} + \sqrt{1 + \mu^2}} \right]^2 \tag{148b}$$

The vertical pressure at any point in the bin will then be

$$V = L/k \tag{148c}$$

Case II. Deep Bin.—To find the pressure on the sides and bottom of a bin, when the depth of grain is such that the plane of rupture meets the oposite side of the bin within the mass of grain. **Let** d be the breadth of the bin, Fig. 156. Then, as in Case I,

$$P = W \times \frac{\tan x - \mu}{1 - \mu.\mu' + (\mu + \mu') \tan x}$$

But

$$W = w \times 1 \times \text{area } AEDCA = w \times CD \times \frac{AC + DE}{2}$$

$$= w \times \frac{d}{2}(2h - d.\tan x)$$

$$P = w \times \frac{d}{2}(2h - d.\tan x) \times \frac{\tan x - \mu}{1 - \mu.\mu' + (\mu + \mu') \tan x}$$

or

$$P = w \times \frac{d}{2} \left\{ 2h \times \frac{\tan x - \mu}{1 - \mu.\mu' + (\mu + \mu') \tan x} \right.$$

$$\left. - d \times \frac{\tan^2 x - \mu.\tan x}{1 - \mu.\mu' + (\mu + \mu') \tan x} \right\}$$

To find the value of x which makes P a maximum, place $\dfrac{dP}{dx} = 0$.

Now

$$\frac{dP}{dx} = w \times \frac{d}{2} \left\{ 2h \left[\frac{1}{\cos^2 x}(1 - \mu.\mu') + \frac{1}{\cos^2 x}(\mu + \mu') \tan x \right. \right.$$

$$\left. - \frac{1}{\cos^2 x}(\mu + \mu') \tan x + \frac{1}{\cos^2 x}(\mu + \mu')\mu \right]$$

$$- d \left[\left(2 \tan x \times \frac{1}{\cos^2 x} - \mu \times \frac{1}{\cos^2 x} \right) \left\{ 1 - \mu.\mu' + (\mu + \mu') \tan x \right\} \right.$$

$$\left. \left. - \frac{1}{\cos^2 x}(\mu + \mu')(\tan^2 x - \mu.\tan x) \right] \right\}$$

all divided by

$$\{ 1 - \mu.\mu' + (\mu + \mu') \tan x \}^2$$

so that

$$2h (1 + \mu^2) - d \{ \tan^2 x (\mu + \mu') + 2 \tan x (1 - \mu.\mu')$$
$$- \mu (1 - \mu.\mu') \} = 0,$$

which by reduction gives finally

$$\tan x = \sqrt{\frac{2h}{d} \times \frac{1 + \mu^2}{\mu + \mu'} + \frac{1 + \mu^2}{\mu + \mu'} \times \frac{1 - \mu.\mu'}{\mu + \mu'} - \frac{1 - \mu.\mu'}{\mu + \mu'}}$$

Substituting this value of tan x in the expression for P, the maximum pressure on the side of the bin of the wedge-shape mass $AEDCA$, 1 foot thick, is obtained; and the pressure on the sides and bottom of the bin can be deduced as before. Thus the fundamental equations for Case II are:

$$\tan x = \sqrt{\frac{2h}{d} \times \frac{1 + \mu^2}{\mu + \mu'} + \frac{1 + \mu^2}{\mu + \mu'} \times \frac{1 - \mu.\mu'}{\mu + \mu'} - \frac{1 - \mu.\mu'}{\mu + \mu'}} \qquad (149)$$

$$P = w \times \frac{d}{2} \times (2h - d.\tan x) \times \frac{\tan x - \mu}{1 - \mu.\mu' + (\mu + \mu') \tan x} \qquad (150)$$

Substituting tan x in (149) in (150)

$$P = \tfrac{1}{2} w.d^2 \left[\frac{\sqrt{\frac{2h}{d} (\mu + \mu') + 1 - \mu \cdot \mu'} - \sqrt{1 + \mu^2}}{\mu + \mu'} \right]^2 \qquad (150a)$$

To calculate the unit pressure, L, at any depth, $h = y$, differentiate P in (150a) with respect to the depth, $h = y$

$$L = \frac{\delta \cdot P}{\delta y} = \frac{w \cdot d}{\mu + \mu'} \left[1 - \frac{\sqrt{1 + \mu^2}}{\sqrt{\frac{2h}{d} (\mu + \mu') + 1 - \mu \cdot \mu'}} \right] \qquad (150b)$$

The vertical pressure at any point in the bin will be

$$V = L/k \qquad (150c)$$

It is seen from Fig. 156 that the value of h for which the plane of separation of the mass of maximum pressure meets the opposite side at the surface level of the grain, is determined by the condition $h = d.\tan x$. If in the expression for tan x in Case II, $d.\tan x$ is substituted for h, then

$$\tan x = \sqrt{2 \tan x \times \frac{1 + \mu^2}{\mu + \mu'} + \frac{1 + \mu^2}{\mu + \mu'} \times \frac{1 - \mu.\mu'}{\mu + \mu'}} - \frac{1 - \mu.\mu'}{\mu + \mu'}$$

or,

$$\tan x = \mu + \sqrt{\mu \frac{1 + \mu^2}{\mu + \mu'}} \qquad (147)$$

the same expression as in Case I. Similarly the value of P from Case II becomes, by putting $h = d \cdot \tan x$ or $d = \dfrac{h}{\tan x}$

$$P = w \times \frac{h^2}{2 \tan x} \times \frac{\tan x - \mu}{1 - \mu.\mu' + (\mu + \mu') \tan x} \qquad (148)$$

the same expression again as was obtained in Case I, showing that the equations for $\tan x$ and P in Case I and Case II are continuous.

A useful law connecting the pressures in bins of different sizes can be obtained immediately from the equations as follows: In Case I, taking the case of a square bin, the length of side of which is d, the total pressure on the sides of the bin is $P \times 4d$. Calling this n, the second equation, Case I, becomes

$$n = 2w \times h^2.d \times \frac{\tan x - \mu}{(1 - \mu.\mu') \tan x + (\mu + \mu') \tan^2 x}$$

which may be written

$$n = 2w \times \frac{h^2}{d^2} \times d^3 \times \frac{\tan x - \mu}{(1 - \mu.\mu') \tan x + (\mu + \mu') \tan^2 x} \qquad (151)$$

therefore, in comparing the pressures on the sides of square bins of different sizes, if $\dfrac{h}{d}$ (the proportion of the depth of the grain to the side of the bin) is the same for both, the pressure varies as d^3, or the pressure per unit of length as d^2.

In Case II, with square bins as before, calling $n = P \times 4d$, the total pressure on the sides of the bin is

$$n = 2w \times d^3 \left(\frac{2h}{d} - \tan x \right) \frac{\tan x - \mu}{1 - \mu.\mu' + (\mu + \mu') \tan x} \qquad (152)$$

Therefore, in this case also, in comparing the total pressures on the sides of square bins of different sizes, if $\dfrac{h}{d}$ is the same for both, the pressure varies as d^3.

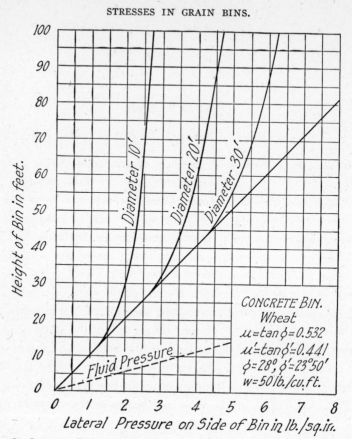

FIG. 158. LATERAL PRESSURE OF WHEAT ON WALLS OF CONCRETE BINS, CALCU-
LATED BY AIRY'S FORMULAS.

Pressures in Bins.—The author has calculated the lateral pressures
in concrete bins with diameters or widths of 10 ft., 20 ft. and 30 ft.
in Fig. 158. The stresses as given by Airy's solution check very well
with the values given by Janssen's solution. For a long rectangular
bin the two solutions check very closely.

The vertical pressures in a deep bin may be calculated by equation
(150c), or the vertical pressures may be calculated as follows: The
grain supported by the side walls is equal to the total lateral pressure
multiplied by μ', the coefficient of friction of the grain on the bin wall.
The grain carried on the bottom of the bin is equal to the total weight
of grain, minus the grain carried by the side walls. This bottom pressure is not uniformly distributed, but is a minimum at the side walls,
and a maximum at the center of the bin. The grain mass producing
bottom pressure might be represented by a portion of an ellipsoid of
revolution, with the major axis of the ellipse vertical. The truth of
this is shown by Bovey's Experiments, Chapter XVII.

CHAPTER XVII.

EXPERIMENTS ON THE PRESSURE OF GRAIN IN DEEP BINS.

Introduction.—The law of pressure of grain and similar materials is very different from the well known laws of fluid pressure. Dry wheat and corn come very nearly filling the definition of a granular mass assumed by Rankine in deducing his formulas for earth pressures. As stored in a bin the grain mass is limited by the bin walls, and Rankine's retaining wall formulas are not directly applicable.

If grain is allowed to run from a spout onto a floor it will heap up until the slope reaches a certain angle, called the angle of repose of the grain, when the grain will slide down the surface of the cone. If a hole be cut in the bottom of the side of a bin, the grain will flow out until the opening is blocked up by the outflowing grain. There is no tendency for the grain to spout up as in the case of fluids. If grain be allowed to flow from an orifice it flows at a constant rate, which is independent of the head and varies as the diameter of the orifice.

Experiments by Willis Whited,[*] and by the author at the University of Illinois, with wheat have shown that the flow from an orifice is independent of the head and varies as the cube of the diameter of the orifice. This phenomenon can be explained as follows: The wheat grains in the bin tend to form a dome which supports the weight above. The surface of this dome is actually the surface of rupture. When the orifice is opened the grain flows out of the space below the dome and the space is filled up by grains dropping from the top of the dome. As these grains drop others take their place in the dome. Experiments with glass bins show that the grain from the center of the bin is discharged first, this drops through the top of the dome, while the grain in the lower part of the dome discharges last.

[*] *Proc. Eng. Soc. of West Penna.,* April, 1901.

The law of grain pressures has been studied experimentally by several engineers within recent years. A brief résumé of the most important experiments follows:

ROBERTS' EXPERIMENTS.*—The first recorded experiments on the pressure of wheat in bins were made by Isaac Roberts in 1882 and 1884. His first experiments were made on small bins, 7 to 20¾ inches in diameter. He observed that "all increase of pressure on the bottom ceases before the cells are filled two diameters." These experiments caused him to make a second series on a rectangular bin 6' 9" × 6' 0" and 52' 2" high. The pressures measured were the pressures on square orifices: 1' 0" × 1' 0", 2' 0" × 2' 0", and 3' 0" × 3' 0". For the bottom pressures the orifices were central, and for the side pressures the orifices were at the bottom of the side. The pressures were measured by levers arranged like a weighing machine. He found considerable difficulty in measuring the pressures with this apparatus, apparently due to the elasticity of the wheat and the movement necessary to raise the lever. To measure the pressure excess weights were placed on the scale, then the grain was put in the bin, and the scale weights were removed one at a time until the scale beam arose. It was found that the beam started at a certain pressure but in order to raise the scale beam it was necessary to remove one weight after another until the pressure indicated was very much less than the initial pressure which started the scale beam. This difficulty is explained in detail because it has in other cases caused erroneous results, as for example, in Prante's experiments.

The second set of experiments by Roberts appeared to confirm the conclusion above—that there is no increase in bottom pressure after the grain has a depth more than twice the width of the bin.

JANSSEN'S EXPERIMENTS.†—H. A. Janssen of Bremen made experiments in 1895 to determine the pressure of grain on bin walls.

---

* *Engineering,* October 27, 1882, and *Proceedings Royal Society of London,* January 31, 1884.

† "Versuche über Getreidedruck in Silozellen," *Zeitschrift des Vereines deutscher Ingenieure,* 1895, p. 1045.

His bins were square model bins having sides 20, 30, 40, and 60 centimeters in length, respectively. The bin walls were supported on 4 jack screws and the loose bottoms were supported directly on a scale. By filling the bin with grain the proportion of the weight resting on the bottom was recorded on the scale. The bin was then slightly raised by the jack screws, and, owing to the friction of the grain on the sides of the bin, this also relieved part of the bottom pressure and allowed the beam to drop. Added weights were then placed on the beam and the filling of the bin proceeded. Janssen made experiments on wheat, corn, and other grains; also on dry sand. The bottom pres-

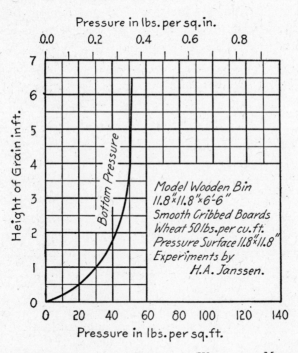

FIG. 159. EXPERIMENTS ON THE PRESSURE OF WHEAT IN A MODEL BIN.

sures were measured as above and the horizontal pressures were calculated by means of Janssen's formulas (144) and (145). The pressures of wheat on a bin 30 cm. × 30 cm. (11.8 × 11.8 inches) as determined by Janssen are given in Fig. 159. *p. 309*

Janssen developed the formulas given in Chapter XVI. The ratio of lateral to vertical pressures for dry wheat as determined from his experiments was $k = 0.67$, and the coefficient of friction of the wheat on the wooden bin walls was $\mu' = 0.3$. The value of k as determined by these experiments appears to be too large for full-sized bins.

Janssen's formulas (144) and (145) and his coefficients are used in grain bin design in Germany.

PRANTE'S EXPERIMENTS.[*]—Prante's experiments were made on two full-sized cylindrical iron bins, 1.5 and 3.8 meters in diameter and 19 meters high. The pressure measurement apparatus consisted of a diaphragm supported on knife edges and connected by a system of levers to a scale pan. Side pressures only were measured. The apparatus as first constructed was not satisfactory, and the details were later slightly changed. These experiments gave the lateral pressure of wheat at rest slightly smaller than the values calculated by Janssen's formulas (144) and (145). With wheat in motion with a velocity in the bin of 1 mm. per second, however, the side pressures rapidly increased until they were as much as four times the static pressures. The discharge gate was located near the bottom of the side, probably just opposite the pressure measurement opening. This would result in pressures on the sides opposite the gate very much in excess of the static pressure. While Prante's experiments were quite elaborate the results may not be reliable on account of the measuring apparatus and the location of the discharge gate. The experiments show that bins should be constructed with discharge gates at or near the center of the bottom of the bin.

Prante's experiments are not considered as reliable in Germany where Janssen's formulas and coefficients are used in the design of grain bins.

TOLTZ'S EXPERIMENTS.[†]—In designing the Great Northern Elevator, Buffalo, N. Y., in 1897, Max Toltz, mechanical engineer Great Northern Ry., based the design on Prante's experiments, and

[*] "Messungen des Getreidedruckes in Silozellen," *Zeitschrift des Vereines deutscher Ingenieure*, 1896, p. 1192.

[†] *Trans. Can. Soc. C. E.*, Vol. XVII, 1903.

designed the bins for fluid pressure. Before building the Great Northern elevator, West Superior, Wis., Mr. Toltz made a series of experiments on the pressure of wheat in a wooden bin 14′ 0″ square and 65′ 0″ deep. In one of the walls near the bottom a hole was cut 1′ 6″ × 3′ 0″, and in the opening a steel plate was placed, which was held rigidly at two ends by steel channels, but the top and bottom edges were free. The bin was then gradually filled with grain, the deflections of the plate for different heights of grain being carefully measured. The process of filling and emptying the bin was repeated several times, using plates Nos. 12, 15, 18, and 22 gage. By testing the plates it was found that the lateral pressures, either when filling or emptying the bin did not exceed 3 pounds per square inch. These experiments were very carefully conducted and the results may be taken as reliable.

AIRY'S EXPERIMENTS.—In a paper to Institute of Civil Engineers, and printed in Proceedings, Vol. CXXXI, 1897, Wilfred Airy gives a valuable discussion on the theory of grain pressures and also the results of a series of experiments to determine the angle of repose of grains, and the coefficient of friction of grain on bin walls. The angle of repose of grain, ϕ, was determined by measuring the slopes of grain in piles. The coefficient of friction, $\mu' = \tan \phi'$, was determined by finding the slope at which a piece of the bin wall would slide down the grain slope. The results of these experiments are given in Table XXXV.

TABLE XXXV.

COEFFICIENTS OF FRICTION OF VARIOUS KINDS OF GRAIN ON BIN WALLS.

	Weight of a Cubic Foot Loosely Filled Into Measure Pounds	Coefficients of Friction.				
		Grain on Grain μ. tan ϕ.	Grain on Rough Board μ'. tan ϕ'.	Grain on Smooth Board μ'. tan ϕ'.	Grain on Iron μ'. tan ϕ'.	Grain on Cement μ'. tan ϕ'.
Wheat..........	49	0.466	0.412	0.361	0.414	0.444
Barley	39	0.507	0.424	0.325	0.376	0.452
Oats	28	0.532	0.450	0.369	0.412	0.466
Corn............	44	0.521	0.344	0.308	0.374	0.423
Beans..........	46	0.616	0.435	0.322	0.366	0.442
Peas	50	0.472	0.287	0.268	0.263	0.296
Tares..........	49	0.554	0.424	0.359	0.364	0.394
Flaxseed	41	0.456	0.407	0.308	0.339	0.414

THE AUTHOR'S EXPERIMENTS.—In 1902 and 1903 a series of experiments on grain pressure was carried on at the University of Illinois by Albert G. Varnes, under the author's direction. The experiments were made with a model bin 1' 0" × 1' 0" and 8' 6" high, made of dressed white pine with the grain vertical. The bottom was movable and the bottom pressures were measured by supporting the movable bottom directly on a platform scale. The side pressures were measured on a diaphragm 12 inches square placed in one side near the bottom. The pressure was transmitted to a platform scale by means of levers.

Experiments were first made on the flow of wheat from an orifice, and it was found that the flow was independent of the head and varied as the cube of the orifice.

Experiments were then made to determine the side pressures and bottom pressures, when the grain was at rest, and in motion. To obtain the pressure of moving grain the bin was filled and the scale beam balanced. Then the orifice was opened and the wheat was allowed to flow out, the drop of the beam being noted at intervals together with the time that had elapsed since the grain started to flow. The orifice having been calibrated, the height of the grain corresponding to the scale readings was easily determined. Bottom pressures were determined with both side and bottom orifices, while the side pressures were determined with a bottom orifice only; the orifices being 2" in diameter. The pressures for the bin filling were determined by placing a hopper above the bin, from which the grain ran into the bin through an orifice.

It was not possible to detect any difference in pressure for the grain at rest or in motion. The means of four tests are given in Fig. 160. It will be seen that the ratio of lateral to vertical pressure is very nearly $k = 0.4$.

JAMIESON'S EXPERIMENTS.[*]—In 1900 J. A. Jamieson, Montreal, Canada, made a series of experiments on a full-sized bin of the Canadian Pacific Ry. Elevator, West St. John, N. B. The bin was of

[*] *Trans. Can. Soc. C. E.,* Vol. XVII, 1903; *Eng. News,* 1904, Vol. 51, p. 236.

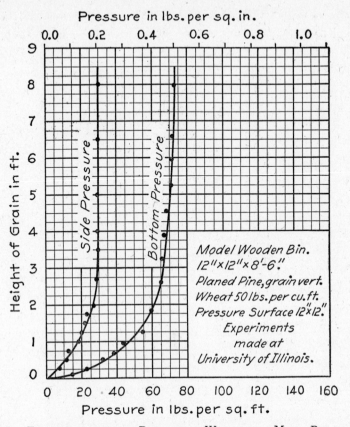

FIG. 160. EXPERIMENTS ON THE PRESSURE OF WHEAT IN A MODEL BIN MADE AT
THE UNIVERSITY OF ILLINOIS, GRAIN IN MOTION.

timber crib construction, 12′ 0″ × 13′ 6″ in cross section and 67′ 6″
high. The grain used was Manitoba wheat weighing 49.4 pounds per
cubic foot.

To obtain the pressure of the grain, diaphragms as shown in Fig.
161 were used. To obtain the lateral pressure the diaphragm was
placed in position a short distance above the hopper bottom, as shown
in Fig. 161. To obtain the bottom pressure the diaphragm was placed
horizontal on top of a small platform attached to the hopper bottom.
The grain was run into the bin in drafts of 30,000 pounds, giving a
depth of 3′ 9″ in the bin. The gage was observed after each draft

and the maximum reading recorded. After the bin was filled it was
allowed to stand 18 hours, during which time the gage reading was

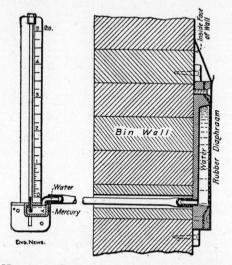

FIG. 161. HYDRAULIC PRESSURE DIAPHRAGM AND MERCURY GAGE.

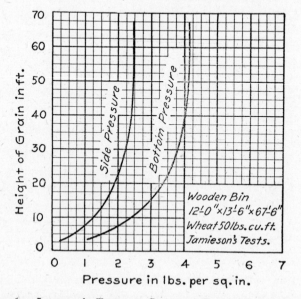

FIG. 162. JAMIESON'S TESTS ON CANADIAN PACIFIC RY. GRAIN BIN.

constant. The grain was then drawn off through the discharge gate in the center of the bottom in 30,000-lb. lots, at the rate of 9,000 bushels per hour. The pressures during emptying fluctuated considerably, the maximum increase of pressure in emptying over the pressure in filling was 4 per cent. Closing the valve during emptying gave a slight increase in pressure, opening the valve a slight decrease. The average pressures of the wheat on the side and bottom of the bin are given in Fig. 162. The coefficient of friction between the grain and the sides was $\mu' = 0.441$. The angle of repose of the grain was $\phi = 28°$, and $\mu = 0.532$. The ratio of the lateral to the vertical pressure was $k = 0.596$, or the vertical pressure $= 1.66$ times the lateral pressure.

The calculated pressures, using Janssen's formulas (144) and (145), using $k = 0.6$, on the same grain bin are given in Fig. 163. The calculated pressures agree very closely with the observed pressures.

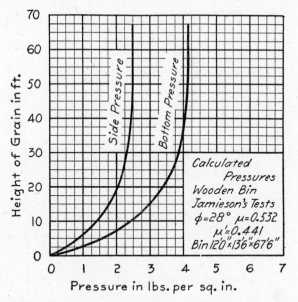

FIG. 163. CALCULATED PRESSURES OF WHEAT, USING JANSSEN'S FORMULAS, ON CANADIAN PACIFIC RY. GRAIN BIN.

Model Bins.—Jamieson also made experiments on model bins. Experiments were made with bins constructed of smooth boards cribbed,

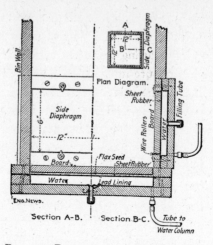

FIG. 164. MODEL BIN AND DIAPHRAGM FOR DETERMINING GRAIN PRESSURE.

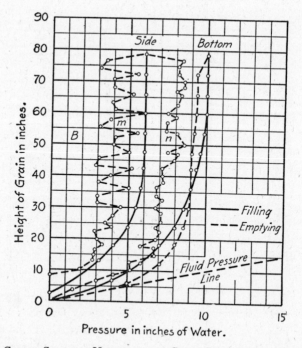

FIG. 165. CURVES SHOWING VARIATIONS IN GRAIN PRESSURES IN FILLING AND EMPTYING BINS WITH OPENING AT SIDE OF BOTTOM. (CURVE *m* SHOWS PRESSURE ON SIDE ADJACENT TO OUTLET AND *n* ON SIDE OPPOSITE.)

flat steel plates, and trough plate bins, the corrugations running horizontally. The bins were 12″ and 6″ square or round, and 6′ 6″ high. The arrangement of the bins and the diaphragms are shown in Fig. 164 and Fig. 167. In testing the bottom pressure the diaphragm

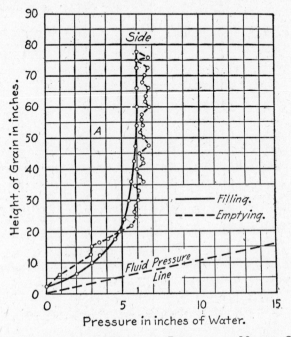

FIG. 166. LATERAL PRESSURE OF WHEAT AT REST AND IN MOTION, OPENING IN CENTER OF BOTTOM.

covered the entire bottom of the bin. In testing the lateral pressure the diaphragm was made a part of the bin wall, the face being set vertical and flush with the inside of the bin. Grain was poured in at the top of the bin in drafts of 6¼ to 25 pounds, depending on the size of the bin, and the height of the water column was recorded for each draft. Tests were all made in duplicate, one set being made with the grain in direct contact with the rubber and the other with a board placed over the rubber to distribute the pressure, as shown in Fig. 164. By tapping the bin with a hammer near the bottom the pressure on the bottom could be decreased. When the tapping was continued from

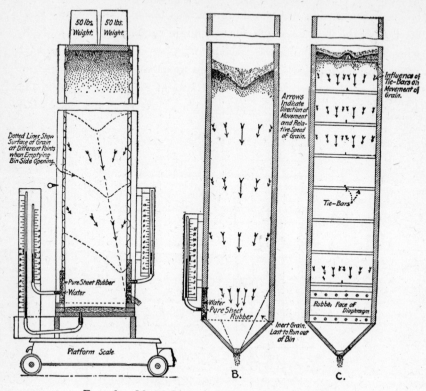

FIG. 167.   Model Bin and Flow of Grain in a Bin.

the bottom to the top on all sides the grain settled 2 to 3 inches, and the bottom pressure was slightly increased.

By placing standard weights of 50 pounds each on top of the grain, the bottom pressure could be only slightly increased by each weight added, the pressure becoming normal on removing the weights. Experiments were made to determine the effect of moving grain on the pressure. The variation of pressure of wheat for grain at rest and in motion, with the outlet in one side of the bottom, is given in Fig. 165, and with the opening in the center of the bottom in Fig. 166. The action of the grain in flowing out of the bin is shown in Fig. 167. It was found that when the grain was drawn from one side of the bin, the pressure was decreased on the side of the opening and increased on the opposite side. When the grain was taken from the middle of the bottom the increase in pressure for grain running at a rate of from 50 to 120 lbs. per minute was from 5 to 7.3 per cent. Jamieson places the maximum increase in pressure due to moving grain in full-sized bins at 10 per cent, where the ratio of area of the gate opening to the area of the bin is not greater than 1 : 150. Tests were also made with

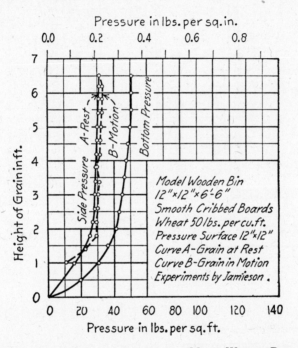

FIG. 168. PRESSURE OF WHEAT IN A MODEL WOODEN BIN.

tie bars of 24 gage steel $\frac{1}{2}$ inch wide, placed on edge across the bins and spaced 6 inches apart. It was found that the tie bars reduced the amount of grain running out of the bottom about one-third, but did not affect the pressures of the grain.

The pressures on a model wooden bin for wheat at rest and in motion are given in Fig. 168. It will be seen that the pressure is only slightly greater when the grain is in motion than when at rest. The percentage of wheat carried by the bottom and sides of the model

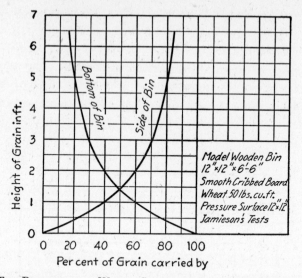

FIG. 169. THE PERCENTAGE OF WHEAT CARRIED BY BOTTOM AND SIDES IN A MODEL WOODEN BIN.

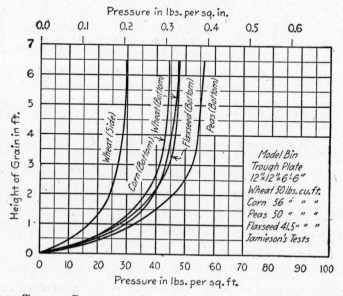

FIG. 170. TESTS OF PRESSURE OF GRAIN IN A MODEL STEEL TROUGH PLATE BIN.

wooden bin are shown in Fig. 169. It will be seen that the amount
carried by the bottom and sides is equal at a height of about 1.4 times
the side of the bin.

Tests were made on a square trough plate bin, 12 inches square and
6' 6" deep, with wheat, peas, corn, and flax-seed. The weights of the
grain per cubic foot were: wheat, 50 lbs.; peas, 50 lbs.; corn, 56 lbs.;
and flax-seed, 41.5 lbs. The tests are shown in Fig. 170. Jamieson

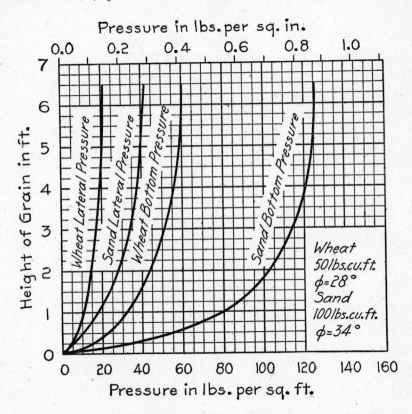

FIG. 171. EXPERIMENTS ON PRESSURE OF WHEAT AND SAND IN A MODEL SMOOTH
STEEL BIN 12" DIAMETER.

states that taking wheat weighing 50 lbs. per cubic foot as a standard,
corn weighing 56 lbs. per cubic foot will give approximately the same
pressure as wheat; peas weighing 50 lbs. per cubic foot will give

22

approximately 20 per cent greater pressure than wheat, while flax-seed weighing 41.5 lbs. per cubic foot will give from 10 to 12 per cent greater pressure than wheat. The coefficients of friction of the different grains vary, which explains the difference in pressure.

The tests of the pressure of dry sand, weighing 100 lbs. per cubic foot, and wheat, weighing 50 lbs. per cubic foot, on a cylindrical bin of smooth steel 12″ in diameter are shown in Fig. 171.

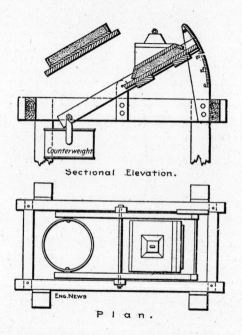

Fig. 172. Apparatus for Testing the Angle of Repose and Coefficient of Friction of Grains on Bin Walls.

Angle of Repose and Coefficient of Friction.—Jamieson made careful tests with the apparatus shown in Fig. 172 to determine the angle of repose of grains, ϕ, and the coefficient of friction, $\mu' = \tan \phi'$, of grains on bin walls. To obtain the angle of repose of grain the tray, which was attached to the pivoted frame, was filled and carefully leveled off, and the frame balanced; the end holding the tray was then carefully raised until the first movement of the grain took place and this angle noted as the angle of repose. By attaching to the pivoted frame a piece of the bin wall material, and again filling the tray with grain, with the tray inverted and with the grain against the material, by raising the pivoted frame the angle of friction of the grain on the material will be found when the tray begins to move. The means of the tests are given in Table XXXVI.

TABLE XXXVI.

COEFFICIENTS OF FRICTION AND ANGLE OF REPOSE OF WHEAT. WHEAT WEIGHING 50 LBS. PER CUBIC FOOT, AND ANGLE OF REPOSE $\phi = 28$ DEGREES.

Materials.	Coefficient of Friction.
Wheat on wheat.........	0.532
Wheat on steel trough plate bin..........	0.468
Wheat on steel flat plate, riveted and tie bars......:..............	0.375 to 0.400
Wheat on steel cylinders, riveted	0.365 to 0.375
Wheat on cement-concrete, smooth to rough.........................	0.400 to 0.425
Wheat on tile or brick, smooth to rough..............................	0.400 to 0.425
Wheat on cribbed wooden bin...........................	0.420 to 0.450

BOVEY'S EXPERIMENTS.[*]—Professor Henry T. Bovey, Mc-Gill University, Montreal, made a series of experiments on full-sized bins in 1901, to check up Jamieson's tests. Four series of tests were made on the Canadian Pacific Ry. grain elevator in Montreal, and one series was made on the Great Northern R. R. grain elevator in Quebec.

The pressures were determined with flat rubber diaphragms similar to those used by Jamieson, the apparatus having been carefully calibrated before and after the experiments.

Series I to IV, Canadian Pacific Ry. Elevator, Montreal.—The bin used was 12 × 14 ft. in cross-section with a hopper gate 12 inches in diameter. Two diaphragms, (B) and (C), were used. Diaphragm (B), having 109.36 sq. in. effective sectional area, was placed horizontally in the center of the bin, and the other, (C), having 26 sq. in. effective sectional area, was placed vertically in the side of the bin, in such a position that the maximum height of grain above the centers of both diaphragms was 44 ft. 10 in. The hopper was filled to the proper height and diaphragm (B) was laid on the grain at the center. The pressures were determined with the grain in motion, and the effect

[*] *Trans. Can. Soc. C. E.,* Vol. XVII, 1903; *Eng. News,* 1904, Vol. 52.

of sudden stopping after each 500 bushels was observed. The sudden stopping produced no appreciable effect.

The lateral and vertical pressures at bottom of bin when filling are given in Fig. 173. The wheat was allowed to stand one day and

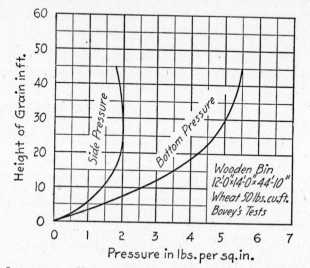

FIG. 173. LATERAL AND VERTICAL PRESSURE, BIN FILLING. DIAPHRAGM (B) AT CENTER OF BIN.

the bin was emptied. The vertical pressures could not be determined, as diaphragm (B) dropped out as soon as the gate was opened. The maximum lateral pressure for bin emptying was 2.142 lbs. per sq. in. as compared with a maximum lateral pressure of 1.951 lbs. per sq. in. when the bin was filling (9.7 per cent increase).

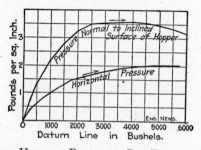

FIG. 174. LATERAL AND VERTICAL PRESSURES, BIN FILLING. DIAPHRAGM (B) ON HOPPER SIDE.

The pressures in Fig. 174 were obtained with diaphragm (C), placed as before, and diaphragm (B) placed parallel to and half-way down the slant of the hopper. All pressures were referred to the top of the hopper. Pressures were determined with the grain in motion, and the effect of a sudden stoppage after each 500 bushels was determined. The sudden stopping produced no appreciable effect. The maximum vertical pressure was 3.592 lbs. per sq. in., as compared with a maximum of 5.654 lbs. per sq. in. with diaphragm (B) at the center. The

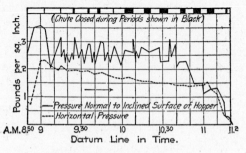

FIG. 175. LATERAL AND VERTICAL PRESSURES, BIN EMPTYING, DIAPHRAGM ON INCLINED HOPPER SURFACE AND ON BOTTOM OF BIN WALL.

grain was left in the elevator over night, the pressure having slightly decreased. The bin was emptied, observations being made at intervals of $\frac{1}{2}$ minute and 1 minute. The pressures and the effect of opening and closing the gates are shown in Fig. 175.

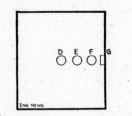

FIG. 176. LOCATION OF DIAPHRAGMS. (FIG. 5.)

Series V. Great Northern R. R. Elevator, Quebec.—The bin used was a timber crib bin, 13.4 × 12.35 ft. in cross-section, with a hopper gate 14 inches in diameter. The hopper was filled to the top and the diaphragms were placed as in Fig. 176. Diaphragms D, E, and *F* had a sectional area of 26 sq. in. each and were placed horizontal, while diaphragm *G* had a sectional area of 109.36 sq. in., and was placed vertical and parallel to the face of the bin. The diaphragms were calibrated before and after the experiments.

The pressures as given by the four diaphragms, readings being taken at intervals of 20 seconds, are shown in Fig. 177. The pressures on the diaphragms *D, E,* and *F* show that the pressures diminish from

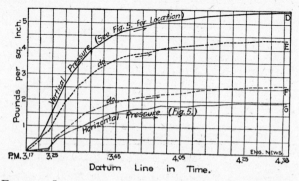

FIG. 177. LATERAL AND VERTICAL PRESSURES, BIN FILLING.

the center to the sides of the bins, and corroborate the theory that the grain in the bin consists of a series of superimposed domes. It will be noted that the lateral pressures determined by the large diaphragm on the Canadian Pacific Ry. elevator correspond very closely with the pressures determined by the small diaphragm, indicating that the size of the diaphragm has no appreciable effect on the pressure. Opening and closing the gates produced no appreciable effect on the pressures.

LUFFT'S EXPERIMENTS.[*]—Eckhardt Lufft made a series of experiments to determine the pressure of grain on full-sized bins in 1902 and 1903, at Buenos Aires, Argentina. These experiments were made before Jamieson's experiments were published. The tests were made on two bins, one 23' 10", and the other 11' 3" diameter, both bins being 54.8 feet deep, arranged as shown in Fig. 178. The inside surface of the bins was faced with rich cement mortar.

[*] *Eng. News,* 1904, Vol. 52, p. 531.

The pressure gage used in making the tests is shown in Fig. 179. The tests were made on bins *A* and *B,* the pressure gages being located as shown in Fig. 178. The bin discharge gates are marked *a.*

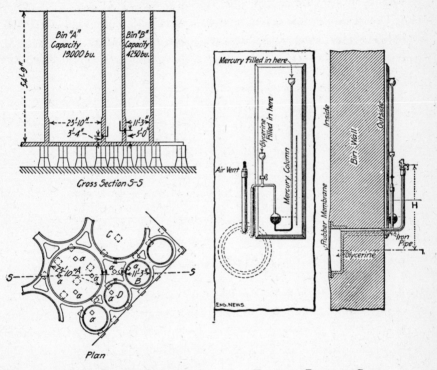

FIG. 178. PART PLAN OF BUENOS AIRES GRAIN ELEVATOR SHOWING LOCATION OF PRESSURE GAGES.

FIG. 179. PRESSURE GAGE.

The pressures of wheat on bin *A,* taken May 4, 1903, for the bin filling and emptying are given in Fig. 180. The grain was conveyed to the bin with a belt conveyor, and was weighed in by an automatic scale. Readings of the gage were taken at intervals of from ten to fifteen minutes. If the outlet nearest the gage was rapidly opened the pressure was decreased, while if the outlet was opened very slowly there was a slight pressure increase. Moving grain made no appreciable increase in the pressure.

The pressure curves for filling and emptying corn weighing 48.4 lbs. per cubic foot are given in Fig. 181. The broken filling curve is due to the fact that the filling was interrupted. In this case the pressure decreased for several hours or days before it became constant. It would appear that this decrease in pressure is due to the settlement of the grains, so that both the angle of repose and the coefficient of friction of the grain on the bin walls are increased.

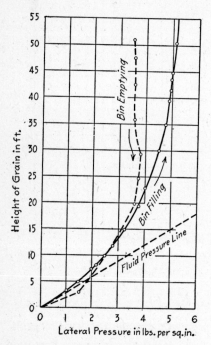

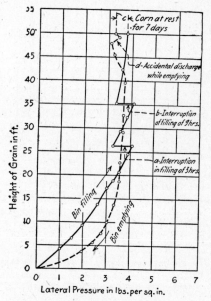

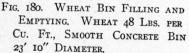

FIG. 180. WHEAT BIN FILLING AND EMPTYING. WHEAT 48 LBS. PER CU. FT., SMOOTH CONCRETE BIN 23' 10" DIAMETER.

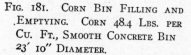

FIG. 181. CORN BIN FILLING AND EMPTYING. CORN 48.4 LBS. PER CU. FT., SMOOTH CONCRETE BIN 23' 10" DIAMETER.

The pressure curves for filling the small bin with wheat of different grades are given in Fig. 182. A typical emptying curve for the same bin is given in Fig. 183. In this bin the gage was almost vertically above the outlet gate, and was exposed alternately to the pressure of flowing grain and the pressure of grain at rest.

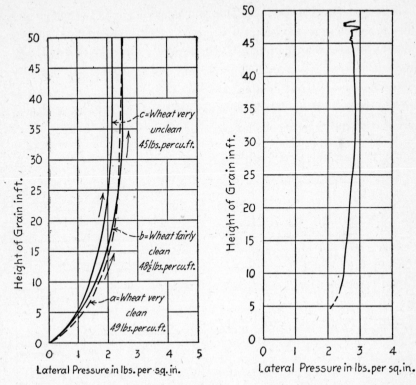

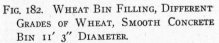

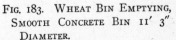

Fig. 182. Wheat Bin Filling, Different Grades of Wheat, Smooth Concrete Bin 11′ 3″ Diameter.

Fig. 183. Wheat Bin Emptying, Smooth Concrete Bin 11′ 3″ Diameter.

PLEISSNER'S EXPERIMENTS.*—In 1902–1905 Mr. J. Pleissner made an extensive series of experiments on the pressure of grain in deep bins for the firm of T. Bienert, in Dresden-Plauen, Germany.

Bins.—The experiments were made (*a*) with a cribbed timber bin, 1.57 meters square and 18 meters deep; (*b*) with a cribbed timber bin, 1.57 meters square and 18 meters deep, with rings spaced 1.6 meters apart vertically and projecting 45 mm. into the bin; (*c*) with a small plank bin with planks vertical, 1.5 meters square and 18 meters deep;

* "Versuche zur Ermittlung der Boden und Seitenwanddrucke in Getreidesilos." *Zeitschrift des Vereines deutscher Ingenieure,* June 23, 30, 1906, p. 976.

(d) with a large plank bin with planks vertical, 2.15 meters $\times$ 2.9 meters in section and 9 meters deep; and (e) with a reinforced concrete bin 2.5 meters $\times$ 3.15 meters in section and 17.24 meters deep, with rings spaced 2.93 meters apart vertically and projecting 80 mm. into the bin.

The surfaces of the cribbed bins (a) and (b) were quite rough, the planks in the plank bins (c) and (d) were unplaned, while the concrete in the reinforced concrete bin (e) had been filled and tamped against rough board forms which left a very rough surface. The coefficients of friction μ' on the bin wall surfaces for different grains are given in Table XXXVII.

TABLE XXXVII.

COEFFICIENT OF FRICTION OF GRAIN ON BIN WALLS.

Bins.	Coefficient of Friction $\mu' = \tan \phi'$.	
	Wheat.	Rye.
(a) Cribbed bin	0.43	0.54
(b) Ringed cribbed bin......................	0.58	0.78
(c) Small plank bin.........................	0.25	0.37
(d) Large plank bin..........	0.45	0.55
(e) Reinforced concrete bin.................	0.71	0.85

Pressure Measuring Apparatus. *Bottom Pressures.*—The bottom pressures in bins (a), (b), and (c) were determined by weighing the pressure directly by supporting the movable bottom by means of a rod passing through the center of the bin to a scale beam above. The bottom pressures in the other bins were measured by observing the deflections of the pitch pine plank bottoms, the pressures being later determined from actual experiments on the deflections of the planks. The planks in the bottom of the reinforced concrete and large plank bins were 300 mm. (12 in.) wide, 90 mm. (3.6 in.) thick, with a clear span of 2.5 meters (8.2 ft.). The bottom pressures were also determined by means of two rubber bags filled with water, placed on the plank bottoms and connected with glass scale tubes.

Side Pressures.—The side pressures were determined by measuring the deflections of plank pressure surfaces, made of planks placed vertically, the pressures being later determined from actual experiments.

The pressure surfaces for (e), the reinforced concrete, and (d), the large plank bin, were each 3.15 m. (10.33 ft.) wide and 2.5 m. (8.2 ft.) high, and were made of planks 300 mm. (12 in.) wide, 70 mm. (2.8 in.) thick, with a clear span of 2.5 m. (8.2 ft.). The pressure measuring surface in each case had the lower edge even with the bottom and extended across an entire side of the bin. The side pressure surfaces in bins (a), (b), and (c) were 1.375 m. (4.5 ft.) wide, by 0.9 m. (2.95 ft.) high, and were made of seven planks 195 mm. (7.8 in.) wide, 25 mm. (1 in.) thick, with a clear span of 860 mm. (2.82 ft.). The side pressures were also determined by means of three rubber diaphragms filled with water and placed on a side next to pressure surface, with their centers at the same height as the center of the plank pressure surface and 560 mm. apart. The sizes of the rubber diaphragms were not given.

The Tests.—The bottom and side pressures were determined for wheat, rye, flax-seed, and rape, with the grain at rest and in motion. The tests were repeated until results that agreed within themselves and with each other were obtained. In all 126 separate tests were made from 1902 to 1905.

Grain at Rest.—The lateral and vertical pressures of wheat at rest in the reinforced concrete bin (e) are given by the full lines in Fig. 184. These pressures were determined by means of the plank pressure surfaces. The pressures calculated by Janssen's formulas (144) and (145) with $w = 50$ lbs. per cu. ft., $\mu' = 0.71$, and $k = 0.3$, are shown by dotted lines. The calculated pressures agree almost exactly in the case of the lateral pressures, and the agreement with the vertical pressures is very close.

The lateral and vertical pressures of wheat at rest in the small plank bin (c) are given by the full lines in Fig. 185. These pressures were determined by means of the plank pressure surfaces. The pressures calculated by Janssen's formulas (144) and (145) with $w = 50$ lbs. per cu. ft., $\mu' = 0.25$, and $k = 0.34$, are shown by dotted lines. The calculated and experimental values of the lateral pressure agree very closely, while the vertical pressures show that k was a variable.

Grain in Motion.—Tests were made to determine the lateral and vertical pressures with the grain in motion. The results with the rein-

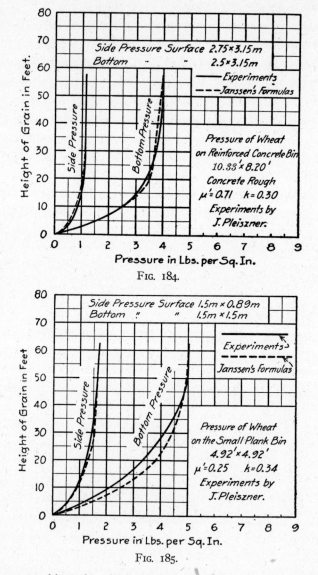

FIG. 184.

FIG. 185.

forced concrete bin only will be discussed. The vertical pressures, as determined by the rubber diaphragms or the deflection of the plank bottoms, showed no appreciable increase with the grain in motion, the average velocity of the grain in the bin being approximately 1 mm. per second, the same as in Prante's experiments.

The lateral pressures, as determined by the plank pressure surfaces, were much increased, while the lateral pressures, as determined by the rubber diaphragms, were erratic; the rubber diaphragm 1 placed midway between the gate and the plank pressure surface showing nearly double the static pressure; rubber diaphragm 3, placed 280 mm. from the side opposite the plank pressure surface, showed only a very slight increase over the static pressure; while the rubber diaphragm 2, placed midway between diaphragms 1 and 3, gave pressures between those given by 1 and 3.

The discharge gates were located in the bottom, one near the center and the other near the side opposite the plank pressure surface. This explains the eccentricities of the pressures indicated by the rubber diaphragms and the increase in pressure on the plank pressure surface opposite the gates; for Fig. 165 and the other experiments show that, with an opening in the bottom of the side of a bin, the pressures due to moving grain are materially increased on the side opposite the gate and slightly decreased on the side in which the gate is placed. Pleissner's experiments confirm the above conclusions, but are of little value in determining the question of increase in lateral pressure due to moving grain, as raised by Prante. To investigate the variation of side pressures for grain in motion the discharge gate must be in the center of the bin. Grain bins should never be constructed with side discharge gates.

A very interesting phenomenon was that the observed increase in pressure for grain in motion was very much less with rye than with wheat, the velocity in the bin being the same.

Value of k, the Ratio of Lateral to Vertical Pressures.—Pleissner found that k, the ratio of the lateral to vertical pressures, was not a constant for a grain in a bin at different depths, being greater for small than for large depths of grain, and that it varies with the different bins and different grains. Average values of k as determined for wheat and rye in the different bins are given in Table XXXVIII.

TABLE XXXVIII.

VALUES OF $k = \dfrac{L}{V}$ FOR WHEAT AND RYE IN DIFFERENT BINS.

Bins.	$k = \dfrac{L}{V}$	
	Wheat.	Rye.
(a) Cribbed bin............................	0.4 to 0.5	0.23 to 0.32
(b) Ringed cribbed bin...	0.4 to 0.5	0.3 to 0.34
(c) Small plank bin.........	0.34 to 0.46	0.3 to 0.45
(d) Large plank bin............................'...	0.3	0.23 to 0.28
(e) Reinforced concrete bin	0.3 to 0.35	0.3

Rape and flax-seed were tested in the small plank bin (c) and gave values of $k = 0.5$ to 0.6 for rape, and $k = 0.5$ to 0.55 for flax-seed.

DISCUSSION OF EXPERIMENTS.—Since the publication of Prante's experiments in 1896 there has been a wide difference of opinion among engineers on (1) the effect of the motion of grain on the lateral pressure, and (2) the effect of the size of the pressure surface on the indicated pressures.

1. Prante obtained lateral pressures four times the static pressures with wheat moving with a velocity of 1 mm. per second, and decided that with increasing velocities the lateral pressures rapidly approach the full hydraulic pressure as a limit. Pleissner obtained lateral pressures twice the static pressures with wheat moving with a velocity of 1 mm. per second. Jamieson found an increase in the pressure of moving wheat of only 4 to 7 per cent. Bovey found an increase of 9.7 per cent in the Canadian Pacific Ry. Grain Elevator. Lufft and the author found no appreciable increase of the pressure of moving grain over the static pressure.

In the experiments of Prante and Pleissner the bin discharge gates were not located in the center of the bins. These experiments therefore show the distorting effect of an eccentric discharge gate, as is evident from a study of Fig. 165, Fig. 166, Bovey and Lufft's experiments, and give no definite information as to the effect of moving grain on the lateral pressure. The experiments made thus far would appear to prove conclusively that with discharge gates in the center of the bottom and a discharge area not greater than 1/150 the area of the bin the increase in pressure due to moving grain will not exceed the static pressure by more than 10 per cent.

The lateral pressure during emptying is less than during filling when the grain is deep, and greater than during filling when the bin is nearly emptied.

2. Pleissner states that the grain arches over a small pressure surface, so that the results of tests with small pressure surfaces do not give absolutely correct results, although they show relative changes correctly. He drew this inference from the readings on the three rubber diaphragms used to determine lateral pressures. The variations in the pressures indicated by the rubber diaphragms were certainly due to the eccentric discharge gate. It will be seen in Fig. 184 and Fig. 185 that Pleissner's tests on grain at rest with large pressure surfaces agree very closely with the pressures calculated by Janssen's formulas. Experiments by Bovey, Jamieson and the author show that the arching action is insignificant, and that the pressures obtained with small and large pressure surfaces give a remarkably close agreement. The results obtained with model bins agree very closely with the results obtained with full-sized bins.

Conclusions.—The following conclusions may be drawn from the foregoing experiments:

1. The pressure of grain on bin walls and bottoms follows a law (which for convenience will be called the law of "semi-fluids"), which is entirely different from the law of the pressure of fluids.

2. The lateral pressure of grain on bin walls is less than the vertical pressure (0.3 to 0.6 of the vertical pressure, depending on the grain, etc.), and increases very little after a depth of $2\frac{1}{2}$ to 3 times the width or diameter of the bin is reached.

3. The ratio of lateral to vertical pressures, k, is not a constant, but varies with different grains and bins. The value of k can only be determined by experiment.

4. The pressure of moving grain is very slightly greater than the pressure of grain at rest (maximum variation for ordinary conditions is probably 10 per cent).

5. Discharge gates in bins should be located at or near the center of the bin.

6. If the discharge gates are located in the sides of the bins, the lateral pressure due to moving grain is decreased near the discharge gate and is materially increased on the side opposite the gate (for common conditions this increased pressure may be two to four times the lateral pressure of grain at rest).

7. Tie rods decrease the flow but do not materially affect the pressure.

8. The maximum lateral pressures occur immediately after filling, and are slightly greater in a bin filled rapidly than in a bin filled slowly. Maximum lateral pressures occur in deep bins during filling.

9. The calculated pressures by either Janssen's or Airy's formulas agree very closely with actual pressures.

10. The unit pressures determined on small surfaces agree very closely with unit pressures on large surfaces.

11. Grain bins designed by the fluid theory are in many cases unsafe as no provision is made for the side walls to carry the weight of the grain, and the walls are crippled.

12. Calculation of the strength of wooden bins that have been in successful operation shows that the fluid theory is untenable, while steel bins designed according to the fluid theory have failed by crippling the side plates.

UNIVERSITY OF COLORADO EXPERIMENTS.—As a check on the foregoing experiments a series of experiments on the pressure of wheat in a model bin was made in 1909 by Professor C. C. Williams under the author's direction.

Bin.—The bin was eight feet high and fifteen inches square inside dimensions, the sides being made of matched Oregon fir boards, with the grain horizontal. A hopper having a capacity equal to one-half the contents of the bin was placed above the bin. Discharge orifices $1\frac{3}{8}$ in., 2 in. and $2\frac{7}{8}$ in. in diameter, giving ratios to the cross-sectional areas of the bin of $1:150$, $1:75$, and $1:37\frac{1}{2}$ were used.

Pressure Measuring Apparatus.—The bottom pressures were measured by resting the movable bottom on a knife edge carried at the middle of a lever, one end of which rested on a fixed knife edge, while the other end rested on a knife edge on a scale platform. In the beginning this apparatus lacked delicacy. To remedy this a strip of canvas was tacked to the side walls about an inch from the bottom, thus forming a fillet without decreasing the area of the bottom.

The side pressures were measured by means of carbon plates carrying an electric current; the pressure of the grain being determined by measuring the electric current passing through the carbon plates. The apparatus was constructed as follows:

An electrode consisting of a steel plate 3 in. by 3 in. by $\frac{1}{16}$ in. with an insulated copper wire soldered to its back was imbedded in the center of one side of a 6 in. by 6 in. by $\frac{1}{4}$ in. wood plate with its surface flush with that of the board. Around this steel plate a box was built having inside dimensions $3\frac{1}{64}$ in. by $3\frac{1}{64}$ in. by $\frac{15}{16}$ in. deep. In this inner box, sixteen carbon plates 3 in. by 3 in. by $\frac{1}{16}$ in. were placed. The 6 in. by 6 in. board was made the bottom of a box $1\frac{1}{4}$ in. deep. A second wood plate containing an electrode exactly like that just described was fitted into the top of this box so that the steel plates might rest exactly on the carbon plates. The steel plates were ground to a plane surface and the carbon plates were carefully prepared by the National Carbon Co., Cleveland, Ohio. Shot were introduced beneath the movable lid of the gage to make as little resistance as possible outside of the carbon plates. The movable plate was tied to the bottom plate by means of loosely tied strings which held the plates in place but did not add to the pressure on the plates. A Weston millammeter and the above apparatus were introduced into the circuit of a wet cell battery, the current being measured by means of the millammeter. The battery consisted of two Daniell's cells connected in parallel and gave a current through this resistance box of 200 to 400 milamperes under the pressures obtaining in the bin. A second gage was made like the one above described, both gages being used where the discharge gates were eccentric. The pressure measuring gages were calibrated by laying weights on the movable lid, the total pressure including both the weight and the weight of the lid. The gages were calibrated before and after each series of tests.

Data for Wheat.—The tests were made with a good grade of wheat weighing 46 lbs. per cu. ft. The coefficient of friction of grain on grain was 0.501; the coefficient of friction of grain on the bin wall was 0.307, while the tangent of the angle of repose of the wheat was 0.421.

Tests.—Tests were made with the grain at rest, with the bin emptying and with the bin filling; with the grain in motion with eccentric discharge gates and with concentric discharge gates; with the discharge gates in the sides and in the bottom. The following conclusions may be drawn from the tests.

1. *Static Pressures.*—The pressures for the grain at rest agree very closely with the calculated pressures and with the pressures determined by other experimenters. The value of k was not a constant but increased with the depth of the grain.

2. *Grain in Motion.*—There was no appreciable increase in pressure for moving grain with a concentric discharge gate. With a discharge gate in the side the lateral pressures above the gate decreased slightly, while the lateral pressures opposite the gate increased from two to four per cent, the larger value being given with the larger orifice. The bottom pressures were not affected by an eccentric discharge gate in the side of the bin. With an eccentric discharge gate in the bottom, the bottom pressures were increased from two to five per cent, but the lateral pressures were not changed.

Conclusion.—These tests confirm the conclusions stated above by the author and printed in the first edition of this book. The author hopes to be able to use a modification of the apparatus just described to determine the actual pressures in full size bins.

The author's conclusions in the first edition have been quoted with approval by Mr. S. Sor in "Handbuch für Eisenbetonbau," Band IV, Teil 2.

CHAPTER XVIII.

The Design of Grain Bins and Elevators.

TIMBER GRAIN ELEVATORS.—The following description and specifications for the timber of the working house of the Missouri Pacific Ry. Elevator, Kansas City, Mo., will give a clear idea of timber elevator construction. For a view of this elevator see Fig. 148. The elevator was designed by the John S. Metcalf Co., Chicago, Ill.

General Description.—The working house is a plank and frame structure 71 ft. wide × 120 ft. long. The first story is built of heavy post and girder work; on top of this are the bins, 45 feet deep, made of laminated 2″ planking, and the bins are surmounted by a cupola five stories in height. The walls are covered with galvanized corrugated steel, and the roof is covered with a tar and gravel roofing. The foundation of the working house is a monolithic concrete slab reinforced with steel rods.

Specifications for Timber and Lumber.—All timber shall be yellow pine, furnished rough. All long leaf yellow pine shall be cut from live, unbled, long leaf pine grown south of Chattanooga. It shall be full size and square-edged, free from all unsound or black knots, splits or shakes. In no case shall wane measure more than $1\frac{1}{2}''$ measured diagonally or extend more than one-third the length or show on more than one corner of the stick. The sap specification shall be "Mercantile Inspection" under Savannah Rules of February 14, 1883, as follows: "All square timbers shall show two-thirds heart on two sides and not less than one-half heart on two other sides. Other sizes shall show two-thirds heart on faces and show heart two-thirds of the length on edges, except where the width exceeds the thickness by 3 inches or over, then it shall show heart on one-half the edges."

All other yellow pine timber shall be No. 1 common yellow pine, cut from live timber, and shall conform to the specifications for No. 1 common timber as set forth in paragraphs 78, 79, and 80 of the

Southern Lumber Manufacturer's Association Standard Classification, Grading and Dressing Rules for yellow pine as revised and adopted at St. Louis, Mo., July 9, 1902, as follows:

" § 78. Rough timber 4″ × 4″, and larger, shall not be more than ¼″ scant when green, shall be well manufactured with not less than three square edges, and shall be free from knots that will materially weaken the piece. Timbers 10″ × 10″ in size may have 2″ wane on one corner, measured on faces, or its equivalent on two or more corners, one-third the length of the piece. Larger sizes may have proportionally greater defects. Shakes extending not over one-eighth of the length of the pieces are admissible, and seasoning cracks shall not be considered defects.

" § 79. Dressed timbers shall conform in grading to the specifications applying to rough timbers of same size.

" § 80. Rough timbers, if thicker than the specified thickness for dry or green stock, may be dressed to such standard thickness, and when so dressed, shall be considered as rough stock."

Bin Planking.—The bin planking shall be thoroughly dry yellow pine, dressed on one side to 1⅝″ and on one edge to the specified width. It shall conform to the specifications for No. 1 common dimension as specified in paragraph 66 of the Standard Classification, Grading and Dressing Rules for yellow pine as revised and adopted by the Southern Lumber Manufacturer's Association at St. Louis, Mo., July 9, 1902, as follows: " No. 1 common dimension may contain sound knots, none of which in 2″ × 4″ should be larger than 2″ in diameter on one or both sides of the piece, and on wider stock which do not occupy more than one-third of the cross-section at any point throughout its length if located at the edge of the piece, or more than one-half the cross-section if located away from the edge; two pits, knots, or smaller or more defective knots which do not weaken the piece more than the knots aforesaid; will admit of seasoning checks; firm red heart, heart shakes which do not go through, wane, pitch, blue sap stains, pitch pockets, splits in the ends not exceeding in length the width of the piece, a limited number of small pin-worm holes well scattered, and such other defects as do not prevent its use as substantial structural material."

Bins.—The bins shall be constructed of planking in courses laid as follows: All walls shall be laid up plumb and true, forming square corners in the bins. Each course of planking shall be securely nailed with 30-d wire nails 4½″ long, said nails not exceeding 22 to the pound.

At all interior crossings two nails shall be driven in each end of each piece of plank in the 4″ and 6″ walls. At all outside crossings five nails shall be driven in each end of each plank crossing the wall and four nails in the plank at right angles to it. The intermediate nails shall be staggered. At the base of the walls and for 11′ 0″ in height the nails shall be spaced not to exceed 14″ centers, and for each additional 11′ 0″ in height the distance apart may be increased 2″, making the spacing in the top 11′ 0″ of planking 20″ centers. The heads of the nails shall be well bedded in the wood.

The floors shall consist of two thicknesses, the first layer to be ⅞″ shiplap, the second layer to be 2″ × 6″ dressed on one side and matched through the trackway, and the second layer over the balance of the floor shall be 1″ × 6″ flooring. All flooring shall be thoroughly dry yellow pine to conform to "C" flooring.

The floor of the engine house shall have the bottom thickness of ⅞″ shiplap and the top thickness of 1″ × 2″ dressed and matched hard maple flooring.

Allowable Stresses in Timber.—The timber parts of grain elevators should be proportioned in accordance with the following unit stresses, given in pounds per square inch:

Kind of Timber.	Transverse Loading.	End Bearing.	Columns Under 10 Diameters. C	Bearing Across Fiber.	Shear Along Fiber.
White Oak..	1,200	1,200	1,000	500	200
Long Leaf Yellow Pine ...	1,500	1,500	1,000	350	100
White Pine and Spruce....	1,000	1,000	600	200	100
Hemlock	800	800	500	200	100

Columns may be used with a length not exceeding 45 times the least dimension. The unit stress for lengths of more than 10 times the least dimension shall be reduced by the following formula:

$$P = C - \frac{C}{100}\frac{l}{d}$$

Where C = unit stress, as given above for short columns;

P = allowable unit stress, in lbs. per sq. in.;

l = length of column, in inches;

d = least side of column, in inches.

CIRCULAR STEEL BINS.—In the designing of steel grain bins particular attention should be given to the horizontal joints, and to the strength of the bin to act as a column to support the grain. To calculate the thickness of the metal the horizontal pressure L is obtained from Janssen's or Airy's formulas, Chapter XVI, and then the thickness will be found by the formula

$$t = \frac{L.d}{2S.f} \qquad (153)$$

where $t =$ thickness of the plate in inches,
  $L =$ horizontal pressure in lbs. per sq. in.,
  $d =$ diameter of bin in inches,
  $S =$ working stress in steel in lbs. per sq. in.,
  $f =$ efficiency of the joint.

The unit stress S may be taken at 16,000 lbs. per square inch, and f will be about 57 per cent for a single riveted lap joint, 73 per cent for a double riveted lap joint, and 80 per cent for double riveted double strap butt joints.

The allowable stresses given in the author's "The Design of Steel Mill Buildings" should be used in design. These allowable stresses are as follows: Tension on net section 16,000 lbs. per sq. in.; shear on cross-section of rivets 11,000 lbs. per sq. in.; bearing on the projection of rivets (diameter $\times$ thickness of plate) 22,000 lbs. per sq. in. Compression in columns $P = 16,000 - 70\,\dfrac{l}{r}$ where $P =$ unit stress in lbs. per sq. in., $l =$ length of member and $r =$ radius of gyration of the member, both in inches.

Rivets in Horizontal Joints.—The side walls carry a large part of the weight of the grain in the bin and this should be considered in designing the horizontal joints. The weight of the grain supported by the bin above any horizontal joint can be calculated as shown in the following example: Assume a steel plate bin 25 ft. in diameter, and it is required to calculate the grain supported by the bin walls above a horizontal joint 75 feet below the top of the grain.

The weight of the grain supported by the bin walls, per lineal foot of bin wall may be calculated by means of formula (145d), page 314. Substituting in (145d), the load per lineal foot of bin wall will be

$$P \cdot \mu' = w \cdot R \left[y - \frac{R}{k \cdot \mu'} \right] \qquad (145d)$$
$$= 50 \times {}^{25}\!/_{4} [75 - 25/(4 \times 0.4 \times 0.375)]$$
$$= 10,415 \text{ lbs.}$$

where $w = 50$ lbs. per cu. ft.; $R =$ diameter divided by four ($= A/U$); $y = 75$ ft.; $k = 0.4$, and $\mu' = 0.375$.

The weight of the steel bin above the joint will be approximately 1,250 lbs. per lineal foot of joint. The horizontal joint should then be designed for a total load of $10,415 + 1,250 = 11,665$ lbs. per lineal foot of joint. Assume that the plates are $\frac{3}{8}$ in. thick and that the rivets are $\frac{3}{4}$ in. in diameter. For allowable stresses of 11,000 lbs. per sq. in. in shear and 22,000 lbs. per sq. in. in bearing, we have from Table XXIX the value of a $\frac{3}{4}$ in. shop rivet in single shear $= 4,860$ lbs., and $\frac{2}{3}$ of $4,860 = 3,240$ lbs. for a field rivet, and in compression $= 6,190$ lbs. for shop rivets, and $\frac{2}{3}$ of 6,190 lbs. $= 4,127$ lbs. for a field rivet. For a lap joint the spacing should not be greater than $3,240 \times 12 \div 11,665 = 3.25$ in. One row of rivets only will be necessary to take direct stress.

Stresses in a Steel Bin Due to Wind Moment.—If M is the moment due to the wind acting on the bin above the horizontal joint, then the stress per lineal inch of joint due to wind moment will be

$$S = \frac{M \cdot d}{2I} \text{ , but } I = \tfrac{1}{8}\pi \cdot d^3 \text{ (approx.) and } S = \frac{4M}{\pi \cdot d^2} \qquad (a)$$

Substituting in (a) we have $S = 300$ lbs. per lineal inch, or 3,600 lbs. per lineal foot. The spacing should therefore not be greater than $3,240 \times 12 \div (11,665 + 3,600) = 2\frac{5}{8}$ in.

Stiffeners.—In large circular steel bins the thin side walls are not sufficiently rigid to support the weight of the grain and it is necessary to supply stiffeners. For this purpose angles or Z-bars may be used. Experience has shown that bins in which the height is equal to or greater than about $2\frac{1}{2}$ times the diameter do not need stiffeners. There is at present no rational method for the design of these stiffeners or the stiffeners in plate girders. In Fig. 210 will be seen the details of a steel bin of the Independent Steel Elevator with Z-bar stiffeners. Angle stiffeners were used in the bins of the Electric Elevator, Minneapolis, Minn.

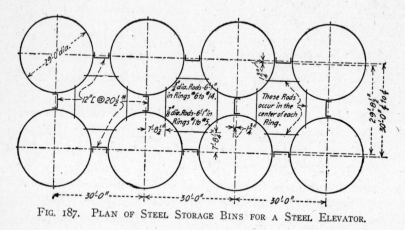

FIG. 187. PLAN OF STEEL STORAGE BINS FOR A STEEL ELEVATOR.

Circular steel bins are used for storage in large elevators and may be used for a complete elevator as in Fig. 187. The space between the bins is sometimes used for auxiliary storage as in Fig. 187. The

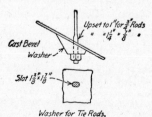

FIG. 188. DETAIL OF THE ROD CONNECTION IN FIG. 187.

circular bin walls are stiffened by means of vertical channels, and the auxiliary bins are cross-braced with steel rods. Complete details of circular steel bins for the Independent Elevator, Omaha, Neb., are shown in Fig. 210.

Reinforced Concrete Country Grain Elevator.—The reinforced concrete grain elevator shown in Fig. 187a, has a capacity of 50,000

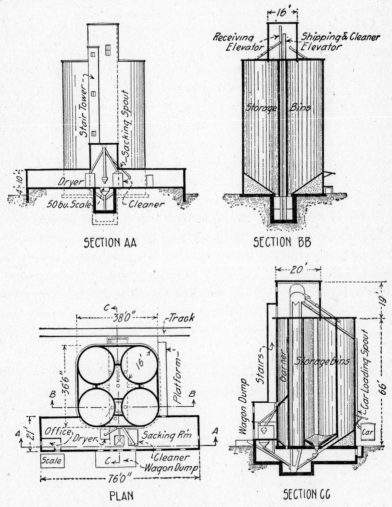

SECTION AA   SECTION BB

PLAN   SECTION CC

FIG. 187 a. REINFORCED CONCRETE COUNTRY GRAIN ELEVATOR.

bushels and is designed for country service. The bins are 16 ft. in diameter and 66 ft. high, and have a capacity of 10,000 bushels each; the garner bin and the interspace bins have a capacity of 10,000 bushels, making a total capacity of 50,000 bushels.

The circular reinforced concrete bins have walls 7 in. thick and are reinforced with horizontal round bars to carry the bursting pressures, and with vertical round bars for temperature and setting stresses. The interspace bin is braced at intervals of 4 feet in height with 2 round bars, passing across the bin and through the walls of the circular bins. The office and sacking room are built of reinforced concrete. The roofs of the elevator, office and sacking room are made of reinforced concrete and are covered with 4-ply tar, gravel and composition roofing. The floors are made of reinforced concrete and have a granolithic finish. This structure is fireproof and will result in a large saving in insurance. With the increased price of timber reinforced concrete country grain elevators will soon be economical to build.

The equipment includes a wagon scale, a wagon dump, a 50 bushel scale hopper, a dryer, a cleaner, a receiving elevator, a cleaning elevator, also spouts for shipping and cleaning. The grain is handled by spouting without screw or belt conveyors. This elevator can be built complete for from $20,000 to $25,000, depending upon the local and other conditions.

Steel Country Elevator.—General plans of a steel grain elevator for the Manhattan Milling Co., designed and constructed by the Minneapolis Steel & Machinery Co., Minneapolis, Minn., are given in Fig. 189. This elevator could easily be changed to a shipping elevator by putting in a wagon dump. Grain is run from the cars into the boot of the receiving leg, and is then elevated and conveyed by a screw conveyor to the large storage bins, or is run into the temporary storage bins, then cleaned and elevated and conveyed to the storage bins by the screw conveyor. The bins are built of steel plates, and the working house is built of steel framework covered with corrugated steel. This elevator has a capacity of 76,300 bushels but the scheme can be used for a 30,000 to 40,000 bushel elevator for either shipping or for milling purposes.

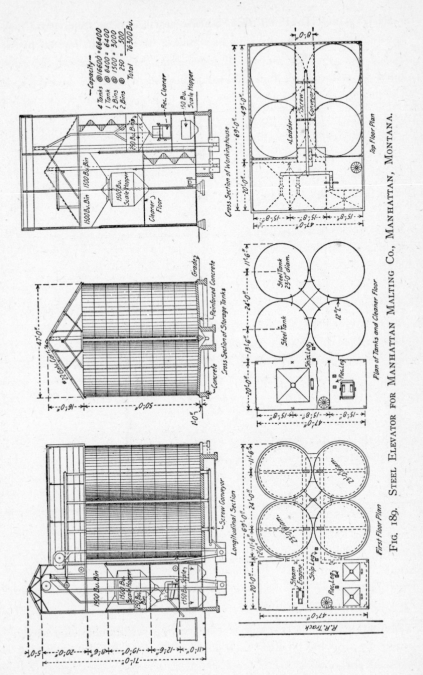

FIG. 189. STEEL ELEVATOR FOR MANHATTAN MALTING CO., MANHATTAN, MONTANA.

RECTANGULAR STEEL BINS.—In designing rectangular bins the thickness of the plates may be found by the diagram for flat plates in Fig. 86. A common size of rectangular bins in grain elevators is about 14 feet square, and in bins of this size it is either necessary to

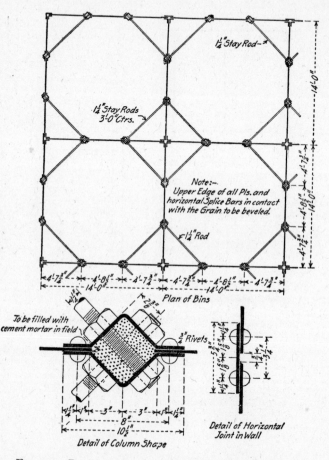

FIG. 190. PLAN OF METCALF RECTANGULAR STEEL BINS.

brace the sides or use very heavy plates. Buckle plates are sometimes used for rectangular grain bins.

Metcalf Bin.—The method of constructing rectangular bins shown in Fig. 190 and Fig. 191 has been patented by the John S. Metcalf Co.,

Chicago. This construction is very economical and satisfactory. The concrete filling makes a continuous column, while the round brace rods are so rigid that the moving grain does not affect them. The Windmill Point steel grain elevator, Fig. 192 and Fig. 193, is an excellent example of an elevator built according to this system.

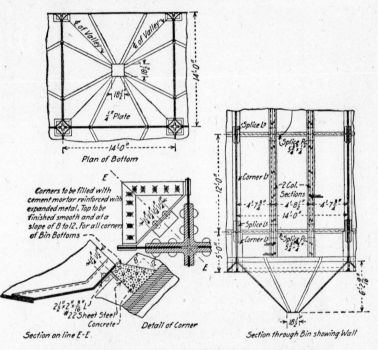

FIG. 191. DETAILS OF METCALF RECTANGULAR STEEL BIN.

Windmill Point Steel Grain Elevator.—The Montreal Warehousing Company's Windmill Point steel grain elevator at Montreal, Quebec, is a fireproof structure of the working house type, and was designed and erected by the John S. Metcalf Co. The building is 84 ft. wide × 238 ft. long. The elevator is shown during construction in Fig. 192 and Fig. 193. The framework is a self-supporting steel structure. The outside covering is of concrete to a height of 7 ft. above the base of rail and brick to a height of 124 ft. above the base of rail; while the cupola is covered with tile. The roofs are made of

FIG. 192. GRAND TRUNK STEEL GRAIN ELEVATOR, WINDMILL POINT,
MONTREAL, QUEBEC.

FIG. 193. GRAND TRUNK STEEL GRAIN ELEVATOR, WINDMILL POINT,
MONTREAL, QUEBEC.

3″ book tile supported on steel T's and covered with felt, tar and gravel. The floors are of concrete and tile. The windows have metal frames glazed with ¼″ wire glass with mesh of wire netting not larger than 1″. A marine tower constructed of fire-proof materials capable of unloading at the rate of 15,000 bushels per hour is provided. A system of conveyor galleries is provided to carry the grain along the wharf. The conveyor belts are 36″ wide and discharge into dock spouts spaced 60 ft. apart.

The elevator is equipped with 5 receiving and 5 shipping elevator legs, having 20″ × 7″ × 7″ metal cups and 7′ 0″ head pulleys. Six belt conveyors 30″ wide are located in the basement to carry grain across the house and discharge it into the five elevators.

In the first story are located 5 pairs of power shovels for unloading, one car puller with four drums, two elevator separators, and a complete sweeper system. On the west side a 36″ belt brings grain from the marine tower and discharges it into any of the 5 receiving elevators.

In the top story of the cupola ten elevator heads discharge into ten 2,000 bushel garners. Below each garner is a 120,000-lb. hopper scale, surmounted by a 2,000-bushel scale hopper. Below the scale hoppers, in the second story of the cupola, is the spouting to the trolley spouts and two 36″ belt conveyors running the entire length of the cupola. These belts are reversible and are provided with loading spouts and trippers. In the first story of the cupola is located a complete system of trolley spouts for discharging into the bins. For an abstract of the specifications for the steel, see p. 298.

Cross-bracing.—In the Great Northern Elevator the plates were too thin to take the change in loading due to emptying and filling adjacent bins, without undue deflection, and vertical Z-bars were riveted to the middle of the sides of the 13′ 6″ × 13′ 6″ bins. The Z-bars were fastened together with flat steel ties 5″ × ⅜″, with long dimension vertical and riveted at the ends. These ties were torn out and the rivets were sheared off by the moving grain. For details of these rectangular bins see Fig. 221.

In the rectangular bins of the Independent Elevator, Omaha, Neb., Fig. 209, vertical stiffener angles were placed about 5 feet apart in

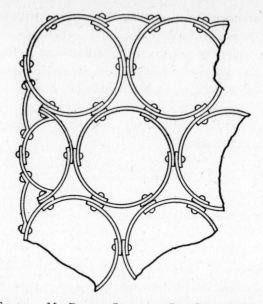

FIG. 194. MACDONALD SYSTEM OF BIN CONSTRUCTION.

FIG. 195. C. H. & D. ELEVATOR "B," TOLEDO, O. JAMES MACDONALD, ENGINEER.

the bin walls and angle diagonal braces were placed 5 feet apart vertically. The ends of the angles were flattened out under the hammer and were then riveted to bin walls, passing between the wall and the vertical stiffeners. Rod bracing was used to brace the bins. For a complete description of this elevator, with plans and details, see Chapter XIX.

For method of bracing the Metcalf bin see Figs. 190 and 191.

MacDonald Bin.—The system of constructing circular bins in clusters, as shown in Fig. 194, is patented by the MacDonald Engineering Co., Chicago, Ill. This system is used for working house storage bins. Three plates are bolted together on the ground and are then lifted into place and bolted in position, no rivets being used. The horizontal joints are butted and covered with butt straps.

Fig. 196. Steel Grain Elevator Constructed on MacDonald System.

24

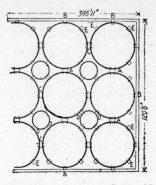

FIG. 197. PLAN SHOWING BIN ARRANGEMENT, GREAT NORTHERN STEEL ELEVATOR,
BUFFALO, N. Y.

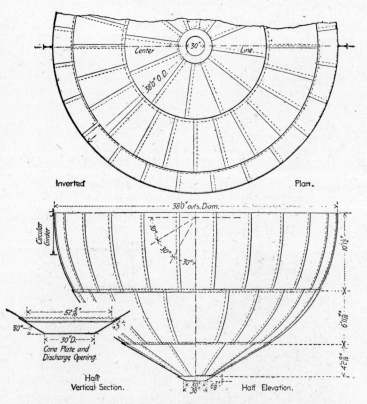

FIG. 198. HEMISPHERICAL BOTTOMS, GREAT NORTHERN STEEL ELEVATOR,
BUFFALO, N. Y.

The elevators shown in Fig. 195 and Fig. 196 illustrate the Mac-
Donald system of steel grain elevator construction. A completed elevator is shown in Fig. 145. The MacDonald Engineering Co. has
erected many elevators under this system.

The " Great Northern " Steel Elevator, Buffalo, N. Y., designed
by Max Toltz in 1897, is of the working house type. This elevator has

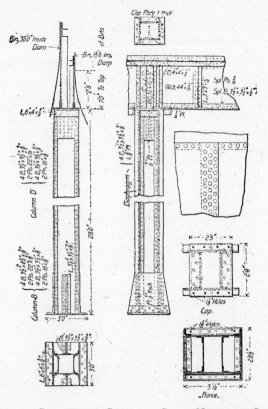

FIG. 199. CIRCULAR GIRDERS AND COLUMNS, GREAT NORTHERN STEEL ELEVATOR,
BUFFALO, N. Y.

a storage capacity of 2,525,890 bushels. The bins are supported on columns and are of two sizes, 30 bins 38 feet in diameter and 85 feet deep,
and 18 bins 15½ feet in diameter, all with hemispherical bottoms. The
arrangement of the bins is shown in Fig. 197, while the hemispherical

bottoms are shown in Fig. 198, and the circular girders and columns in Fig. 199. The bins were designed for full fluid pressure, assuming wheat to weigh 50 lbs. per cu. ft. The hemispherical bottoms were made the same thickness as the bottom side plates. The steel work was designed for a safe fiber stress of 17,000 lbs. per square inch in tension. For a complete description see Engineering News, April 7, 1898.

SPECIFICATIONS FOR STEEL WORK.—The specifications for steel grain bins should be the same as for bins, for which see Chapter XI and Appendix IV. For specifications for structural steel work see the author's specifications for Steel Frame Mill Buildings, published in "Steel Mill Buildings." For reinforcing concrete soft steel is used with an allowable stress of 16,000 lbs. per sq. in.; and high steel with an ultimate strength of 90,000 to 100,000 lbs. per sq. in. is used with an allowable stress of 25,000 lbs. per sq. in.

The following extracts are from the specifications prepared by the John S. Metcalf Co. for the Windmill Point Steel Grain Elevator. The clauses not given are essentially standard clauses.

Method of Manufacture.—All steel used shall be made by the open hearth process. The bin bottoms, garner bottoms and all bent plates shall be of flange steel; all other plates, shapes and bolts shall be of structural steel.

Chemical and Physical Properties.—The steel when tested shall show the following properties:

TABLE OF CHEMICAL AND PHYSICAL REQUIREMENTS.

	Flange Steel.	Structural Steel.	Rivet Steel.
Maximum Phos., Basic Steel	.04 per cent.	.04 per cent.	.04 per cent.
Maximum Phos., Acid Steel	.08 per cent.	.08 per cent.	.04 per cent.
Maximum Sulphur	.04 per cent.	.05 per cent.	.03 per cent.
Ultimate Tensile Strength, lbs. per Sq. In.	Desired 56,000	Desired 62,000	Not over 55,000
Yield point to be observed and recorded in all tests made			
Elongation (in 8 inch and in 2 inch)	26 per cent.	25 per cent.	28 per cent.
Cold Bending	180° flat	180° flat	180° flat
Quench Bending	180° flat		
Nicked Bending Test.			

Stay Rods in Bins.—The stay rods in the regular 14 ft. square bins shall be 1″ diameter upset to 1¼″, and in the divided bins ⅝″ diameter upset to ¾″. They shall be threaded at ends, as indicated on drawings, with full U. S. standard thread. The rods shall be straight, free from flaws, and shall be annealed after being upset.

Painting.—In shop riveted work the surfaces coming in contact shall be painted one good coat before being put together.

All iron and steel work before leaving the shop shall be thoroughly cleaned, and shall be given one good coat of paint, well worked into all joints and open spaces.

Surfaces which are not accessible for painting after assembling shall have two coats of paint before being assembled. The surfaces in contact of all pieces put together in the field shall each be painted one good coat before being put together.

The paint shall be of a good quality of oxide of iron paint, and shall be approved by the engineers. No painting shall be done in wet or freezing weather, and care shall be taken to have all surfaces dry before treatment.

After erection all of the steel work shall be thoroughly cleaned and all surfaces except the interior surfaces that come in contact with grain (interior surfaces of bins, garners, and hoppers) shall be painted with one coat of the iron oxide paint. After this coat has thoroughly dried all of the above mentioned paint surfaces shall be given a second coat of paint. This coat shall consist of white lead mixed with pure boiled linseed oil colored as may be directed by the engineers. The quality of said paint shall be such as to meet with the approval of the engineers.

All paint shall be thoroughly and evenly applied and well worked into all joints and open spaces. Finished surfaces shall be given one heavy coat of white lead and tallow before being shipped from the shop.

Inspection.—The manufacturer shall furnish all facilities for inspecting and testing the weight and quality of workmanship at the shop where material is manufactured. He shall furnish a suitable machine for testing full-sized members, if required.

When an inspector is furnished by the company he shall have full access at all times to all parts of the shop where material under his inspection is being manufactured.

The inspector shall stamp each piece accepted with a private mark. Any piece not so marked may be rejected at any time and at any stage of the work. If the inspector, through an oversight or otherwise, has accepted material or work which is defective or contrary to the specifications, this material, no matter in what stage of completion, may be rejected by the company.

Material shall not be rolled nor any work done before the company has been notified and arrangements have been made for the inspection.

The engineer shall be furnished complete shop plans and must be notified well in advance of the start of the work in the shop, in order that he may have an inspector on hand to inspect material and workmanship. The inspector shall be paid by the company.

Clips.—Steel clips of an approved make shall be used to connect the T's supporting the book tile to the girders.

Erection.—The center of each base must be made true to the column center, as given on the plans, within $\frac{1}{16}$ of an inch, and its height shall be adjusted exactly, using an engineer's level and referring to a fixed bench mark. The anchor bolts for the cast bases will be set in place by the company.

Each cast base shall be set in exact position both as to alignment and to height, using cement grout for this purpose. The casting shall be supported on wooden wedges until the grout has set. Each base shall be thoroughly bedded in the grout. Cement grout for this purpose shall be made with Portland cement and sand. The Portland cement for the work will be furnished by the company. An equal quantity of cement and sand shall be used, and the two thoroughly mixed dry in a tight box. Enough water shall then be added to make the whole just flow under its own weight. The whole operation of mixing and setting shall be performed as rapidly as possible. No grout shall be used that has begun to set. After the bases are set, their heights will be inspected by the engineers, and if they are found to vary more than $\frac{1}{32}$ of an inch from the correct height, they shall be taken up and re-set.

The use of iron sledges in driving or hammering beams or columns or other structural steel will not be allowed where it can be avoided. Wooden mauls shall be used wherever their use is possible. Care shall also be exercised to prevent the materials from falling or from being in any way subjected to heavy shocks.

Especial care shall be used to keep the columns and bin walls plumb and in proper line during erection, and they shall be plumbed to the satisfaction of the engineers as often as they may desire. In case the columns or bin walls are not kept plumb, the entire work of erection shall stop, upon receipt of a written order from the engineers to that effect, and the measures to be employed to remedy the defect shall be approved by the engineers before the erection proceeds.

The use of steel wedges or shims to plumb up columns will not be permitted, the intention being to have the work so accurately done that such practice will be unnecessary.

The sections of columns, truss members, beams or girders must nowhere be cut without first obtaining the approval of the engineers.

Every failure of the material to come together properly shall be noted and reported daily to the engineers. If any serious difficulty occurs during erection, it shall be reported to the engineers before any unexpected measures are used to meet the difficulty.

The contractors shall furnish and erect temporary timber bracing whenever necessary during the erection of the building and whenever so directed by the engineers.

Bins.—The bins shall be made grain tight; any openings in the bin walls, at points where the splices are made, or at any other place in the walls, or bottoms, shall be securely stopped up in a workmanlike manner. After a complete section of bin wall has been erected, the spaces between the column shapes shall be filled with cement grout made in the manner specified for the grout for the column bases, except that it shall be composed of one part Portland cement to four of sand. Care must be taken to stop openings at bottom of the column shapes of lower section until the grout has set.

After each complete section is riveted up and before the grout is poured into the openings between the column shapes, the stay bolts shall be adjusted so as to true up the bin wall. After this has been done, the grout shall be applied in the aforesaid manner.

The work of erection shall be done in a workmanlike manner and to the satisfaction of the engineers.

CONCRETE BINS.—Circular reinforced concrete bins have horizontal and vertical reinforcement. The horizontal reinforcement is either single, when it is placed at the center of the walls, as in the Santa Fe Elevator, Fig. 228; or double, when bars are placed near the surface, as in the Canadian Pacific Ry. Elevator, Port Arthur, Ontario, Fig. 230. The horizontal reinforcement may be continuous, rising from the bottom to the top as a spiral, as in the Santa Fe Elevator, or may be in separate rings. When spiral reinforcement is used the reinforcement is usually high steel wire. The vertical rods are equally spaced and are wired or clamped to the horizontal rods at intersections, see Fig. 228.

Design of Horizontal Reinforcement.—The horizontal reinforcement is usually designed to take all the tensile stresses due to the pressure of the grain. Now let $g =$ vertical spacing of the bars in inches, $p =$ grain pressure per square inch on a point midway between the bars, $d =$ the diameter of the bin in inches, $A =$ net area of steel rods in a height g, and $f_s =$ allowable unit stress in the rods.

Then the net area of the steel for spacing g will be given by formula

$$A = \frac{p.g.d}{2f_s} \tag{a}$$

and the spacing for rods with an area A will be

$$g = \frac{2A.f_s}{p.d} \tag{b}$$

Design of Vertical Reinforcement.—The vertical reinforcement carries the load between the horizontal reinforcement and takes its proportion of the vertical load. The walls will have negative bending moments at the horizontal reinforcement, and positive bending moments midway between the horizontal reinforcement. The bending moments on a unit width are approximately

$$M = \pm \tfrac{1}{12} p.g^2 \tag{c}$$

The area of the steel can be calculated by formula (6a), Appendix I.

The pressure on any horizontal section is equal to the weight of the wall plus the weight of the grain carried by the walls. This pressure is carried by the concrete and the steel, the stress in the steel being n times the stress in the concrete, where $n = E_s \div E_c$.

Wind Stresses.—The stresses due to wind moment in grain bins are small and the concrete and steel may both be assumed to take tension and compression. The wind pressure will act at one-half the height and will produce a moment M, about the center of any horizontal section.

Then the extreme fiber stress in the concrete will be given by the formula

$$f_c = \pm \frac{M.d}{2(I_c + n.I_s)} \tag{d}$$

Where d is the external diameter of the bin.

The stresses in the steel will be given by the formula

$$f_s = \frac{n.M.d'}{2(I_c + n.I_s)} \tag{e}$$

Where d' is the diameter of the reinforcement. With vertical reinforcement of $\frac{1}{2}''$ square bars spaced $12''$ to $18''$ in grain bins of ordinary sizes the total stresses are nominal.

Example 1.—As an example the reinforcement in the reinforced concrete grain bin in Fig. 228 will be investigated. A section 70 feet below the top will be taken. The diameter $= 24'$ $2''$; the spacing $g = 7''$ and $f_s = 16,000$ lbs. per sq. in., and $p = 4.3$ lbs. per sq. in. (Fig. 153).

Horizontal Reinforcement.—Then

$$A = \frac{4.3 \times 7 \times 24.16 \times 12}{2 \times 16,000} = 0.27 \text{ sq. in.}$$

The rods are $\frac{3}{4}''$ round with an area of 0.44 sq. in., which makes a stress of 10,000 lbs. per sq. in. in the gross section of the horizontal rods. If the splice has an efficiency of 0.75, the stress in net area will be about 13,400 lbs. per sq. in.

Vertical Reinforcement.—The approximate weight of the concrete above this horizontal joint, $= 396,000$ lbs., $= 5,000$ lbs. per lineal foot. The weight of the grain carried by the walls is from Fig. 157, $= 859,000$ lbs., $= 11,900$ lbs. per lineal foot. The vertical bars are $\frac{1}{2}'' \square$ and are spaced $18''$ centers. The area of steel per lineal foot is then, $A = 0.167$ sq. in. The area of concrete $= 84$ sq. in. The concrete is $1 : 2\frac{1}{2} : 4$ and $n = 10$.

Then

$$f_c = \frac{5,000 + 11,900}{84 + 10 \times 0.167}$$

$$f_c = 195 \text{ lbs. per sq. in.}$$

and

$$f_s = 1,950 \text{ lbs. per sq. in.}$$

The wind pressure will be taken at 20 lbs. per sq. ft. of vertical projection, and $M = 20 \times 70 \times 24.16 \times 35 \times 12 = 14,206,080$ in.-lbs.

Now

$$I_c = \frac{\pi}{64} [(24.16 \times 12)^4 - (23 \times 12)^4] = 61,957,600 \text{ in.}^4$$

The value of I_s will be very nearly $\frac{1}{36}$ of I_s for a $\frac{1}{2}''$ ring of steel.

$$I_s = \frac{\pi}{64} \times \frac{1}{36} [(283\frac{1}{2})^4 - (282\frac{1}{2})^4] = 123,520 \text{ in.}^4$$

Now from (d)

$$f_c = \pm \frac{M.d}{2(I_c + n.I_s)} = \pm 35 \text{ lbs.}$$

and

$$f_s = \pm 350 \text{ lbs,}$$

The stress in the vertical reinforcement as given by formula (c) is nominal. The maximum compression in the concrete is then $c = 195 + 35 = 230$ lbs. per sq. in. This gives a factor of safety of about 10 in the concrete. The vertical reinforcement is ample.

STRESSES IN RECTANGULAR BINS. Case I. Bin Walls of Uniform Thickness.—The rectangular bin in Fig. 199a has a breadth b and length l, and sustains the pressure of the grain p. Now if the bin is hinged at the corners 1, 2, 3, 4 as in (b), Fig. 199a, the maximum bending moments in the sides b will be $M = \frac{1}{8}p.b^2$, and in the sides l will be $M = \frac{1}{8}p.l^2$. The moments being a maximum at the middle of the sides and zero at the corners.

The sides of the bin in (c) and (d), Fig. 199a, have a constant cross-section, so that the moment of inertia, I, is constant, and in addition the bin is rigid at the corners. It is required to calculate the bending moments in the bin walls. Now it has been proved in " The Design of Steel Mill Buildings," Chapter XVA, that to fix a simple beam at the

ends there must be introduced a negative bending moment polygon
equal to the positive bending moment polygon in amount, and having
its center of gravity in the same vertical line. This is expressed by
the equations

$$\Sigma M = 0 \qquad\qquad (a)$$

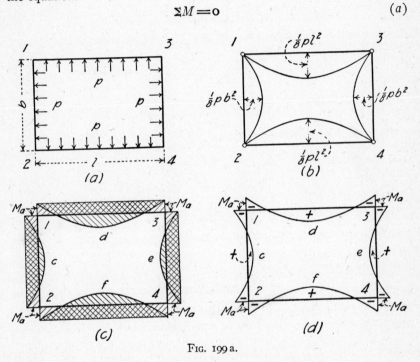

Fig. 199 a.

and

$$\Sigma M.x = 0 \qquad\qquad (b)$$

It will also be seen in (c) and (d), Fig. 199a that the negative bending
moments at the corners, M_a, will be the same in both spans meeting at
the point. It will then be seen that the bin may be considered as a
beam fixed at the ends, with square bends and loaded with a normal
load. It therefore follows (1) that the sum of the areas of the positive
bending moment polygons equals the sum of areas of the negative
bending moment polygons, and (2) that the negative bending moment
at the end of each side is M_a.

The area of the positive bending moment polygons is

$$+\Sigma M = \tfrac{4}{3}(\tfrac{1}{8}p.b^3 + \tfrac{1}{8}p.l^3) = \tfrac{1}{6}p(b^3 + l^3) \qquad (c)$$

and the area of the negative bending moment polygons is

$$-\Sigma M = -2M_a(b + l) \qquad (d)$$

Now since $+\Sigma M - \Sigma M = 0$, we have by equating (c) and (d)

$$M_a = -\tfrac{1}{12}\frac{p(b^3 + l^3)}{b + l} = -\tfrac{1}{12}p(b^2 - b.l + l^2) \qquad (e)$$

The bending moment in the middle of the side l is

$$M_f = M_d = \tfrac{1}{8}p.l^2 - \tfrac{1}{12}\frac{p(b^3+l^3)}{b + l} = \tfrac{1}{24}p(l^2 + 2b.l - 2b^2) \qquad (f)$$

and also the moment in the middle of the side b is

$$M_c = M_e = \tfrac{1}{24}p(b^2 + 2b.l - 2l^2) \qquad (g)$$

Now if the bin is square, $l = b$ and

$$M_a = -\tfrac{1}{12}p.l^2 \qquad (h)$$

$$M_f = M_c = +\tfrac{1}{24}p.l^2 \qquad (i)$$

Case 2. Walls b and 1 of Different Thickness.—If the bin walls on sides b and l in (c) and (d), Fig. 199a, do not have the same thickness the bending moments may be calculated as follows: It is assumed that the moment of inertia of the sides b and l are I_b and I_l, respectively.

As in case 1 the negative moment M_a will be the same at the corners of all sides. To equilibrate the positive and negative bending moments it will be necessary to divide the bending moment at every point by the moment inertia of the side at that point.

The area of the positive bending moment polygons is

$$+\Sigma(M/I) = \tfrac{4}{3}(\tfrac{1}{8}p.b^3/I_b + \tfrac{1}{8}p.l^3/I_l) \qquad (j)$$

and the area of the negative bending moment polygons is

$$-\Sigma(M/I) = -2M_a(b/I_b + l/I_l) \qquad (k)$$

Now since $+\Sigma(M/I) - \Sigma(M/I) = 0$, we have by equating (j) and (k)

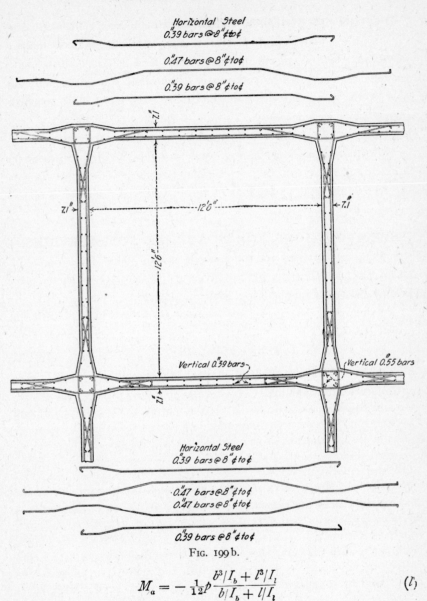

FIG. 199 b.

$$M_a = -\tfrac{1}{12}p\frac{b^3/I_b + l^3/I_l}{b/I_b + l/I_l} \qquad (l')$$

Pull at Ends of Walls.—The pull at the ends of the walls will be

$P = \tfrac{1}{2}p.l$ at ends of wall b, and

$P = \tfrac{1}{2}p.b$ at ends of wall l.

DESIGN OF SQUARE BINS.—In designing a reinforced concrete working house grain elevator, square or rectangular bins make a more convenient arrangement than circular bins. Square or rectangular bins require practically the same amount of concrete as circular bins of the same diameter and number of bins, but require approximately twice as much steel. Care must be used to tie the walls in at the corners and to reinforce for negative moment at the corners.

The square bin shown in Fig. 199b was designed by Professor E. Morsch and represents the best German practice. The reinforcing in the rectangular and square bins of the F. C. Ayres Elevator is shown in Fig. 250.

SPECIFICATIONS FOR CONCRETE STORAGE BINS.—Complete specifications for the concrete storage bins of the Santa Fe Grain Elevator, Chicago, Ill., are given in Chapter XIX. These specifications were prepared by the John S. Metcalf Co., Chicago, Ill.

The following description and abstract of the specifications for the concrete storage bins of the Missouri Pacific Ry. Co. at Kansas City, Mo. (see Fig. 148), will give a clear idea of the details of construction. These specifications were prepared by the above company.

Concrete Storage Bins.—The storage bins are 42′ 0″ outside diameter and 81′ 6″ high, with walls of concrete 9″ thick, reinforced with steel rods. The concrete is composed of one part Portland cement, 2½ parts sand, and 4 parts broken stone that will pass a 1″ ring, or such proportions of cement, sand, and stone as will completely fill the voids. The horizontal reinforcing rods are ¾″ in diameter; they are spaced 3″ apart for a distance of 11′ 6″ from the bottom of the bin; 3½″ apart for the next 12′ 3″; 4″ apart for the next 12′ 0″; 5″ apart for the next 8′ 9″; 6″ apart for the next 9′ 0″; 8″ apart for the next 6′ 0″; 10″ apart for the next 5′ 0″; and 12″ apart for the remaining 17′ 0″. These rods are bent to the curve of the bin, and have their ends bent and connected by links with wedges as shown in Fig. 228. The ends of each band are lapped at least 18″. The several bands of horizontal rods are erected so as to break joints. The vertical rods are ⅝″ in diameter and are spaced 18″ centers, or 86 in each bin. They are composed of sections not less than 6 feet long, connected by cast iron couplings, and the adjacent rods are arranged to break joints with each other. The lapped portions of the horizontal rods and the crossings of the horizontal and vertical rods are to be properly fastened together with No. 14 annealed wire, or with steel clips.

The forms are to be so constructed and manipulated that the walls of the bins shall be perpendicular, and free from ledges or pockets on which the grain can lodge. The concrete shall be deposited in a state sufficiently fluid to form walls that are smooth and free from voids. After the molds are removed all pits or voids are to be carefully pointed up with one to one Portland cement mortar. No plastering of any surface will be allowed. The bottoms of the bins are to be made of concrete of the same proportions as for the bin walls. The surface of the bottoms are to be given a trowel finish. The molds and the method of erection are shown in Fig. 200.

FIG. 200.   PROGRESS VIEW OF MISSOURI PACIFIC RY. CONCRETE GRAIN BINS, SHOWING FORMS FOR CONCRETE.

The roofs of the tank are to be made of 3″ book tile supported on steel purlins, covered with a tar and gravel roofing. The floor of the conveyor gallery is to be made of 3″ book tile, supported on a steel framework, and covered with a top dressing composed of one part Portland cement and two parts sand. Each cylindrical bin shall be provided with a bin ladder, and one fire escape shall be provided as shown.

The interspace bins are frequently used for grain storage. Where these bins are used they should be braced with rods and the intersections of the circular bins should be thickened and strengthened. Several failures due to faulty construction have occurred in concrete bins where the interspaces have been used for storage.

SPECIFICATIONS FOR TILE BINS.*—" The tank walls will be constructed of special semi-porous hollow tile made to conform to the circle of the tank. The main wall tile shall be 12" × 12" × 6", the channel tile 12" × 4" × 5", the outside facing tile made of similar material, but semi-glazed are 12" × 12" × 1¼". All the tile shall be well manufactured, hard burned and reasonably free from cracks and

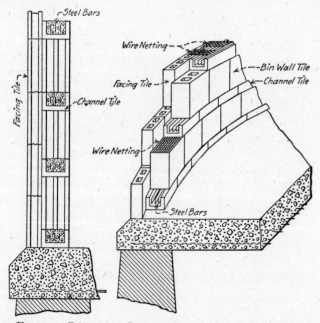

FIG. 201. DETAILS OF BARNETT-RECORD TILE GRAIN BIN.

defects. The wall tile shall be set in the wall with the cells running vertically and all set with full flush mortar joints sides and bottoms. The joints shall be thoroughly pointed on both sides of the wall and the top of each course of wall tile shall be covered with a metal wire fabric, about four meshes to the inch, so as to give a full mortar joint for the next course of channel tile. The channel tile shall be set to

* Prepared by the Barnett-Record Co.

break joints with the wall tile and, after a full course has been set, steel bands of the sizes shown on the drawings shall be placed in same and carefully spaced so as to be separate from each other and from the sides of the tile. Each course of channel tile shall contain at least two complete steel bands. When the bands have been properly placed in the channel tile the same shall be filled with thin Portland cement mortar, composed of one part sand and two parts Portland cement, and thoroughly worked around the bands to insure that all the bands are thoroughly coated and that all the crevices are filled. The facing tile are laid in courses with a full mortar bed and are tied to the main wall of tanks by wire fabric, similar to that used for the main wall tile."

The method of laying the tile and the general appearance of the bins is shown in Fig. 151 and Fig. 201.

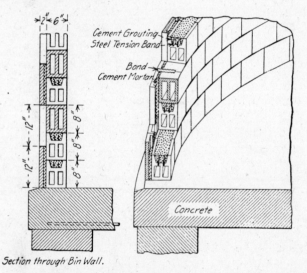

FIG. 202. DETAILS OF WITHERSPOON-ENGLAR TILE GRAIN BIN.

For a complete description of a tile storage elevator, see description of the Canadian Pacific grain elevator, Port Arthur, Ontario, in Chapter XIX.

The details of the Witherspoon-Englar tile bin are shown in Fig. 202. This system appears to be somewhat more simple than the system shown in Fig. 201.

BIN ROOFS. *Steel Bins.*—The most satisfactory roof for steel bins is a conical steel sheet roof supported on a radial framework.

25

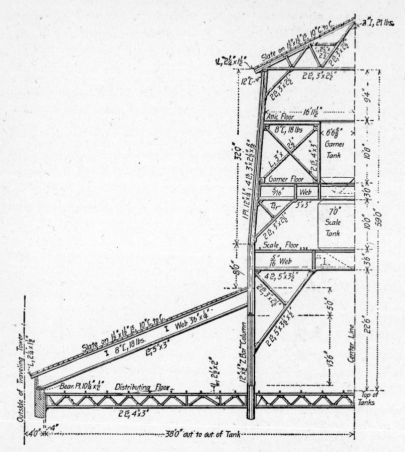

FIG. 203. STEEL ROOF FRAMING OF GREAT NORTHERN ELEVATOR, BUFFALO, N. Y.

For this roof No. 14 sheet steel is about the lightest metal that can be calked. The sheets should be cut radially and should be riveted with light rivets spaced $2\frac{1}{2}$ to 3 inches; the rivets are usually driven cold.

The roof sheets are sometimes detailed developed and the sheets are bent to shape. In this case the sheets are rectangular. It is very difficult to make a presentable job in this way. The radial framework for the steel bins of the Independent Elevator at Omaha, Neb., is shown in Fig. 212, the detail plans of the steel roof are shown in Fig. 213, and the details of a radial steel truss are shown in Fig. 214. Steel roofs sometimes sweat on the inside. This may be prevented by the use of an "anti-condensation" lining as described in "The Design of Steel Mill Buildings."

The steel framing and roof above the bins of the Great Northern elevator, Buffalo, N. Y., is shown in Fig. 203.

Tile Roofs.—The roofs of tile and concrete bins are usually made of book tile supported on sub-purlins carried on a radial framework, as shown in Fig. 212. The book tile are then covered with a composition tar and gravel roof covering.

See detailed descriptions of the tile roof of the reinforced concrete storage bins for the Missouri Pacific Ry., given on a preceding page. For additional details see Chapter XIX.

Cement Roofs.—A reinforced concrete roof supported by the radial framework is often used on concrete, tile or brick bins. The concrete is usually covered with a tar and gravel roof covering.

FOUNDATIONS.—Grain bins should be built on solid foundations, or on monolithic foundations if the soil is yielding. Bin failures have occurred in bins with inadequate foundations by the outside ring being forced down by the load of the grain on the bin walls, and the center being forced up by the upward pressure of the soil.

Bin bottoms are commonly made of concrete, reinforced or plain, carried on a sand or gravel filling placed inside the bin. The conveyor tunnels pass under the bins, the grain discharging from the bin through one or more spouts onto the conveyor belts. The bins should discharge from as near the center as practicable. Care should be used to waterproof the floor of the bins or the grain will absorb moisture and spoil. The floor should be drained with drain tile set just below the finish or a layer of asphalt or other waterproofing should be used in the concrete layer.

Small storage bins are sometimes made with flat bottoms, in which case part of the grain must be shoveled out. Plate bottoms are sometimes used for small bins, and the grain is sometimes discharged from the side. Eccentric discharge gates cause excessive lateral stresses when the bin is emptying (see Chapter XVII).

For details of bin foundations see Figs. 211, 228, 231, 232, 236, and 238.

CONVEYORS.—Grain is commonly moved in a horizontal direction in large elevators by means of belt conveyors, while in small elevators the screw conveyor is most in use for this purpose. Movement in a vertical direction is by belt or chain conveyors in closed boxes called elevator legs. For details of conveyors see Chapter XIV.

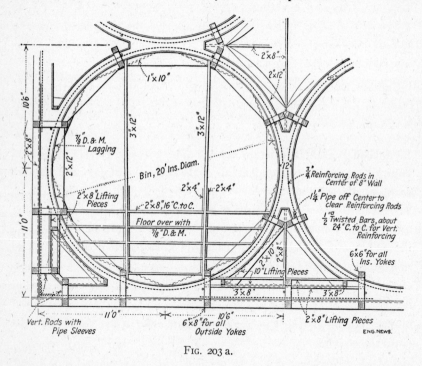

FIG. 203 a.

CONSTRUCTION OF BINS.—The cost of reinforced concrete structures depends very much upon the cost of the forms. In massive concrete work which can be constructed in sections the cost of the forms comprises but a small part of the entire cost of the work, but in reinforced concrete bin and grain elevator construction, where the walls are thin and are heavily reinforced and where the entire structure must be carried up as a unit, the cost of stationary forms becomes very high. In Germany it is the general practice to wire every piece of reinforcing steel in place and to use stationary forms, thus making a high cost per cubic yard for thin reinforced concrete walls. In the United States bins and grain elevators are now commonly constructed by means of moving forms.

Moving Forms.—The forms and the jack used by the MacDonald Engineering Company are shown in Fig. 203a and Fig. 203b. The vertical forms were made of 2½-in. long leaf yellow pine staves 48 inches long, and were fastened together by means of the jacks as shown in Fig. 203b. The forms carry joists that support a floor upon which the men may work in placing the steel and the concrete. In Fig. 203b the posts B and B are of long leaf yellow pine $6'' \times 8'' \times 8'$ 0″ long and hold the forms together and are so placed that the forms may be moved up without deforming the walls. The rod G is supported on 2-in. gas pipes, 4 ft. long, placed in the walls, the successive sections being added as the forms are raised. The forms are raised by means of the jacks, made as shown in Fig. 203a. The jacks can lift the forms about ¾ inch at a stroke. The forms are jacked up from 6 in. to 12 in. at one filling, depending upon the spacing of the reinforcing steel. The horizontal steel is placed in position during the filling while the vertical steel is wired in position. The concrete is elevated to the platform and is carried to the place of deposit in carts. With four foot forms in fair weather from 4 to 6 feet of wall may be placed in 24 hours. With the jack shown in Fig. 203b the gas pipes are sometimes thrown out of line, thus causing cracks or blow-outs. To obviate this difficulty a solid rod is now used as a jacking rod, the rod being used in sections 10 to 12 feet long. The ends of the rods are held in line by means of dowels, while the jack grips the rod and no rod G is used.

Another type of jack, used by the Canadian Stewart Co., is shown in Fig. 203c. The yoke is made of steel channels, while the forms are raised by jacking against reinforcing rods. The forms are made of staves 2 inches wide and 4 feet long. The jack is less liable to cause

break-outs in the wall, but takes more time in jacking up. An additional description of this jack is given in the description of the "Re-

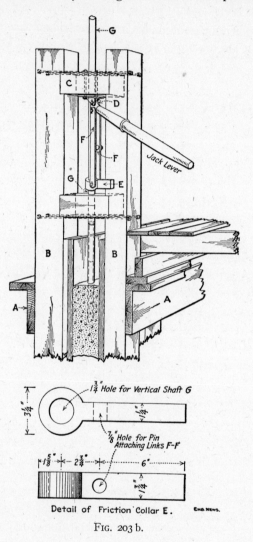

Detail of Friction Collar E.   ENG.NEWS.

FIG. 203 b.

inforced Concrete Grain Elevator, Fort William, Canada," in Chapter
XIX.

Additional details of forms are shown in Fig. 233 and Fig. 234.

The staves of which the forms are made should be not to exceed 2½ inches in width and should have a saw-kerf down the middle, leaving only ⅛ to 3/16 inch of wood which will be crushed when swelling takes place. The staves are commonly tongued and grooved and should be placed as far apart in the beginning as can be and still have the forms tight.

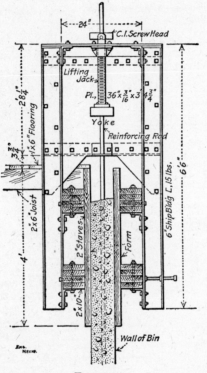

FIG. 203 C.

To prevent excessive swelling the staves should be boiled in paraffine before being used. Even with extreme care the forms of large bins are almost certain to swell so that one or more staves must be removed during the course of the work. Sheet metal lining may be used; however, it is very liable to stick to the concrete so that it is of doubtful utility.

Bin Forms for Fisher Flouring Mills.—The moving forms for the

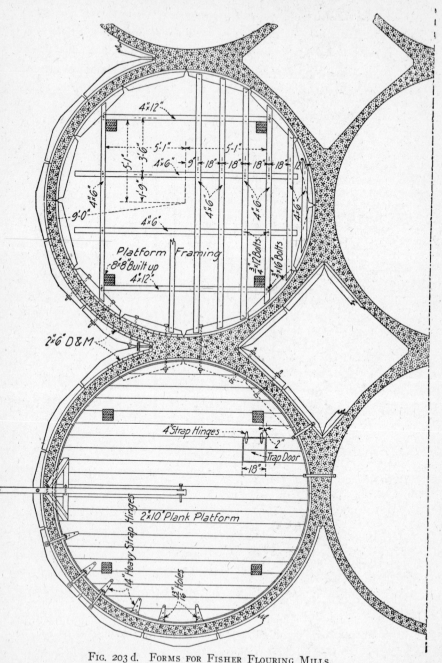

Fig. 203 d. Forms for Fisher Flouring Mills.

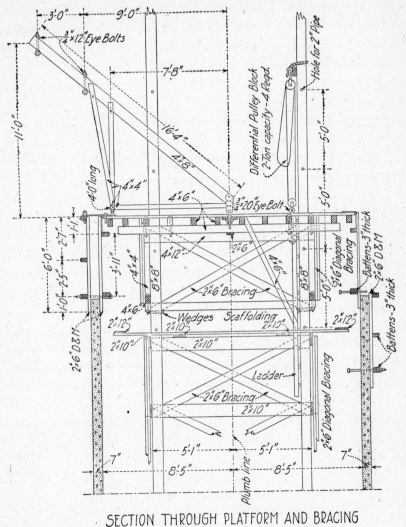

SECTION THROUGH PLATFORM AND BRACING

FIG. 203 e. FORMS FOR FISHER FLOURING MILLS.

Fisher Flouring Mills, Seattle, Wash., designed by the Stone & Webster Engineering Corporation are shown in Fig. 203 d and Fig. 203 e. The reinforced concrete storage consisted of 21 circular bins 18 ft. diameter and 12 interspace bins, all bins 82 ft. 2 in. high.

The bin wall forms were made of $2'' \times 6''$ pine, dressed and matched, by 6 ft. long. The platform framing carrying the $2'' \times 6''$ plank platform was carried on a 4-post tower with $8'' \times 8''$ built-up posts, and which passed through the platform floor. The wall forms were fastened to the plank platform with $14''$ heavy strap hinges so that they were raised up with the platform. When the concrete was sufficiently set the bolts passing through the forms and the wall were removed, and the platform and wall forms for a bin were raised 5 ft. by means of four 2-ton differential pulley blocks. The wall forms were then bolted together and the platform was blocked up. After the circular bin forms were raised the interspace forms were raised with the differential pulley blocks. The details of the forms and the towers are clearly shown in Figs. 203 d and 203 e.

For additional details of construction see the descriptions of the F. C. Ayres Mercantile Elevator and the Grand Trunk Pacific Elevator in Chapter XIX.

The author has used moving forms for walls and columns. The method is quite satisfactory where the columns are heavy and the stories high. With light columns and walls and heavy forms there is danger of shattering the concrete and stationary forms are more satisfactory. When the moving forms have reached a floor it is necessary to block up the platform and build stationary forms for the girders, beams and columns, the only part of the moving form that can be used above the floor being the outside forms. Moving forms are economical only for bin walls.

CHAPTER XIX.

Introduction.—In this chapter complete descriptions are given of the Independent Steel Elevator, Omaha, Neb.; the Great Northern Ry. steel elevator, West Superior, Wis.; the Santa Fe Ry. concrete elevator, Chicago, Ill.; the Canadian Pacific Ry. Co.'s concrete grain elevator, Port Arthur, Ontario; and the Canadian Northern Ry. Co.'s tile grain bins, Port Arthur, Ontario.

The author is under obligations to the Minneapolis Steel & Machinery Co., Minneapolis, Minn., for plans and specifications for the Independent Steel Elevator; also to the John S. Metcalf Co., Chicago, for plans and specifications of the Santa Fe Ry. elevator.

THE INDEPENDENT STEEL ELEVATOR, OMAHA, NEB.

General Description.—This elevator consists of a steel working house having a bin capacity of 240,000 bushels and 8 steel storage bins having a storage capacity of 100,000 bushels each, making a total storage capacity of 1,040,000 bushels. A view of the completed structure is shown in Fig. 204, and a progress view is shown in Fig. 205.

The steel working house is 64′ 0″ × 70′ 0″, with 14′ 0″ sheds on two ends and one side, as shown in Fig. 206. The sub-story of the building is 26′ 0″. The bins are 65′ 4″ high, as shown in Fig. 209, and are supported on steel columns, as shown in Fig. 207 and Fig. 208. The spouting story is 24′ 6″ high; the garner and scale story is 26′ 6″ high; and the machinery story is 13′ 8″ high. The walls below and above the bins are covered with No. 24 corrugated steel laid with 1½ corrugations side lap and 3 inches end lap. The roof is covered with No. 22 corrugated steel laid directly on the steel purlins with 2 corrugations side lap and 6 inches end lap.

On the first or working floor the floor between the tracks is made

FIG. 204. THE INDEPENDENT ELEVATOR, OMAHA, NEB. 1,040,000 BUSHELS.
CAPACITY.

FIG. 205. THE INDEPENDENT ELEVATOR UNDER CONSTRUCTION.

of $\frac{1}{4}$ inch plate bolted to the beams, while the remainder of this floor is made of concrete filled in above concrete arches which rest on the flanges of the beams with a finish $1\frac{1}{4}''$ thick of Portland cement mortar consisting of one part cement to one part clean, sharp sand. The concrete is composed of one part Portland cement, two parts sand, and five parts crushed stone.

The floor of the cupola throughout the different floors and in the gallery leading over the bins is made of No. 24 corrugated steel rest-

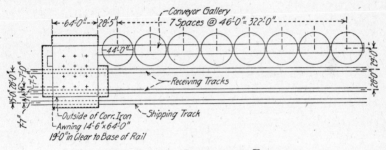

FIG. 206. PLAN OF INDEPENDENT ELEVATOR.

ing on steel framework, and covered with 3 inches of concrete and a one-inch finish of one to one Portland cement mortar troweled smooth. All doors are of the rolling steel type. The window frames were made of $2'' \times 6''$ timbers and are covered with No. 26 sheet steel. All windows are provided with $1\frac{1}{4}''$ checked rail sash and are glazed with double strength glass.

Painting.—All steel work of every description was painted with one coat oxide of iron paint at the shop and a second coat after erection. The tank plates and corrugated steel were painted on the exterior surface only after erection.

Bins.—The eight steel storage bins are 44' 0'' in diameter and 80' 0'' high, have a capacity of 100,000 bushels and rest on separate concrete foundations. The bins are constructed of steel plates stiffened with Z-bars, as shown in Fig. 210. The bins are covered with a steel plate roof, Fig. 213, supported on roof trusses, as shown in Fig. 212 and Fig. 214. A conveyor gallery 10' 0'' wide and 8' 0'' high

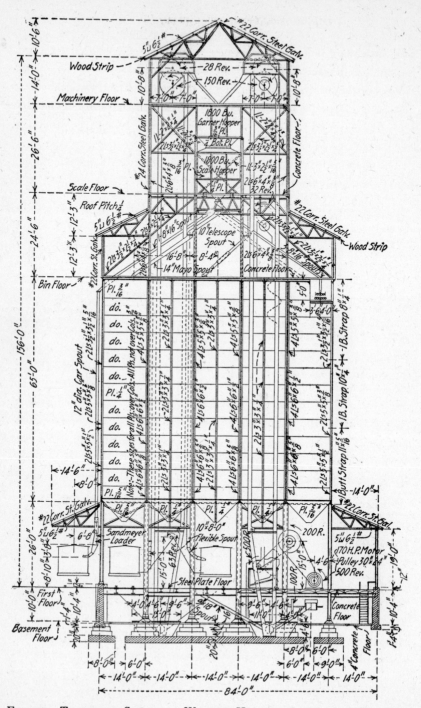

FIG. 207. TRANSVERSE SECTION OF WORKING HOUSE OF INDEPENDENT ELEVATOR.

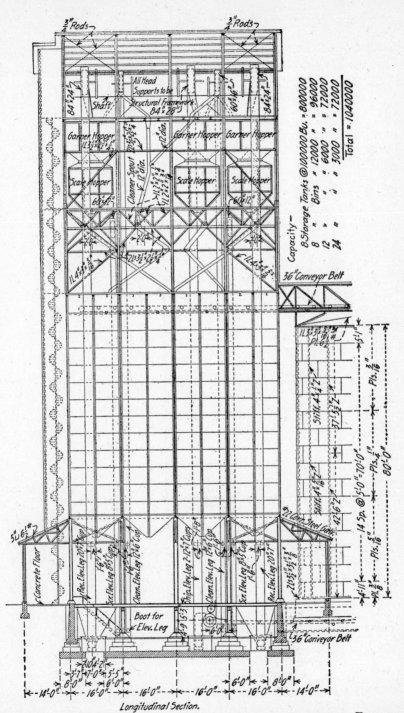

FIG. 208. LONGITUDINAL SECTION OF WORKING HOUSE OF INDEPENDENT ELEVATOR.

extends from the working house over the bins. A conveyor tunnel extends from the working house under the bins. The rivet spacing in the circular bins is shown in Fig. 211.

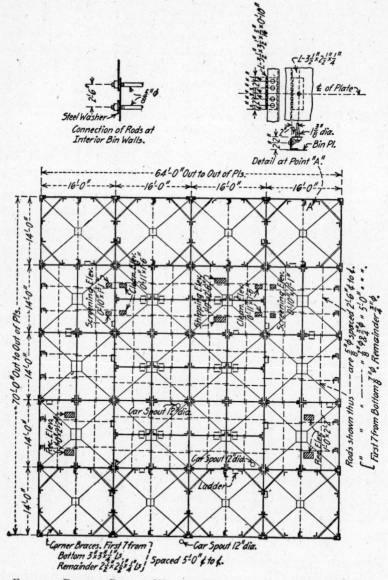

FIG. 209. PLAN OF BINS IN WORKING HOUSE OF INDEPENDENT ELEVATOR.

The bins in the working house are arranged as shown in Fig. 209, and are constructed of plates, as shown in Fig. 207 and Fig. 208. The bins, 14′ 0″ × 16′ 0″, are braced in the corners with angle braces spaced 5′ 0″ centers vertically, and of the sizes shown in Fig. 209. The large bins are also braced with ⅞ and ¾-inch round rods spaced 5′ 0″ apart as shown. All the smaller bins are braced with ⅝-inch round rods spaced 2′ 6″ apart as shown. Vertical angles in the sides of the bins are provided, as shown in Fig. 207, Fig. 208, and Fig. 209.

EQUIPMENT.—There are two stands of receiving elevators with receiving pits on either side. These elevators have 22-inch 6-ply belts and 20″ × 7″ × 7″ buckets spaced 14 inches apart; the receiving pits are covered with steel grating, and a pair of Clark's automatic grain shovels are located at each unloading place. These elevators are driven with an electric motor of 100 H. P., each elevator being driven with a clutch and pinion so that the elevator may be stopped and started at will.

There is one stand of shipping elevators constructed in the same manner, having a 26-inch 6-ply belt and 2 lines of 12″ × 7″ × 7″ buckets spaced 14 inches apart.

There are two stands of cleaning elevators with 14-inch 6-ply belts with 12″ × 6″ × 6″ buckets spaced 12 inches apart.

There are also two screenings elevators with 9-in 5-ply belts with 8″ × 5″ × 5″ buckets spaced 12 inches apart.

The shipping, screenings, and cleaner elevators are driven from a line shaft which is driven by a 100 H. P. motor, each elevator being driven by a core wheel and pinion.

Three scale hoppers, having a capacity of 1,800 bushels, are located in the cupola, and three garner hoppers of 1,800 bushels capacity are located above the scale hoppers.

The main line shaft on the first floor is driven by a 170 H. P. motor. A car puller capable of moving 25 loaded cars is provided.

Elevators.—The boots of the receiving and shipping elevators rest in water-tight steel boot tanks made of $\frac{5}{16}$-inch steel plates. The ele-

26

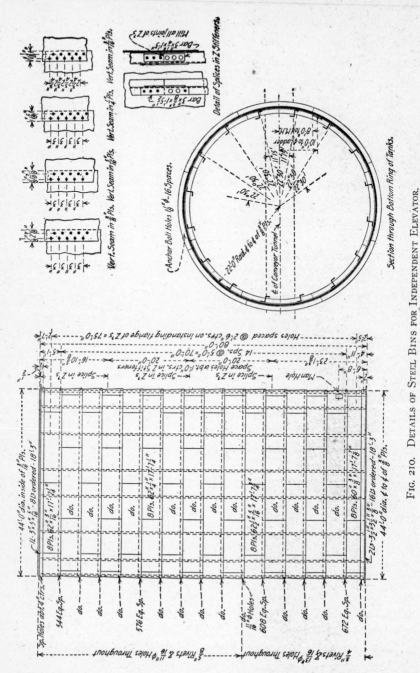

FIG. 210.   DETAILS OF STEEL BINS FOR INDEPENDENT ELEVATOR.

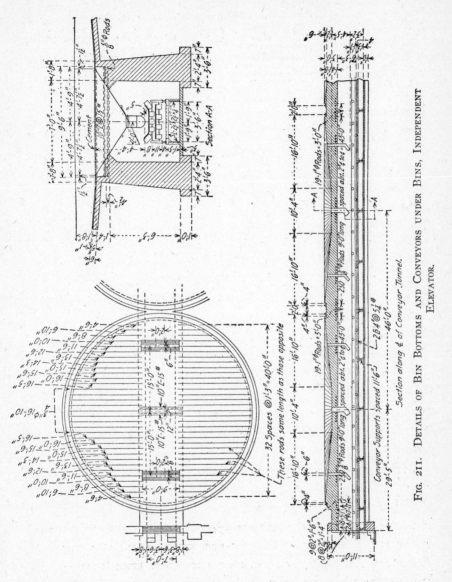

vator boots are made of $\frac{3}{16}$-inch steel plates, the boot pulleys having a vertical adjustment of 8 inches. The elevator cases are made of No. 12 steel up to the bins, and of $\frac{3}{16}$-inch plates in the bins, and No. 14 steel above the bins. The cases are strengthened by angles at the corners. The elevator heads are made of No. 14 steel. At each receiving elevator is a large elevator pit extending from the leg back to the center of the track. This pit is constructed of beams and $\frac{3}{16}$-inch plates and is covered with a grating of $1\frac{3}{4} \times \frac{1}{4}$-inch bars spaced $1\frac{1}{4}$ inches apart.

The elevator buckets are " Buffalo " buckets; those for the receiving elevators are $20'' \times 7'' \times 7''$; for the shipping elevators two lines of $12'' \times 7'' \times 7''$ buckets; for the cleaning elevators one line of $12'' \times 6'' \times 6''$ buckets; and for the screenings elevator one line of $8'' \times 5'' \times 5''$ buckets. The buckets in the receiving, shipping and cleaning elevators are spaced $14''$ apart, while those in the screenings elevator are spaced $12''$ apart.

The elevator belts in the receiving elevators are 22 inches wide and 6-ply, the shipping belts are 26 inches wide and 6-ply; the cleaning belts are 14 inches wide and 6-ply, and the screenings belts are 9 inches wide and 5-ply. The belting is made of 32 ounce duck and is first-class.

Spouts.—The building is provided with a complete system of spouts. The general distributing spouts from the scales to the shipping spouts are double-jointed Mayo spouts. There are three shipping spouts which are provided with telescoping bottom sections. All bin bottoms are provided with a revolving spout with a cut-off gate operated with a rack and pinion, with cords leading to within reaching distance of the floor.

Conveyors.—The conveyor belt leading from the working house over the bins is a $36''$ 4-ply conveyor belt, is carried on disc rolls consisting of 3 straight-faced 6-inch pulleys and 2 special discs; the discs run loose on the shafts, which are $1\frac{3}{16}$-inch diameter and are spaced 5 ft. centers. The return rolls are 5-inch straight-faced rolls spaced 15 ft. centers. At each point in the elevator where grain is loaded onto the belt there are two pairs of special concentrating rolls. Movable trippers provided with spouts are provided, so that grain may be discharged on either side of the belt. The entire conveyor is carried on a steel framework. The conveyor belt is driven by a 40 H. P. motor.

The conveyor in the tunnel leading from the storage tanks to the working house is of the same type as the conveyor above the bins, and is supported on a steel framework, except that the top or carrying rolls are all of the concentrating types, as shown in Fig. 211. The concen-

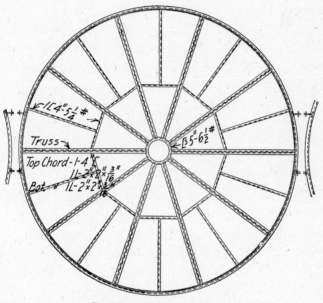

Roof Framing Plan for Tanks.

FIG. 212. FRAMING FOR ROOF OF CIRCULAR BINS, INDEPENDENT ELEVATOR.

trating rollers are composed of two straight-faced rolls from the main shaft, and two concentrating rolls meeting at an angle of 45° to the straight rolls. The lower conveyor is driven by a rope drive from the main line shaft in the working house.

Scale Hoppers.—There are three scale hoppers of 1,800 bushels capacity, each mounted on a Fairbanks-Morse and Company's scales, having a capacity of 84,000 lbs., and have steel frames. The hoppers have $\frac{3}{16}$-inch steel plate sides, and $\frac{1}{4}$-inch plate bottoms, stiffened with angle irons, and are tied together with tie rods. Each hopper is provided with a 22-inch cast iron outlet with a steel plate cut-off gate.

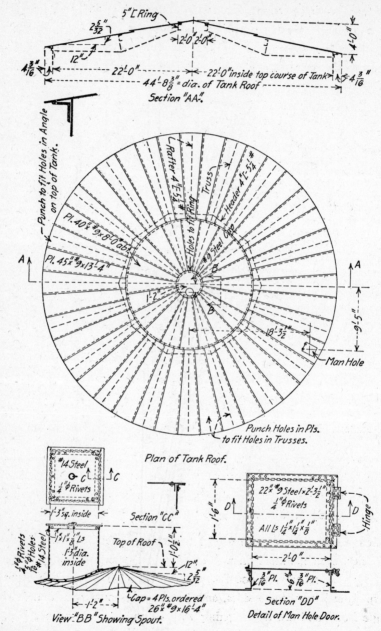

FIG. 213. DETAILS OF STEEL ROOF FOR STEEL BINS FOR INDEPENDENT ELEVATOR.

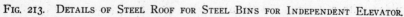

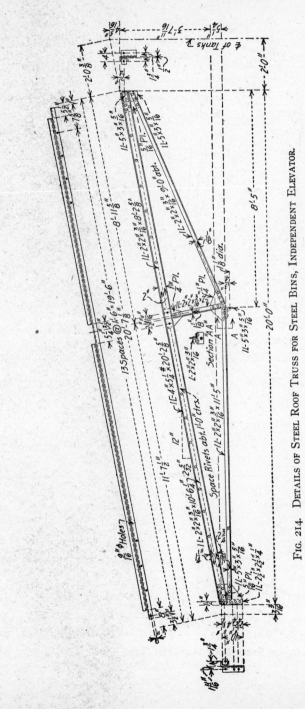

FIG. 214. DETAILS OF STEEL ROOF TRUSS FOR STEEL BINS, INDEPENDENT ELEVATOR.

Garners.—A steel garner hopper is placed directly over each scale hopper. The garners have a capacity of 1,800 bushels, and are constructed with $\frac{3}{16}$-inch side plates and $\frac{1}{4}$-inch bottom plates. The bottoms of the garners are hoppered to four openings, which are provided with gates sliding on steel rollers.

Cleaning Machines.—A large size cleaning machine and a large size oat clipper are provided. These machines are connected with a large dust collector which discharges the dust from the cleaning machines and from the sweepings outside of the building.

Car Puller.—A car puller having a capacity of 25 loaded cars is provided. The car puller has two drums, each provided with 400 feet of $\frac{5}{8}$-inch crucible steel cable.

Shovels.—A pair of Clark automatic grain shovels, with all necessary counterweights, sheaves, scoops, etc., are provided.

The total weight of steel in the elevator is 1,700 tons; approximately 900 tons in the working house, and 800 tons in the circular bins and conveyors.

The total cost was $205,000, of which the 8 steel bins and conveyors cost $80,000.

General Description.—The elevator is rectangular in form, 364' 6" long by 124' 6" wide and 246' 0" high, and has a storage capacity of 3,100,000 bushels (see Fig. 215). The rectangular "house" is surmounted by a longitudinal superstructure or cupola. The house contains a basement floor and a main floor, and above the main floor is filled with storage bins. The cupola contains the bin floor, a spout floor, a scale floor, and a machinery floor. On the receiving side of the elevator there rise 9 towers which are continuations of the receiving legs. On the opposite sides are 9 shipping legs, and between the two rows of receiving and shipping legs there are 9 cleaning legs. The towers and the exterior walls and the floors of the house and cupola are of steel frame construction, and are covered with steel roof trusses.

Foundations.—The elevator structure rests on a pile and concrete foundation. The piles were sunk by a water jet and a 4,200-lb. hammer, through a mixture of sand and clay, to a depth of from 25 to 45 feet, where hardpan was struck. The lower timbers of the grillage are 8" × 12" white pine timbers spaced 2' 6" center to center, while the upper layer are of 6" × 6" timbers spaced close together. On top of the grillage were built the concrete pedestals to carry the columns. The concrete was made of 1 part Portland cement, 2½ parts clean, sharp sand, and 5 parts Kettle River sandstone. The maximum allowable pressure on the concrete was 500 lbs. per sq. in., and the maximum load on a pile was 22 tons.

Steel Framework.—The rectangular bins are carried on girders, which are in turn carried by 280 Z-bar columns about 42 feet long, arranged as shown in Fig. 217. The Z-bar columns rest on cast bases which are anchored to the concrete pedestals. Details of the columns are shown in Fig. 218. The bin corners are directly above the columns and carry the columnar structure to the level of the bin floor where the columns supporting the upper part of the house begin, as shown

*Engineering News, Sept. 26, 1901.

FIG. 215. GENERAL VIEW OF 3,100,000 BUSHEL GRAIN ELEVATOR FOR GREAT
NORTHERN RY., AT WEST SUPERIOR, WIS.

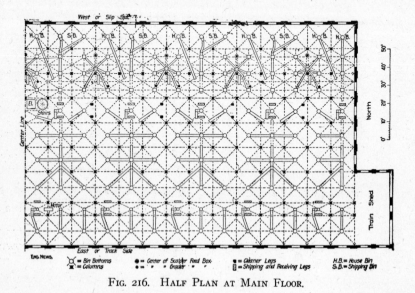

FIG. 216. HALF PLAN AT MAIN FLOOR.

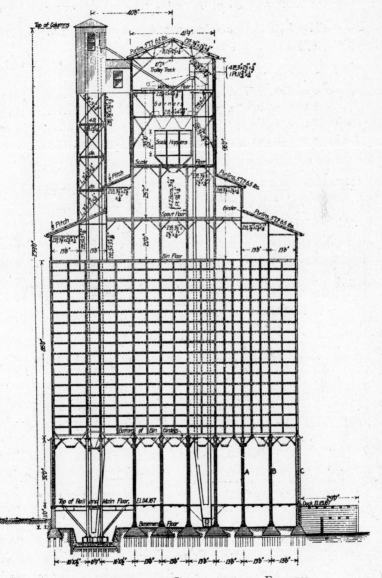

FIG. 217. TRANSVERSE SECTION THROUGH ELEVATOR.

in Fig. 217. To the height of the bottoms of the bins the exterior walls are of brick, and above this level they are of corrugated iron.

Bins.—The building contains 505 rectangular bins 85 feet high, divided as follows:

		Bushels.
8 shipping bins, 13′ 6″ x 27′ 0″		24,900
91 standard bins, 13′ 6″ x 13′ 6″		12,800
54 large bins, 16′ 10½″ x 13′ 6″		15,600
28 small bins, 6′ 9″ x 13′ 6″		6,300
324 house and cleaner pocket bins, 6′ 9″ x 4′ 6″		2,100

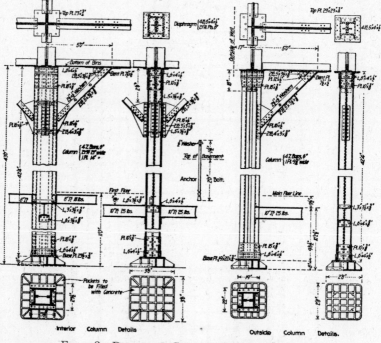

FIG. 218. DETAILS OF COLUMNS SUPPORTING BINS.

The bins are constructed of plates and angles, there being 17 courses of plates 5′ 0″ wide. Starting from the bottom the thickness of plates are 2 courses $\frac{5}{16}$″, 4 courses ¼″, and the remaining 11 courses are $\frac{3}{16}$″ thick. The horizontal seams of the bin plates are spliced together with splice plates or butt straps. On every second seam, or at intervals of

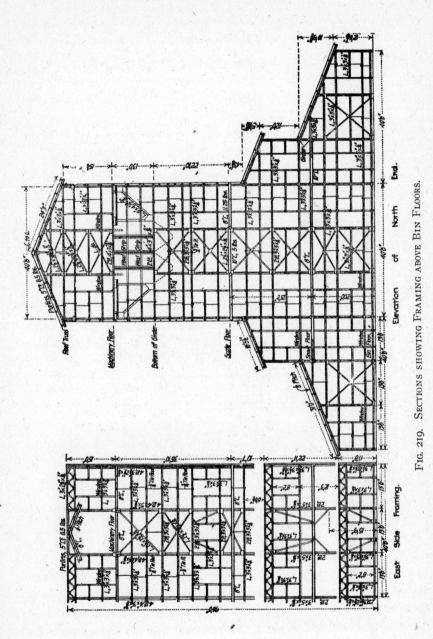

FIG. 219. SECTIONS SHOWING FRAMING ABOVE BIN FLOORS.

10 feet the lower end of these butt straps is bent out toward the center lines of the bin. This construction was adopted for the purpose of arching the grain so that the pressure would be transferred directly to the corners of the bin, thus relieving the pressure on the bin bottom.

The details of the bottom portion of one of the 13′ 6″ × 13′ 6″ bins are shown in Fig. 221. The column and bin construction are shown in Fig. 220. The arrangement of the bins is shown in Fig. 216. Above the bins are four floors and below them two floors, as shown in Fig. 217.

FIG. 220. INTERIOR VIEW ON MAIN FLOOR SHOWING COLUMN AND BIN CONSTRUCTION.

Basement Floor.—On the basement floor are the nine receiving hopper pits, into which grain is discharged from the cars. These pits are concrete lined and into them extend the hopper-shaped boot legs of steel plates. The receiving elevator legs extend up through the bins and are then continued in steel frame towers to the level of the top floor of the cupola. The cleaning leg hoppers do not project below the floor line and the cleaner legs also reach from the basement to the top floor of the cupola, but do not require separate towers.

Main Floor.—The main floor is 11 feet above the basement floor, and is constructed of concrete over brick arches carried by I-beams. This floor contains the dust collecting machinery, car shovels, unloading trucks, etc. A representative section is shown in Fig. 217. Loaded cars are run into the house and to the transfer table located 600 feet from the house by a car haul. There are 18 receiving hoppers 12' 0" × 35' 0", two being provided for each receiving leg. To unload there are 18 movable power shovels. Details of these power shovels are shown in Fig. 224.

The dust collection system is unusually elaborate and gathers dust from all floors and delivers it into the furnaces in the boiler rooms.

Cupola Floors.—The cupola floors contain four floors, as shown in Fig. 219: (1) The bin floor.   (2) The spout and conveyor floor with two 40-in. conveyor belts.   (3) The scale floor, containing 18 scale

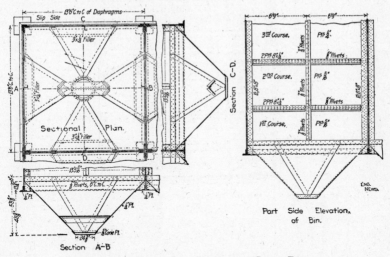

FIG. 221. DETAILS OF BOTTOM OF STEEL BIN.

hoppers having a capacity of 1,000 bushels each, and 18 Fairbank's scales with a capacity of 120,000 lbs. each. Above the scale hoppers are 18 scale garners and 9 cleaner garners. The capacity of the garners is 25 per cent larger than the capacity of the scale hoppers. (4) The machinery floor, which contains all the motors which drive

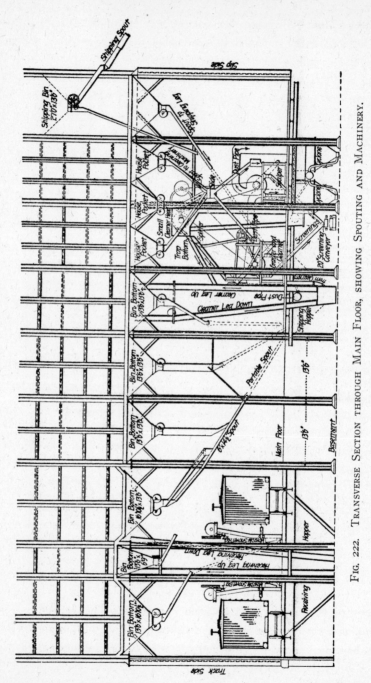

FIG. 222. TRANSVERSE SECTION THROUGH MAIN FLOOR, SHOWING SPOUTING AND MACHINERY.

the 9 receiving, 9 shipping and 9 cleaner legs. The capacity of the
receiving and shipping legs is 12,000 bushels per leg per hour, and the

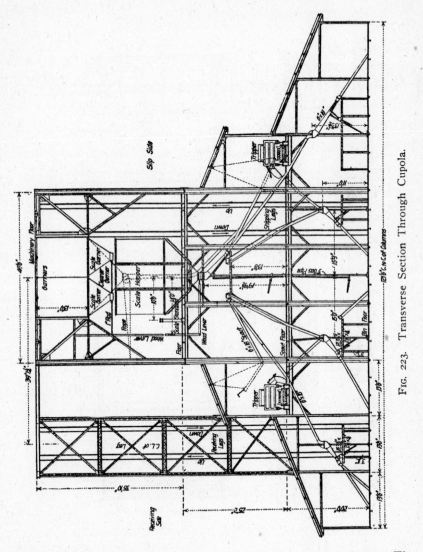

FIG. 223. Transverse Section Through Cupola.

capacity of the cleaner legs is 3,000 bushels per leg per hour. The
screenings from the machines are discharged on a 20-in. conveyor belt
in the basement, which empties into the boot of the cleaner leg.

27

Operation.—When wheat is brought into the elevator in cars, of which nine can be pulled in by a grip cable at one time, it is pushed by the automatic shovels out of the car onto a grating over one of

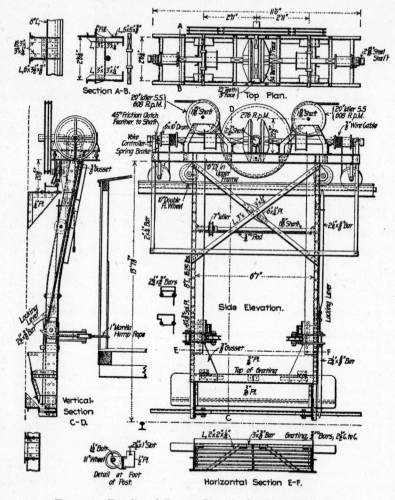

FIG. 224. Details of Power Shovels for Unloading Cars.

the nine receiving hoppers. Running to the bottom of these are endless belts carrying small buckets which scoop up the grain and hoist it to the very top of the house, the upper part of each belt running in one of the nine steel towers. Dumped from the belt the grain is shot into a spout and directed across the top of the building to the garners, from which it falls into the scales. It then drops through a swinging turn-head into any one of numerous spouts and is conducted perhaps to a belt conveyor by which it can be handled longitudinally of the building, perhaps by way of another series of turn-heads and spouts to its bin. If it is to be cleaned it falls through the cleaner bin to one of the cleaning machines and passes over the sieves on the main floor, whence it returns again to the top of the house and down into a bin. If it is to be shipped it is sent a second time to the scales and thence to the shipping bins, which have a capacity sufficient to load a ship of 160,000 bushels at one draft. All screenings from the cleaner are directed to a belt in the basement and then collected. The dust is gathered and conveyed to furnaces in the boiler house.

Materials and Quantities.—The following is a summary of materials used in the construction of the elevator:

Foundation and Walls in Main Story:

Number of piles driven	4,570
Timber and sheet piling, ft. B. M.	380,000
Excavation, cu. yds.	23,000
Masonry, cu. yds.	1,500
Concrete, cu. yds.	3,000
Cut stone, cu. ft.	1,300
Brick work, cu. ft.	45,000

Superstructure:

Structure below bins, consisting of columns, knee braces, car and shipping hoppers, grillage beams and girders, etc., tons	1,850
Bins proper, consisting of bin plates, corner angles, tie bars, bin bottoms, etc., tons	6,500
Cupola material, tons	1,450
Legs and spouts below bin floor, tons	450
Legs and spouts above bins manufactured at elevator site, tons	350
Total tons	10,600

Total length of legs and spouts (nearly) 8 miles.

Total number of field rivets.................................. 2,000,000

Machinery:

1 20" screening conveyor, in basement.

2 40" conveyors, on spout floor.

24 cleaners, on main floor.

12 flax machines, on main floor.

18 movable power shovels, on main floor.

9 receiving legs.

9 shipping legs.

9 cleaner legs.

16 marine loading spouts.

18 120,000-lb. scales.

42 3-phase 60 cycle, 440 volt electric motors, total 2,122 H. P. Lighting:

1,000 16-candle-power incandescent lamps.

Cost.—The following unit costs were furnished the author by Max Toltz, mechanical engineer, Great Northern Ry., who had charge of the design and erection of the elevator:

Piles cost 10 cents per lineal foot.

Driving 40-ft. piles, $1.00 each.

Concrete cost $6.25 per cu. yd.

Structural steel work cost $50.00 per ton f. o. b. Pittsburg, Pa.

Erection of structural steel work, including the driving of all rivets, $13.25 per ton.

The total cost of the elevator was 39.65 cents per bushel of storage.

The costs, especially the cost of structural steel and erection, are very low.

The work was begun May 1, 1899; the erection of steel January 1, 1900; the first car of grain was received on February 26, 1901.

Note.—A reinforced concrete annex with a capacity of 2,400,000 bushels was built in 1908–1909. A description of this annex is given in the latter part of this chapter.

GRAIN ELEVATOR, SANTA FE SYSTEM, CHICAGO.

General Description.—The elevator comprises a frame working house of 400,000 bushels capacity, with car shed, marine tower, 35 reinforced concrete storage bins, having a total capacity of 1,000,000 bushels, a drying and bleaching equipment, and a 1,500 H. P. power plant. A general view of the elevator is shown in Fig. 225, and a plan is given in Fig. 226. This elevator was designed by the John S. Metcalf Co., Chicago.

Working House.—The working house is 225 feet long and 56 feet wide, and is of timber cribbed construction, covered on the outside up to the top of the bins with brick, and above that point with corrugated steel. There are 5 receiving and 5 shipping legs, having a capacity of 15,000 bushels per hour each, making it possible to receive and ship 75,000 bushels per hour. In addition to these there are 15 smaller legs for serving the five clippers, five cleaners, one screener, and the drying and bleaching plants; also one leg for the disposal of screenings from the machines.

In the cupola are 10 scale hoppers, each of 1,600 bushels capacity. In addition to the above are a dust collecting system, a large car pulley, a longitudinal conveyor in the cupola for conveying grain lengthwise of the house, a passenger elevator, etc. There is a marine tower with a capacity of 6,000 bushels per hour; also eight vessel loading spouts. The arrangement of the bins and the elevating machinery is shown in Fig. 227. The working house bins are made of timber, with steel hopper bottoms and gates. Elevator legs and heads throughout are of steel, and most of the spouts are of steel.

Loading and Unloading.—A steel shed extends over four tracks, as shown in Fig. 227. On each track are five unloading places spaced 45-foot centers, in order to accommodate the longest cars. Beneath each unloading place is a steel track hopper with a capacity of a full car load. Each hopper discharges through four openings to a 15,000 bushel conveyor running below a line of four hoppers, across the basement under the track shed to one of the receiving legs. It is so arranged that but one of the four hoppers can be discharged into the

FIG. 225. GRAIN ELEVATOR FOR SANTA FE RY., CHICAGO, ILL.

conveyor at one time. Ten car loading spouts are arranged to load cars at five places on two tracks. The design of the working house is unusual in having the cars unload in an unloading shed.

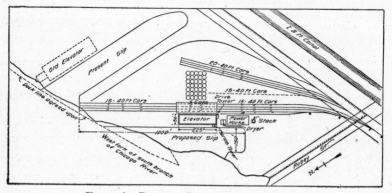

FIG. 226. PLAN OF ELEVATOR AND TRACKS.

Concrete Bins.—The reinforced concrete storage bins are 35 in number, and are 23 feet inside diameter and 80 feet high. In addition to this there are 24 interspace bins. The detail plans for the bins are given in Fig. 228. The conveyors have a capacity of 15,000 bushels per hour for filling and emptying the tanks. The detailed specifications follow:

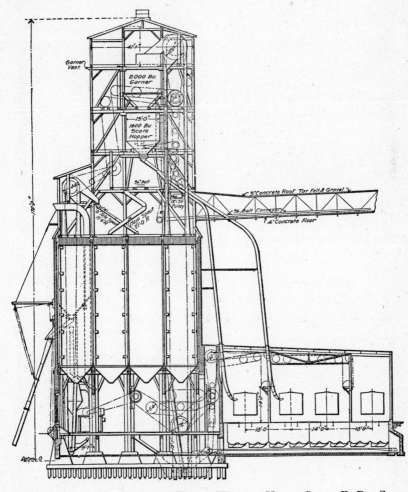

FIG. 227. TRANSVERSE SECTION OF TIMBER WORKING HOUSE, SANTA FE RY. GRAIN ELEVATOR.

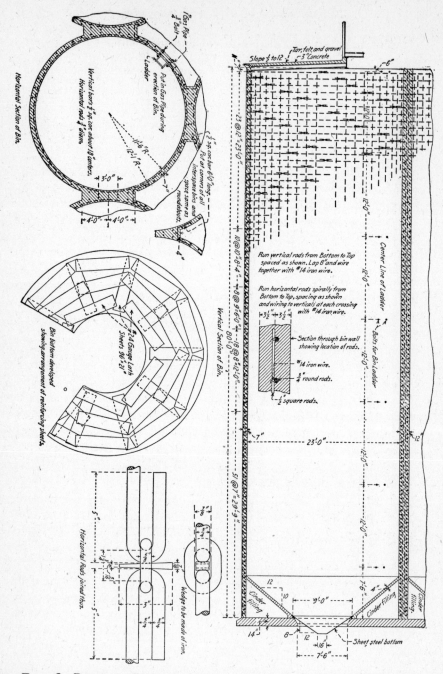

FIG. 228. DETAILS OF REINFORCED CONCRETE GRAIN BINS, SANTA FE RY. GRAIN ELEVATOR.

Detailed Specifications for Concrete Storage Bins.*

CONCRETE BINS.—Thirty-five cylindrical concrete bins, 23′ 0″ in diameter inside, shall be built as shown on the drawings. The interspaces between these bins shall also be used for the storage of grain. The walls shall be of concrete of the ingredients hereinafter specified.

Concrete.—Concrete shall be composed of the broken stone or gravel, sand and cement hereinafter specified. A batch mixing machine approved by the chief engineer may be used. The ingredients shall be placed in the machine in the volumes specified, and sufficient water added to form a mixture fluid enough to give clean, smooth surfaces when deposited in the forms. The mixing shall be continued until the mass is uniform; it shall be done as rapidly as possible and the batch deposited in the work without delay. If the mixing is done by hand, it shall be performed in a manner satisfactory to the chief engineer.

The concrete in the bin walls and in the hopper bottoms shall be mixed in the following proportions: One measure of Portland cement, not more than 2½ measures of sand, and not more than four measures of broken stone; and the proportions of sand and stone shall be reduced if necessary, so that in all cases the sand will thoroughly fill the voids in the stone and the cement will thoroughly fill the voids in the sand. Cement shall be measured in the original packages. The sand and broken stone must be actually measured in bulk. No counting of shovelsful or other approximations will be allowed.

All concrete shall be mixed in small and convenient quantities and immediately deposited in the work. It must be carefully placed, and not dropped from sufficient height to separate the mortar from the broken stone. It shall be laid in sections and in horizontal layers. It shall be deposited in a state sufficiently fluid to form walls which are smooth and free from voids.

In no case shall concrete be permitted to remain in the work if it has begun to set before the ramming is completed. Layers of concrete must not be tapered off in wedged-shaped solids, but must be built with square ends. The concrete must be so thoroughly compact that

* These specifications were prepared by the John S. Metcalf Co., Chicago, Ill., who has kindly granted permission to have them published.

there shall be no pores or open spaces between the stone of which it consists that are not thoroughly filled with mortar.

The walls during the progress of the work shall be kept as near a uniform height as possible. Before depositing any concrete after work has been discontinued for over one hour, the forms shall be cleaned of any concrete adhering to them, and all fins or broken pieces on the top of the wall removed; and the forms and upper surface of the concrete shall be thoroughly wetted. On all exposed surfaces of concrete, a wedge-shaped rammer shall be used to force the stone back and leave a clean cement-mortar face, without voids, on the surface. Before any weight is placed on the concrete, it shall have as much time to set as can conveniently be allowed, and in no case less than 24 hours. Concrete laid in cold weather shall be protected from freezing.

Pointing.—After the molds are removed, if there should be found any small pits or voids on the exposed surfaces of the concrete, such porous places shall be neatly stopped with pointing mortar. The mortar shall be composed of one part cement and one part sand. This mortar shall be mixed in small quantities and used before it shall commence to set. No plastering of any surfaces will be allowed.

Finishing Outside Walls.—After the walls have been carried to the full height, the contractor shall go over the entire outside surface with a cement wash evenly put on with a brush, leaving the entire surface of the bin walls of a uniform color.

Broken Stone.—The broken stone used in this work shall be so crushed that it will pass through a 1″ ring. All stone used shall be a good hard quality of limestone, free from clay, dust, or other impurities, but the smaller particles of stone that come from the crusher shall be left in. Clean washed gravel, so crushed as to pass through a 1″ ring, may be substituted for the above stone on the written consent of the chief engineer.

Sand.—All sand used in this work shall be clean, coarse, sharp river, bank, or lake shore sand, free from all loam or vegetable matter, and shall be subject to the approval of the chief engineer.

Portland Cement.—All Portland cement will be furnished by the company, f. o. b. cars at the elevator site, for all of the building. It shall be of such quality as to conform to the standard specifications for Portland cement as adopted November 14, 1904, by the American Society for Testing Materials. Tensile tests shall not fall below the lower limit of minimum tensile tests as given in the specifications referred to. If the cement furnished fails in any particular to conform to the above-mentioned specifications it may be rejected. All cement shall be kept housed and dry by the contractor until wanted in the work. The contractor shall furnish the chief engineer a report of the tests of the cement in each car supplied, which report shall be made by a competent engineer and shall not be a factory test. Reports shall be furnished to the chief engineer sufficiently in advance of using the cement so that he may give his approval of at least the seven-day tensile tests before the material is used. Factory tests will be accepted if the contractor obtains express written permission from the chief engineer to that effect.

Molds for Concrete.—The contractor shall furnish and construct all necessary molds to form the concrete to the exact sizes shown on the drawings. They shall be of a substantial character, made of planks dressed one side and two edges, or of dressed and matched flooring, and the frames holding them shall be of sufficient strength so they will be practically unyielding during the process of filling and tamping. The forms shall be so constructed and manipulated that the walls of the bins will be perpendicular and free from ledges or pockets upon which grain could lodge, and when the molds are used more than once they shall be thoroughly cleaned before using a second time. All surfaces of forms which come in contact with the concrete shall be treated with soap or crude oil before the concrete is deposited. When the forms are ready to be filled with the concrete, the chief engineer shall be notified, and no concrete shall be deposited in the forms until he has inspected the arrangement of the steel and the various fastenings of the reinforcing rods, and given his approval of the work.

Reinforcing Rods.—The horizontal reinforcing rods shall be round rods made of mild merchantable steel, $\frac{3}{4}''$ in diameter. These rods shall be bent to the curve of the bins and shall have their ends hooked, and be connected by links, held securely in place by wedges, in the manner indicated on the drawings. The several bands of horizontal rods shall be arranged in a spiral, running continuously from the bottom to the top of the wall. The couplings of the rods shall break joints with each other, and the bands shall be spaced as shown on the drawings.

The vertical rods shall be $\frac{1}{2}''$ corrugated square steel bars spaced as shown on the drawings. The vertical rods shall be not less than 12' 0" long except at the starting and the finishing of the wall. The ends shall be wired together, lapping them 8″. Adjacent rods shall be arranged to break joints with each other. The crossings of the horizontal and vertical rods, and the ends of the vertical rods, shall be properly and securely fastened together with No. 14 annealed wire, as shown on the drawings, or with steel clips, samples of which have been submitted to the chief engineer, and have received his approval.

All other reinforcing rods shall be put in place wherever necessary or wherever shown on the drawings.

Corrugated Bars.—The vertical bars in the bin walls shall be corrugated square steel bars known as " Johnson " bars. Other square reinforcing bars shall be " Johnson " bars or " Ransom " bars.

Anchor Bolts.—Anchor bolts shall be set in the concrete as shown on the drawings for attachment of structural steel, etc.

Bin Ladders.—Each bin in the storage annex shall be supplied with a steel ladder, erected at the location shown on the drawings, and painted with a good coat of oxide of iron paint before erection.

General Description.—The elevator consists of a steel working house 16′ 0′ × 36′ 0′ and 166′ 0″ high, which contains the working machinery, and a reinforced concrete grain storage consisting of 9 circular reinforced concrete grain bins 30 feet in diameter and 90 feet high, with a capacity of 43,500 bushels each, and four interspace bins, with a capacity of 13,100 bushels each, making a storage capacity of 443,000 bushels. The working house is connected with the drying

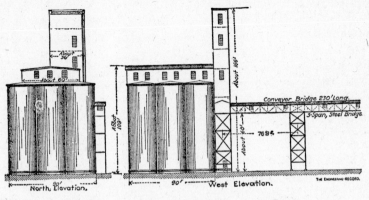

FIG. 229. ELEVATION OF CONCRETE GRAIN BINS.

plant by a three-span steel conveyor bridge 230 feet long, carried on steel towers 60 feet high. The conveyor gallery contains a 36-inch reversible belt conveyor. An elevation of the bins is given in Fig. 229.

Machinery.—The equipment includes an elevator leg with a capacity of 15,000 bushels per hour; two 36-inch belt conveyors over the bins; three 36-inch belt conveyors under the bins to receive grain from them and one 36-inch belt conveyor transverse to the three to carry grain to the leg; three garner weighing bins and shipping scales. The elevator machinery is run by a rope drive from an engine house.

Bins.—The reinforced concrete bins, Fig. 230, are 30 feet in diameter, 90 feet high and have walls 9 inches thick carried on foundations 24 inches thick. The concrete was made of 1 part American Portland cement, 3 parts sand, and 5 parts Lake Superior gravel. The con-

*Engineering Record, April 9, 1904.

crete was reinforced with steel bars placed horizontally and vertically. The horizontal reinforcement consisted of pairs of steel bars, one bar near each surface of the wall, and placed 12 inches apart vertically. For the first 15 feet above the base the steel had an area of 1 sq. in. per foot of height $(2\text{--}2'' \times \frac{1}{4}''$ bars) ; for the next 35 feet an area of

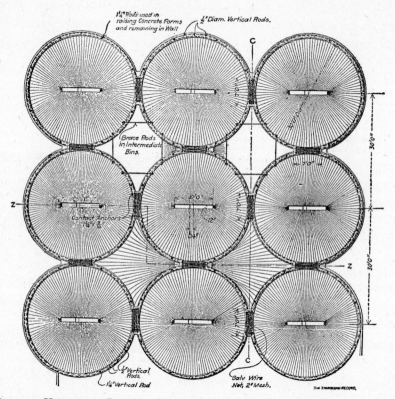

FIG. 230. HORIZONTAL SECTION THROUGH BINS, SHOWING INTERMEDIATE BINS AND HOPPER BOTTOMS.

0.88 sq. in. per foot $(2\text{--}1\frac{3}{4}'' \times \frac{1}{4}'')$; for the next 20 feet an area of 0.75 sq. in. per foot $(2\text{--}1\frac{1}{2}'' \times \frac{1}{4}'')$; for the next 20 feet an area of 0.50 sq. in. per foot $(2\text{--}1'' \times \frac{1}{4}'')$; and above this 0.38 sq. in. per foot $(2\text{--}1'' \times \frac{3}{16}'')$. Besides the horizontal bars there are 27 vertical bars $\frac{1}{2}$-inch diameter equally spaced. Where the walls are thickened at the contact points of tangencies they are reinforced by horizontal layers of 2-inch

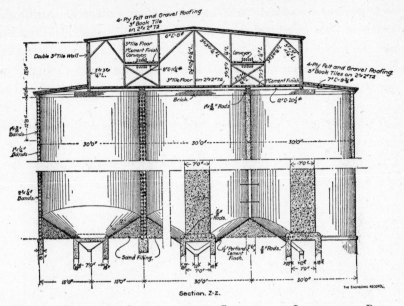

FIG. 231. TRANSVERSE SECTION THROUGH CIRCULAR AND INTERMEDIATE BINS.

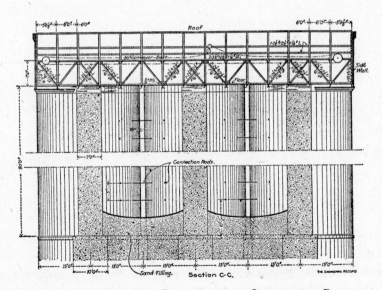

FIG. 232. LONGITUDINAL SECTION THROUGH INTERMEDIATE BINS.

mesh galvanized netting placed 12 inches apart vertically. Also by 2 horizontal $1\frac{1}{4} \times \frac{5}{16}$-inch anchors 12 inches apart vertically, which hook over the bars.

The interspace bins are braced by tie bars, as shown in Fig. 230, spaced 5 feet apart vertically. These bars have a diameter of $1\frac{3}{4}$ inches up to 20 feet high; $1\frac{5}{8}$ inches for the next 30 feet; $1\frac{1}{2}$ inches for the next 20 feet; and $1\frac{3}{8}$ inches to the top. The ends of adjacent bars are connected by a horizontal steel band.

The floors of the bins are made of 3 inches of concrete placed on a

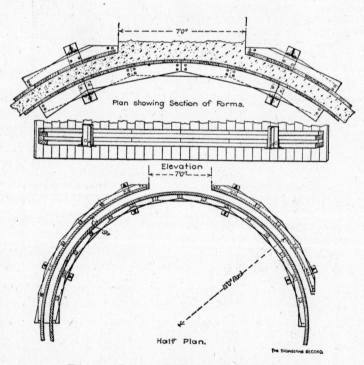

FIG. 233. PLAN OF FORMS FOR CIRCULAR BINS.

sand filling, and $1\frac{1}{2}$-inch wearing Portland cement coat. Additional details are given in Figs. 231 and 232.

Construction of Concrete.—The walls of the bins were made in movable cylindrical forms 4 feet high, as shown in Fig. 233 and Fig.

234. The curved surfaces of the forms were made of 2-inch vertical planks spiked to inside and outside circular horizontal chords. The chords were made like ordinary arch centers with four thicknesses of 2 × 8-inch scarf planks bolted together to break joints and make complete circles inside the bins and circular segments of 270 degrees or

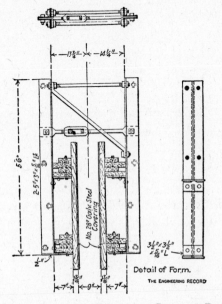

FIG. 234. DETAIL OF FORMS FOR CIRCULAR BINS.

less on the outside surface of the bins. The molds were faced on the inside with No. 28 galvanized steel and were maintained in concentric positions with fixed distances between them by means of eight V-shaped steel yokes in radial planes. Each yoke consisted of an inside and an outside vertical post with a radial web and flanges engaging the inner and outer faces of the circular chords. The posts projected about 2 feet above the tops of the molds and were rigidly connected there by means of heavy braces and an adjustable tension bar. The yokes were bolted to the inner and outer chords of the molds and vertically united them into a single structure. The lower ends of the vertical yoke posts were seated on jack-screws which were supported on false

28

work built up inside the tanks as the work progressed. The inside surface of the mold was a complete cylinder, but the outer surface was made in 2, 3 or 4 sections, to allow for the connections between the concrete walls at the points of tangency of the different tanks.

Steel Construction.—The steel framework on the tops of the bins is shown in Figs. 231 and 232, except the conveyor bridge which consisted of three 61′ 8″ spans composed of two connected trusses 8′ 4″ deep and spaced 1c′ o″ center to center. The construction is similar to the trusses over the bins, as shown in Fig. 232.

The steel garner bin is 13′ o″ square and 5′ o″ deep, with W-shaped bottom, and is made of ¼″ plates and 3″ × 3″ × ¼″ angles. The steel scale hopper is 12′ o″ square and 9′ o″ deep, with a pyramidal top, and is made of $\frac{3}{16}$″ plates. The steel shipping bin, 13′ o″ × 15′ o″ is made of ¼″ plates.

The total weight of the steel work in the elevator is 400,000 pounds.

The elevator was designed by the engineering department of the Canadian Pacific Ry., Mr. E. H. McHenry, chief engineer, and was constructed by the Barnett-Record Company. The contract was let January, 1903, and the elevator was ready for service January 3, 1904.

THE CANADIAN NORTHERN RAILWAY TILE GRAIN BINS, PORT ARTHUR, ONTARIO.

General Description.—The grain storage consists of 80 circular tile grain bins arranged as shown in Fig. 235, Fig. 236, and Fig. 237,

FIG. 235. GRAIN ELEVATOR FOR CANADIAN NORTHERN RAILWAY, PORT ARTHUR, ONTARIO. (THE ORIGINAL ELEVATOR "B" IS DESCRIBED HERE.)

and located 50 feet south of the working house. The bins are each 21′ 0″ outside diameter and 83′ 0″ from the floor to the eaves, and are The capacity of the bins is as follows:

	Bushels.
48 circular bins, each 21,825 bu...............................	1,047,600
32 circular bins, each 21,440 bu...............................	686,080
63 intermediate bins each 6,300 bu...........................	396,900
Total capacity of bins..................................	2,130,580

The tile bins rest on a pile and concrete foundation surrounded by a retaining wall on three sides of the building to protect it from the waves. The piles are of pine, spruce, and tamarac, 40 to 50 feet long, 12 and 8 inches in diameter at the butt and top, respectively. They were driven so that there was not to exceed one inch penetration for a 2,000-lb. hammmer dropping 20 feet. The concrete was composed of 1 part Portland cement, 3 parts clean gravel, ranging in size from the size of a pea to that which would pass a 2½-inch ring. The floors were made of reinforced concrete, as shown in Fig. 238.

Bin Walls.—The walls of the tanks were constructed of Barnett-Record semi-porous tile, constructed as shown in Fig. 201. The main tiles were 12″ × 12″ × 5″, alternating with channel tiles 12″ wide, 3″ deep and 5″ thick, laid as shown. The outside tile were hard burnt semi-glazed tile 12″ × 12″ × 12″. The facing tiles were firmly an-

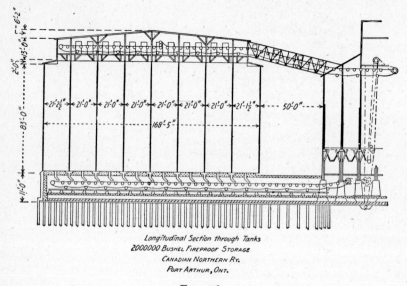

Longitudinal Section through Tanks
2000000 BUSHEL FIREPROOF STORAGE
CANADIAN NORTHERN RY.
PORT ARTHUR, ONT.

FIG. 236.

chored to each other and to inner tile in every fourth course where the joints came together with a piece of 3″ × 4″ galvanized wire netting, four meshes to the inch, one anchor to each tile. The openings in the upper end of the main wall tile were covered with wire netting, three meshes to the inch, to permit of a full mortar bed to receive the channel tile. In the channel tile were placed steel bands, not less than two steel bands in each channel, the weight of the bands decreasing from the bottom to the top. All the tile were laid in Portland cement mortar, composed of 1 part Portland cement and 3 parts clean, sharp sand, tempered with lime mortar. No lime was put in the mortar used to imbed the steel bands. Tiles in the cupola walls were of two thicknesses of 3″ hollow tile laid in the same manner as the main wall tiles.

Roof.—All roof surfaces except the bridges and tunnels were covered with 12″ × 18″ × 3″ hollow book tile, laid in a bed of Portland cement mortar on the flanges of tee sub-purlins. On top of the tile

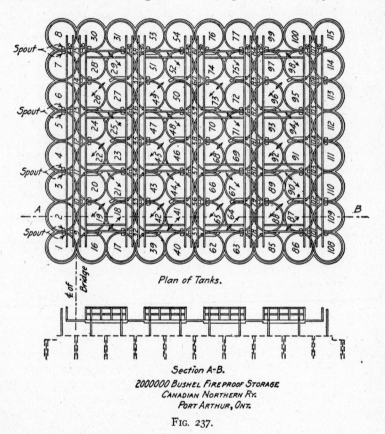

Plan of Tanks.

Section A-B.
2000000 BUSHEL FIREPROOF STORAGE
CANADIAN NORTHERN RY.
PORT ARTHUR, ONT.

FIG. 237.

thus laid was laid a four-ply composition felt and gravel roofing. The exposed edges of each ply were cemented down with hot pitch and the entire surface was covered with straight-rim medium soft domestic coal tar roofing pitch, 100 lbs. to the square of 100 square feet. The gravel was screened through a ¾-inch wire mesh screen, ⅛ cu. yd. being used to the square.

Conveyors.—Each bin coming over the tunnels or conveyors is provided with a cut-off spout with an extension made of No. 14 steel,
arranged to load the grain on the belts.   In the upper part of the building no spouts are needed except for the intermediate bins, which are

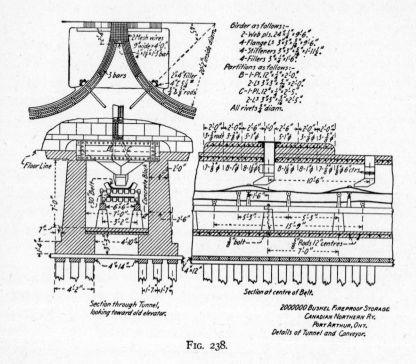

Section through Tunnel,
looking toward old elevator.

2000000 Bushel Fireproof Storage
Canadian Northern Ry.
Port Arthur, Ont.
Details of Tunnel and Conveyor.

FIG. 238.

provided with spouts of No. 14 steel to take the grain from the tripper
spouts.

There are 5 belt conveyors, with 36-inch belts, running from the
working house out over the bins, and supported by disc rolls 5′ 3″
apart.   The return belt is carried on straight rolls, 15′ 9″ center to
center.   The shafts for these rolls are $1\frac{3}{16}$″, with standard oscillating
bearings fixed to wood supports resting on the steel framework, the
wood support being covered with No. 26 plain sheet steel.   The conveyor belts in the basement are 36″ wide, carried as in the upper conveyors.   In the upper conveyor belt there is one 2-pulley tripper
for each belt.   These trippers are provided with self-propelling de-

vices, platform levers, etc., and with spouts discharging to either side, so that the circular bins can be filled without any other spout than that provided by the tripper. These spouts are provided with cut-off gates and arranged with spouts to the intermediate bins. All trippers are carried on 16-lb. tee rails attached to the round supports which carry the rolls.

The capacity of each of the five top conveyor belts is 15,000 bushels per hour, and each of the five lower belts is 10,000 bushels per hour. The conveyor belts are four-ply rubber belting made of 30-oz. cotton duck, pliable with hard surface stretched and spliced with Smith's patent No. 1 belt fastener. These belts are driven by light leather belting. The conveyor head pulleys are covered with four-ply rubber belting. The bridges for each of the five belt conveyors consist of two steel trusses, as shown on the plans; the floor is of book tile and concrete resting on tees and angles as in the upper belt conveyor galleries. The walls of the bridge are covered with No. 24 and the roof with No. 22 galvanized corrugated steel. The bridges are provided with telescope joints to provide against settlement.

Miscellaneous Details.—All woodwork for window and door frames is covered with crimped galvanized iron. The 15 galvanized iron frame skylights in the roof are glazed with $\frac{1}{4}''$ unpolished glass. The cornices and flashing are made of No. 26 plain galvanized iron.

The bin ladders are made of iron bars built into the walls, one ladder to each bin, extending from the top to the bottom. Two fire-escape ladders were also provided on the outside walls.

Painting.—The structural steel work received in the shop one coat of boiled linseed oil mixed with 10 per cent of lampblack and oil. All woodwork around windows received two coats of red lead and oil.

Miscellaneous Data.—Each eight feet in height of each bin required the following materials:

378 tiles, $12'' \times 12'' \times 5''$,
378 channel tiles, $12'' \times 3'' \times 5''$,
216 facing tiles, outer bins only,

336 facing tiles, corner bins only,

250 brick,

375 pieces wire netting, 12″ × 4″,

12 pieces wire netting, 4′ × 8″,

126 pieces wire netting, 12″ × 1″, for facing tile,

12 clips, 12″ × 1½″ × ⅛″,

6 crooked steps, 3′ 7″ × ⅝″ φ iron,

6 straight steps, 2′ 6″ × ⅝″ φ iron,

4 tie rods, 11′ 0″ × ¾″ φ iron.

Each thousand tiles took ¾ cubic yard mortar grout.

Each bricklayer laid 364 tiles per day of 10 hours in the month of November.

Each inside bin has four double channels 75 feet long to carry the rods which support the intermediate bins.

Each outside bin has two double channels 75 feet long.

The hoops or bands in the channel tiles consisted of 1½″ × 3/16″ and 1½″ × ⅛″ steel bars, three complete hoops being used in the lower and two in the upper, thus varying the section to suit the pressure.

Cost.—The entire cost of the building, including revetment and everything complete except the earth filling around and under the foundation was $397,095.80, or 19 cents per bushel of storage capacity.

General Description.—A reinforced concrete grain storage annex to the steel grain elevator of the Great Northern Railway, built in 1900, was built in 1908–1909. The steel working house shown in Fig. 215 has nine separate receiving and shipping units. In building the storage annex eight circular bins were placed opposite each of the nine south units of the steel elevator. The storage units thus formed have no connection with each other except through the longitudinal conveyors and partial system of cross spouting in the main elevator. The storage annex consists of 72 reinforced concrete bins 19 ft. 7 ins. inside diameter, and 110 ft. high, and 51 interspace bins. The circular and interspace bins have a capacity of approximately 2,400,000 bushels. The general arrangement of the bins is shown in Fig. 239.

Design.—The reinforced concrete bins are carried on 5,000 piles, each pile carying a load of 26 tons. The entire load of $3\frac{1}{2}$ tons per square foot is transferred to the piles through the bottom slab. Over the conveyor tunnels the slab is reinforced with 1 inch square corrugated bars spaced 4 ins. center to center. Three-fourths of these bars were turned down to take shear and diagonal tension. The fourth bar was made continuous for the full length of the basement, using 27 inch laps at points of no stress as shown in Fig. 241. The load on the bin walls at the bottom was approximately 45,000 pounds per lineal foot of wall. To distribute this load 20-in. I beams @ 80 pounds per foot were used over the conveyor tunnels. Reinforced concrete girders 3 ft. deep and 8 ft. 9 ins. long were used for the shorter spans between subdividing walls. In some cases the basement subdivision walls were required to take stresses as beams. In such cases they were considered as very large reinforced T-beams, the 2-ft. bottom slab taking

* *Engineering News,* August 4, 1910.

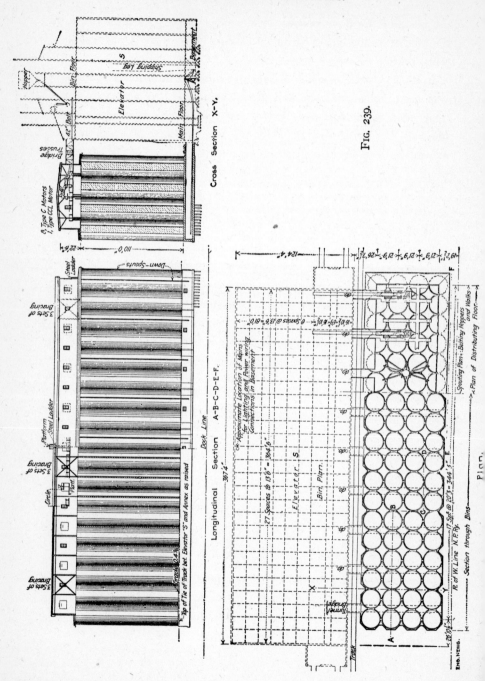

FIG. 239.

the place of the floor slab in ordinary T-beams. Grain pressures on the bottom of the bins were taken care of by reinforced concrete slabs 6 ins. thick.

In the construction of the basement slabs and walls 1 : 2½ : 5 concrete was used, both sandstone and gravel being used as aggregate. The upper 3 ft. of the basement is of 1 : 2 : 4 concrete. The concrete in the bin walls is 1 : 2 : 4 concrete. Medium steel corrugated bars were used except for the horizontal bin reinforcement where plain bars were used.

The following stresses were used in design:

Steel in tension, 16,000 lbs. per square inch.

Concrete in compression, 600 lbs. per square inch.

Concrete in shear, 40 lbs. per square inch.

Adhesion of concrete to bars, 100 lbs. per square inch.

Ratio of moduli of elasticity of steel and concrete = 12.

The outer walls were made 7 ins. thick, while the inside walls, having grain pressure on both sides, were made 7½ ins. thick. The walls were made the same thickness from bottom to top to permit the use of sliding forms in the construction. The circular bins were reinforced with plain round ⅝-in. and ½-in. diameter bars, spaced to carry the bursting pressures. The circular bins were tied together at the corners by corrugated bars bent into U shape, and placed in the intersections of the bins as shown in Fig. 240. The bottoms of the bins were hoppered with a very lean concrete.

The cupola consists of a steel frame-work resting on the bin walls, which carries 6-in. reinforced concrete side walls. The roof consists of reinforced concrete tile resting on steel T's and covered with 4-ply pitch and gravel roof. The roofing tiles are 18-in. span, 24 ins. long and 1⅛ ins. thick, reinforced with woven wire.

Conveyors and Spouts.—All grain spouts were made rectangular in cross-section, the tops and sides being made of No. 14 and the bottoms of No. 8 sheet steel. To facilitate the renewal of worn sections the spouts were bolted instead of being riveted.

The upper conveyor belts are 42 ins. wide and the lower belts 46 ins. wide. These belts are made of solid woven canvas with a thin rubber coating, and are spliced with copper belt fasteners. The lower belts are driven by new 15-H.P. alternating current motors, while the upper belts are driven by eight 15-H.P. motors of an old type and one new 20-H.P. motor.

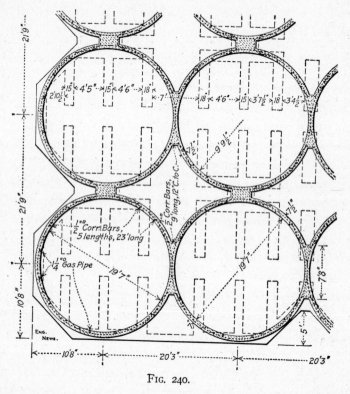

FIG. 240.

Construction.—The bin walls were constructed with sliding forms of the type commonly used in grain elevator construction. These forms were of wood covered with galvanized sheet iron and were 4 ft. deep. The outer and inner forms were connected by wooden yokes, so as to move together. The forms were raised by jacks connected to the yokes and working on 1¼-in. gas pipes fixed in the wall. In order to prevent the concrete from being raised with the forms the inner forms

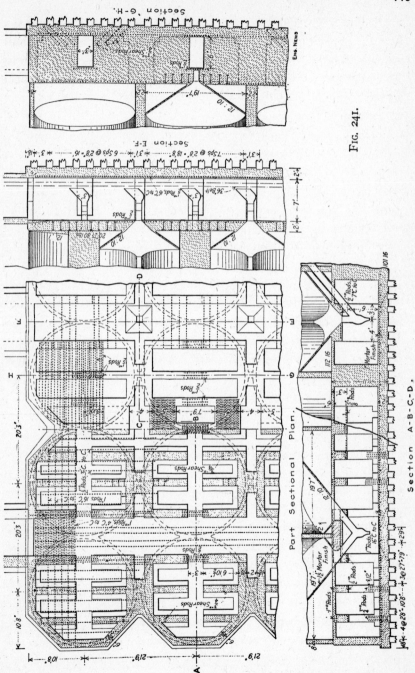

FIG. 241.

of the bins were slightly tapered toward the bottom and the connection between outer and inner forms was made such that the distance between them could be slightly increased after the concrete had set up. All inner forms were planked over to provide a place for wheeling concrete and placing bars.

Corrugated bars were used for vertical reinforcement in the bin walls. The specifications required that the horizontal bars be wired to each of the vertical bars as well as to the vertical gas pipes. In placing the horizontal bars it was found impossible to push the bars down into the concrete after they had been wired to the corrugated bars. The horizontal bars were therefore wired to gas pipes only, which method was found to be very satisfactory. The horizontal bars were specified to be bent into a hook at the end. This was done in the material yard, but otherwise the bars were sent up to the placing crew straight. There was no difference noticeable in the labor of placing $\frac{5}{8}$- and $\frac{1}{2}$-in. bars, but $\frac{3}{4}$-in. bars would probably be too stiff to handle this way. The horizontal bars were plain bars, as it was found that it was almost impossible to handle corrugated bars, as the corrugation would cause them to bind while being put in place. Two lengths of bars were used to form one hoop. In placing the hoops the splice of each hoop was placed 45° ahead of splice in the preceding hoop, giving at each point of the circumference not less than three unspliced bars to each bar that was spliced.

The bin walls were concreted at an average rate of 30 ins. in height per day of ten hours. During the latter part of the work a rate of 36 to 40 ins. per day was usually attained. Each inch of height required about 9 cu. yds. of concrete for the whole group of bins. As a rule the concrete was put in in two layers per day. The night force got the forms ready for the day's run, putting the tops of the forms about 30 ins. above the top of the concrete placed the day before. About 16 ins. of concrete was placed in the forenoon, finishing up about eleven o'clock. The forms were then raised a few inches to give a sufficient depth for the afternoon. This raising was done when the new concrete was three to four hours old. The balance of the day's run was placed in the afternoon, beginning about half-past two. The night force then came on and raised the forms for the next day's work. By this method concrete placed in the forenoon was left exposed by the raising of the forms about midnight of the same day.

After the completion of the concrete work, all exterior concrete surfaces were treated with a cement and alum wash, both as a partial waterproofing and as a finish.

Excavation for the foundations began January, 1909, and the storage house was practically completed by September 15, 1909. The bins were filled about October 1, 60 days after the concrete was placed.

The work was designed and constructed under the direction of Mr. A. H. Hogeland, Chief Engineer, Great Northern Ry. Mr. Max Toltz was consulting engineer on design and construction. The construction was under the direction of Mr. O. B. Robbins, acting under Bridge Engineer Mr. George A. Casseday, and his successor, Mr. John A. Bohland. The contractors were the Barnett & Record Company, Minneapolis, Minnesota.

GRAND TRUNK PACIFIC RY. REINFORCED CONCRETE GRAIN ELEVATOR, FORT WILLIAM (ONT.), CANADA.*

Introduction.—To handle the grain of the Canadian Northwest a grain elevator plant with a capacity of 40,000,000 bushels will be built at Fort William by the Grand Trunk Pacific Ry. The entire plant will be built in four seperate units of 10,000,000 bushels each. The first section of the first unit was completed in December, 1910, and has a storage capacity of 3,500,000 bushels, together with equipment for handling and cleaning.

Description.—The present completed section consists of the following structures: (1) a four track receiving shed; (2) a working and receiving house with 75 cylindrical bins, 12 ft. inside diameter and 79 ft. high; (3) a storage annex of 2,750,000 bushels capacity, having 70 bins 23 ft. 3 ins. inside diameter and 95 ft. high; (4) a house for the electrical transformer and switchboard; (5) a drying plant. The general arrangement of the bins is shown in Figs. 242 to 244. Interspace bins are used both in the working house and the storage annex. The smaller buildings and the main structures are built of reinforced concrete. The cupolas of the working house and storage annex are of steel frame construction, with concrete roofs and floors. The roofs are covered with 5-ply roofing felt and composition covering. The doors are steel covered. Sheet metal window frames glazed with $\frac{1}{4}$ in. ribbed wire glass are used in all buildings.

Foundations.—The elevator was built on reclaimed land and is founded on piles 55 ft. long driven to solid rock. A heavy concrete mattress and walls distribute the load evenly over this footing. A concrete wharf 337 ft. long and 12 ft. wide forms the water front.

Construction of Bins.—The forms for the cylindrical bins consisted of inner and outer wall staves 4 ft. high, held in place by built-up wooden rings. These form walls were held in place by rigid yokes built of steel plates and channels and were bolted to the forms. The

*Engineering News, Feb. 23, 1911, p. 221.

forms were raised continuously as the work progressed and gave a smooth surface without breaks or offsets. The construction of the yokes and jacks for the forms is shown in Fig. 203c.

The device for raising the forms, Fig. 203c, consisted of a hollow jack screw, through which was passed one of the vertical rods for reinforcing the concrete; the jack was made to climb this rod and thereby raises the forms. In operating, a bar was inserted in one of the sockets

FIG. 242. REINFORCED CONCRETE GRAIN ELEVATOR, FORT WILLIAM, CANADA.

in the cast head of the jack, and with this leverage the screw was turned. By turning to the right the forms are lifted, and by turning to the left, the jack itself climbs the rod, while the forms remain stationary, supported by the adjacent jacks. The load was applied concentrically to the reinforcing rod and there was no tendency of the forms to bind. Additional vertical rods were merely inserted in the tops of the jacks, thus causing no delay. The forms of the separate tanks though constructed in sections were tied together to prevent spreading from the pressure of wet concrete by a system of horizontal rods attached from yoke to yoke.

29

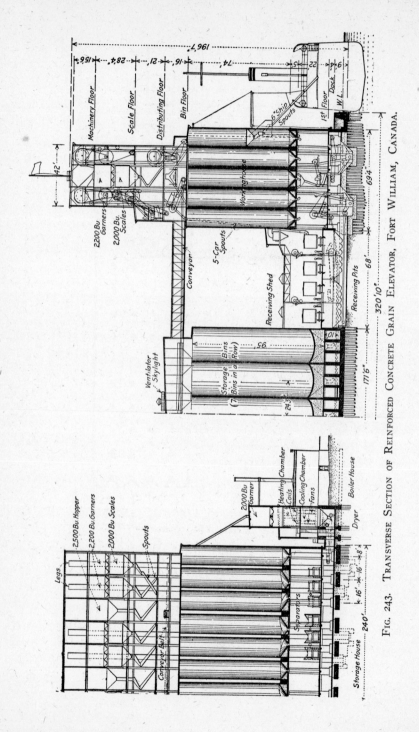

FIG. 243. TRANSVERSE SECTION OF REINFORCED CONCRETE GRAIN ELEVATOR, FORT WILLIAM, CANADA.

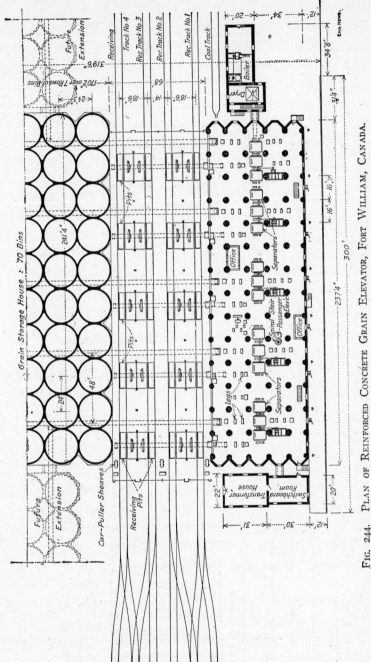

FIG. 244. PLAN OF REINFORCED CONCRETE GRAIN ELEVATOR, FORT WILLIAM, CANADA.

Concrete.—The concrete was composed of Portland cement, sand and gravel in proportions of 1 : 2 : 4, mixed very wet. The aggregate varied in size from 2½ ins. down to coarse sand. The sand and gravel was dredged from Lake Superior. From the stock piles the materials were loaded into the cars by a locomotive revolving crane. There were two concrete mixing plants, one at either end of the elevator and each had two concrete mixers. The aggregate was lifted to the charging hoppers where cement and water were added. The proper amounts of materials for a batch of concrete were then introduced into the mixer, from which the concrete was poured directly into a large hoisting bucket in an elevator tower. The loaded bucket was then raised and emptied into a hopper above the level of the work. From here the concrete was distributed to the various sections of the works by means of concrete carts. With this equipment as much as 800 cu. yds. of concrete were placed in one 20-hr. day, and a total of 60,000 cu. yds. in the entire work.

Steel Reinforcement.—The reinforcement of the bins consisted of vertical rods and horizontal hoops of flat steel of varying widths and thicknesses. For the reinforcing of the concrete columns supporting the bins of the working house a spiral of ½ in. steel wire forming a helix 41 inches in diameter was used, supplemented by vertical rods. Round steel rods were used for reinforcing girders and floor slabs.

Operation of Plant.—There are 20 receiving pits giving a capacity of 500 cars per 24 hours. Each track pit has a capacity of 2,000 bushels and has a gate for delivering its contents upon a 36-in. lateral belt conveyor leading to the five receiving legs. The grain may be sent to the storage bins by belt conveyors overhead, or to the working house, or to cleaning machines in the first story below. It then may be elevated again and sent to the storage bins or may be delivered directly to the steamers. If grain needs drying it may be delivered by spouts from the working house to the drying plant. Grain from all storage bins is fed by gravity through hoppers upon belt conveyors which deliver it to elevators in the working house. There are 5 car spouts for loading into cars and 6 dock spouts for loading into vessels.

In the cupola, there are 10 hopper scales of 2,000 bushels capacity, fitted with recording devices; each is served by an overhead garner of 2,200 bushels capacity. Fans and cyclone separators are used for the removal of dust from various departments and this is discharged into dust bins. The entire plant is operated by electric power.

The cost of this section was $1,250,000, or approximately $.36 per bushel.

The elevator was designed and constructed by the Canadian Stewart Co., Mr. R. H. Folwell, Chief Engineer, and Mr. W. R. Sinks, General Manager. Mr. John S. Metcalf was consulting engineer for the owners, the Grand Trunk Pacific Ry.

Reinforced Concrete Grain Elevator for the F. C. Ayres Mercantile Co., Denver, Colo.

Description.—The elevator is 72 ft. 10 ins. long by 60 ft. 3 ins. wide, is 127 ft. 6 ins. from the track grade to the top of the monitor and the basement is 6 ft. 6 ins. below grade, making a total height of 134 ft. above the basement floor. The elevator is of the working house type and has a storage capacity of 190,000 bushels. The basement has a clear head room of 6 ft. 8 ins.; the storage bins a depth of 70 ft.; the spouting floor a height of 15 ft. and the monitor a height of 17 ft. There are seven bins 12 ft. 11 ins. by 14 ft. 4 ins.; six bins 6 ft. 10½ ins. by 13 ft. 0 ins.; eight bins 6 ft. 4 ins. by 14 ft. 4 ins.; sixteen bins 6 ft. 10½ ins. by 8 ft. 4½ ins., and two bins 6 ft. 10½ ins. by 12 ft. 10½ ins. A general view of the elevator is shown in Fig. 245; transverse sections are shown in Figs. 246 and 247; the plan of the working floor in Fig. 248; a cross-section of the bins in Fig. 249; a detail of the bins in Fig. 250; while progress views are shown in Figs. 251 to 254.

The sacking room extends along the west side and south end of the building with its floor on the level of the bottoms of the bins. A receiving track passes through the north end of the building. A circular iron stairway connects the working floor with the top of the bins, while iron ladders are provided over the tops of the bins to the walk around the cupola. All windows have metal sash glazed with wire glass and bear the approval stamp of the National Board of Fire Underwriters. The roof is a reinforced concrete slab covered with a tar and gravel roofing. All bins have hopper bottoms made by depositing a cinder concrete filling on top of the bin slabs. The upper surface of the filling is covered with a neat cement mortar two inches thick, troweled smooth.

Equipment.—The machinery equipment consists of one track scale, 100 tons capacity, 50 ft. long; one hopper scale with hopper having 1,500 bushels capacity and registering 90,000 lbs.; one short receiving elevator leg; one large elevating or lofter leg reaching to the top of

454

the cupola; one small leg extending from the basement floor through the side roof outside the cupola and the same height as the lofter leg;

FIG. 245. REINFORCED CONCRETE GRAIN ELEVATOR, DENVER, COLO.

a sulphur bleaching machine with fans and apparatus; one separator of 1,000 bushels capacity, with motor and necessary drives; one double drum car puller with double ropes, located in the basement, arranged

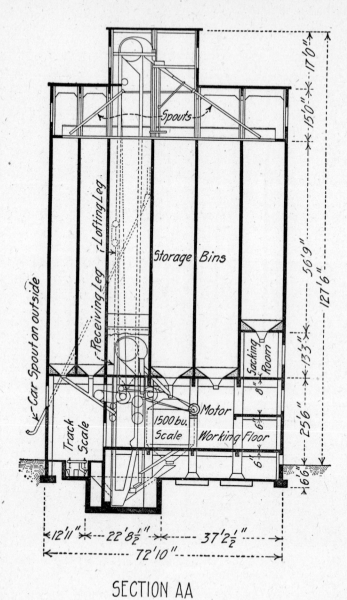

SECTION AA

FIG. 246. TRANSVERSE SECTION, REINFORCED CONCRETE GRAIN ELEVATOR,
DENVER, COLO.

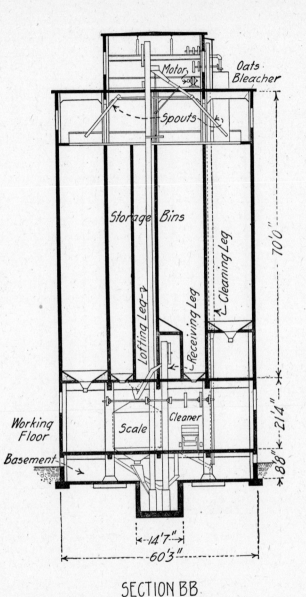

SECTION BB

FIG. 247. TRANSVERSE SECTION, REINFORCED CONCRETE GRAIN ELEVATOR, DENVER, COLO.

with ropes and sheaves to pull cars on two tracks; one set of car shovels; one bifurcated car loading spout connected with the spouting system in the cupola to load cars on outside tracks; a permanent steel spouting system in the cupola having one spout reaching each bin and also a connection for the car spout. All bins are provided with hoppers with valve and spout, and adjustable spouting is furnished for

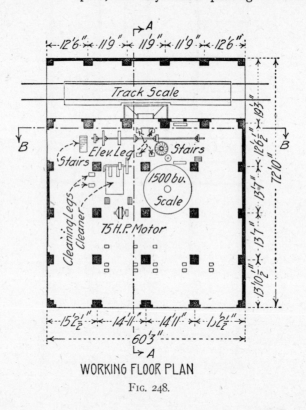

WORKING FLOOR PLAN

Fig. 248.

special machines. A view of the tops of the bins is shown in Fig. 255.

Design.—The stresses in the bins were calculated by Janssen's solution as given in Chapter XVI, wheat being assumed to weigh 50 lbs. per cu. ft.; the angle of repose of wheat, $\phi = 28°$, and the coefficient of friction of wheat on the concrete walls, $\mu' = 0.5$, while k was taken as equal to 0.4. The reinforced concrete was designed for working

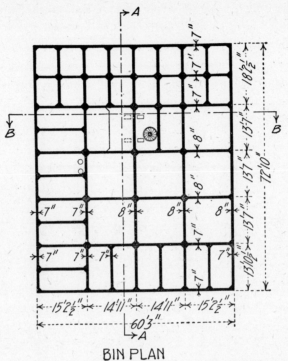

BIN PLAN

FIG. 249.

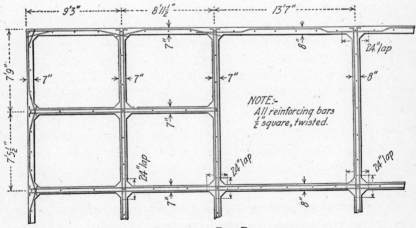

NOTE:-
All reinforcing bars
½" square, twisted.

FIG. 250. DETAILS OF BIN REINFORCEMENT.

stresses of 650 lbs. per sq. in. in concrete and 16,000 lbs. per sq. in. in the reinforcing steel, and $n = 15$.

Construction.—The Portland cement used in the work was tested by the Consulting Engineers and conformed to the standard specifications of the American Society for Testing Materials. The concrete was composed of one (1) part Portland cement, two (2) parts fine aggregate, and four (4) parts coarse aggregate. The sand was clean bank sand, a large part of which was taken from the site of the elevator.

FIG. 251. MOVING FORMS, READY TO START ON MAIN COLUMNS.

Coarse aggregate consisted of equal parts of gravel and Lyons sandstone broken to pass a one-inch ring.

The concrete was mixed in a Ransome batch mixer with a capacity of 11 cu. ft. From the mixer the concrete was run into charging carts, which were then elevated to the form platform and the concrete was wheeled and dumped into the forms. The concrete was thoroughly mixed and was deposited very wet.

Inasmuch as all of the concrete was deposited during cold weather special precautions were taken to prevent the freezing of the concrete. The water used in mixing the concrete was heated to approximately 180°, and was introduced in the mixer after the fine and coarse aggregate had been put in. The mixer was then rotated for a sufficient length of time to remove all frost from the aggregate and the cement was added. The temperature of the concrete coming from the mixer varied from 60 to 70° F. Floor slabs and other freshly exposed surfaces were covered with tarpaulin until the concrete was set. The concrete

FIG. 252. MOVING FORMS ON BIN WALLS.

set up very rapidly even in cool weather and gave very satisfactory results.

The reinforcing steel was open hearth steel twisted cold. A typical detail of the reinforcing in the bin walls is shown in Fig. 250. The vertical reinforcing rods were kept as near the center of the wall as possible, while the horizontal rods were laid in place as the work progressed. The columns supporting the first floor and the bins were reinforced with longitudinal rods and hooped reinforcement.

Forms.—Stationary forms were used for the basement columns and first floor beams and slabs; moving forms were used for the columns supporting the bins, the walls of the working story and for the bin walls. The moving forms used in constructing the main columns supporting the bin walls were four ft. high and were jacked up about 12 inches at one time. These columns were built at the rate of about 5 ft. per day of 8 hours, so that the fresh concrete was exposed after it

FIG. 253. MOVING FORMS AT TOP OF BINS.

had been placed 5 or 6 hours. When the moving forms reached the level of the bin slabs they were blocked up and the bin floor and girders were poured in the usual manner.

The forms used in constructing the bin walls were four ft. high and were fastened together with yokes as shown in Figs. 203*a* and 203*b*. From 6 to 12 ins. of concrete were deposited in the forms at one

time, the depth depending upon the spacing of the horizontal reinforcement steel. After the concrete had all been deposited and the horizontal
reinforcement put in place the forms were jacked up to receive the next

FIG. 254. MOVING FORMS NEAR TOP OF ELEVATOR.

filling. The jacks lifted the forms approximately ¾ of an inch at
one jacking. The gas pipe used for jacking was cut into pieces
approximately 48 ins. long, and in a few cases the gas pipe crushed or

was thrown out of line and caused a blow-out in the wall. These blow-outs were immediately repaired by a man working on a platform suspended from the bottom of the fr·ms, nails being driven in the concrete wall to give a firm bond. The concreting of the bin walls was carried on by a day and a night shift. The average height for two shifts was 48 ins., while the maximum height for two shifts was 66 ins. The staves for the bin walls were 2½ ins. wide by ¾ ins. thick with a saw-kerf in the middle of the stave to within ⅛ of an inch of the

FIG. 255. VIEW OF TOP OF BINS SHOWING SPOUTING SYSTEM.

inside. The staves were coated with paraffine oil before being fastened to the form timbers. Even though the staves were placed as far apart as practicable, considerable difficulty was experienced from the swelling of the staves, it being necessary in many instances to remove an entire stave.

Bin Reinforcement.—All bins were reinforced with ½″ □ twisted bars. The large bins were reinforced from the bottom as follows: 4 spaces @ 9½″, 81 spaces @ 4″, 48 spaces @ 5″, and 34 spaces @ 7″, making a total of 166 bars in a height of 70′ 0″. The small bins were reinforced from the bottom as follows: 4 spaces @ 9½″, 41 spaces @ 8″, 24 spaces @ 10″, and 16 spaces @ 14″, making a total of 87 bars in a height of 70′ 0″. The rectangular bins over the sacking floor were reinforced as follows: 4 spaces @ 9½″, 41 spaces @ 8″, 24 spaces @ 10″, and 4 spaces @ 14″, making a total of 72 bars in a height of 55′ 0″. A typical plan of reinforcement is shown in Fig. 250. Bent bars were placed in the corners at frequent intervals to tie the corners together.

Cost.—The total cost of the elevator was $50,000 for the building and $16,000 for machinery and equipment, or a total of $66,000. The cost of the storage was $0.34 per bushel, of which $0.085 per bushel was for machinery and $0.255 was for the building.

Cost of Concrete in Basement.—There were 440 cu. yds. of concrete and 14 tons of steel in the basement. The cost per cu. yd., using stationary forms, was as follows:

Portland cement	1.57 bbls. @ $1.30	$ 2.04
Sand	0.44 cu. yds. @ 1.00	.44
Gravel	0.88 cu. yds. @ 1.00	.88
Form lumber		.64
Building forms		2.16
Mixing and placing concrete		3.86
Engineering, inspection and profit, 20 per cent		2.00
Total cost of concrete, per cu. yd.		$12.02
Cost of reinforcing steel, per cu. yd.		1.43
Bending and placing steel		1.00
Engineering, inspection and profit, 20 per cent		.49
Total cost per cu. yd.		$14.94

Cost of bending and placing steel, $18.60 per ton.

Cost of Concrete in First Story.—There were 325 cu. yds. of concrete and 21 tons of steel in the first story. The cost per cu. yd., using moving forms, was as follows:

Portland cement	1.57 bbls. @ $1.30	$ 2.04
Sand	0.44 cu. yds. @ 1.00	.44

30

Gravel	0.44 cu. yds. @ 1.00	.44
Stone	0.44 cu. yds. @ 1.75	.77
Form lumber		1.00
Building forms		5.08
Mixing and placing concrete		4.57
Engineering, inspection and profit, 20 per cent		2.87
		$17.21
Cost of reinforcing steel, per cu. yd.		2.90
Bending and placing steel, per cu. yd.		1.00
Engineering, inspection and profit, 20 per cent		.78
Total cost per cu. yd.		$21.89

Cost of bending and placing steel, $18.84 per ton.

Cost of Concrete in Bin Walls.—There were 1,400 cu. yds. of concrete and 169.5 tons of reinforcing steel in the bin walls. The cost per cu. yd., using moving forms, was as follows:

Portland cement	1.57 bbls. @ $1.30	$ 2.04
Sand	0.44 cu. yds. @ 1.00	.44
Gravel	0.44 cu. yds. @ 1.00	.44
Broken stone	0.44 cu. yds. @ 1.75	.77
Form lumber		.50
Building forms		1.91
Mixing and placing concrete		2.24
Engineering, inspection and profit, 20 per cent		1.67
Cost per cu. yd.		$10.01
Cost of reinforcing steel, per cu. yd.		5.41
Bending and placing steel, per cu. yd.		.50
Engineering, inspection and profit, 20 per cent		1.18
		$17.10

Cost of bending and placing steel, $4.32 per ton.

The moving forms used in constructing the first story were not economical, due to the time required to deposit the concrete, and the labor required to build the moving forms. The cost of building the forms includes the cost of maintaining the moving forms and of tearing down and removing the forms.

The following wages were paid on the work: Superintendent, 60 cts.

per hour; foremen, 40 cts. per hour; carpenters, 60 cts. per hour; blacksmith and hoisting engineer, 40 cts. per hour; skilled labor, 25 cts. per hour; common labor, 20 cts. per hour. The cost of materials was as follows: Cement, $1.30 per bbl.; lumber, $25.00 per M; reinforcing steel, $45.00 per ton.

Crocker and Ketchum, Denver, Colo., were the Consulting Engineers, Mr. John Barr was General Manager of the F. C. Ayres Mercantile Co., and the MacDonald Engineering Company, Chicago, Ill., were the contractors. The design and construction were under the direct supervision of the author. The work was begun in November, 1909, and completed August 1, 1910.

CHAPTER XX.

Cost of Grain Bins and Elevators.

COST OF STEEL GRAIN ELEVATORS.—For a detailed cost of the different parts of steel grain elevators and for methods of estimating, see Chapter XIII. The following actual costs of steel elevators will give a fair idea of the range of costs.

Cost of Great Northern Ry. Grain Elevator, Superior, Wis.—The following unit costs were furnished the author by Max Tolz, mechanical engineer, Great Northern Ry., who had charge of the design and erection of the elevator:

Piles cost 10 cents per lineal foot.

Driving 40 ft. piles cost $1.00.

Concrete cost $6.25 per cu. yd.

Structural steel cost $50.00 per ton f. o. b. Pittsburg, Pa.

Erection of structural steel work, including the driving of all rivets, $13.25 per ton.

The elevator weighed 7 lbs. per bushel of storage capacity.

The total cost of the elevator was 39.65 cents per bushel of storage. This cost was very low.

For quantities of materials see Chapter XIX.

Cost of Independent Elevator, Omaha, Neb.—The total weight of steel in the elevator was 1,700 tons; the steel in the working house weighing 900 tons and the steel in the circular bins and conveyors 800 tons. The weight of steel in the working house was therefore about 7 lbs. per bushel of storage capacity, while the weight of the circular bins was 2 lbs. per bushel. The total cost, including machinery and foundation was $205,000, of which the working house cost approximately $125,000, and the circular bins $80,000.

468

Cost of Steel Elevator, Winona Malting Co., Winona, Minn.— The steel working house has a storage capacity of 55,000 bushels, and the 12 steel storage bins are 20 ft. in diameter by 80 ft. high and contain 295,000 bushels. The working house cost about $1.00 per bushel of storage, and the steel bins cost about 14 cents per bushel of storage capacity. The cost of the working house was high on account of the small amount of storage capacity. For a description see Figs. 146 and 147, and Chapter XV.

Miscellaneous Costs.—Eight steel storage tanks, with a capacity of 335,000 bushels in Minnesota cost, including machinery and conveyor galleries, 13 cents per bushel of storage capacity. The Electric Steel storage bins, Minneapolis, Minn., cost, including foundations, about 10 cents per bushel of storage capacity.

Steel working houses will at present (1906) cost from 50 to 80 cents per bushel of storage capacity for large elevators. Steel working houses for small elevators may cost $1.00 to $1.25 per bushel of storage capacity.

A steel grain elevator of the working house and independent storage bin type, with a capacity of 200,000 bushels in the working house and 800,000 bushels in the 8 steel storage bins, has recently been constructed in the middle west for the following unit costs: The steel in the bins and the steel conveyor supports above and below the bins cost 7 cts. per bushel of storage capacity; the conveyor machinery cost 1 ct. per bushel of storage capacity; and the foundations cost $1\frac{1}{2}$ cts. per bushel of storage capacity; making a total cost of $9\frac{1}{2}$ cts. per bushel of storage capacity. The steel in the working house, including leg casings, hoppers, machinery supports, and all steel except the machinery cost 36 cts. per bushel of storage capacity; the machinery, including cleaning machines, motors, etc., cost 15 cts. per bushel of storage capacity; and the foundations cost 3 cts. per bushel of storage capacity; making a total cost of 54 cts. per bushel of storage capacity. These costs are a fair average.

The total cost of the machinery for a 100,000- or a 300,000-bushel steel working house will be approximately the same as for the 200,000-

bushel working house, while the cost of the steel work and foundations will be approximately the same per bushel as for the 200,000-bushel working house. The cost per bushel of the 100,000-bushel working house will be approximately $36 + 30 + 3 = 69$ cts.; while the cost per bushel of the 300,000-bushel working house will be approximately $36 + 7\frac{1}{2} + 3 = 46\frac{1}{2}$ cts.

Steel storage bins cost from 10 to 15 cents per bushel for large bins to 15 to 20 cents per bushel for small bins, varying with local conditions.

A 30,000 bushel storage for a country mill, consisting of four steel tanks, $17\frac{1}{2}$ ft. diameter and 30 feet high, with an interspace bin and a conveyor shed, contained 41 tons of plates and structural steel and 3 tons of corrugated steel, or about 3 lbs. per bushel of grain storage. The shop labor cost, including distribution, was about $15.00 per ton, while the erection, including riveting and painting, cost $19.00 per ton.

Cost of Country Elevators.—Country elevators in the middle west, having a capacity of from 20,000 to 40,000 bushels, will cost complete from 20 to 25 cents per bushel of capacity if built of timber, and 30 to 40 cents per bushel if built of steel.

COST OF REINFORCED CONCRETE GRAIN BINS.—The

cost of forms for concrete bins is high per M of lumber, but since each section is raised and used for a complete bin, the cost for forms is not excessively large. Framing the forms costs from $10.00 to $15.00 per M. The concrete in place in the walls will cost from $12.00 to $20.00 per cubic yard. To this must be added the cost of the reinforcing steel.

The timber working house of the Santa Fe Elevator, Chicago, Ill., cost $1.00 per bushel of storage capacity exclusive of power plant, while the reinforced concrete storage bins cost 20 cts. per bushel of storage capacity. The machinery in the working house was unusually expensive, which makes the cost per bushel high. In this connection it should be remembered that the machinery and not the storage capacity is the governing consideration in estimating the cost of a working house.

The working house of the Santa Fe reinforced concrete elevator at Argentine, Kas., cost 60 cts. per bushel of storage capacity, exclusive of power plant; while the reinforced concrete bins cost 20 cts. per bushel of storage capacity.

Cost of Reinforced Concrete Stand Pipe.—The 50' × 100' reinforced concrete stand pipe at Attelborough, Mass., cost $34,000 complete, including foundation and roof. This makes 18 cts. per bushel of storage capacity. The walls are 18 inches thick at the bottom, and 8 inches thick at the top. The concrete was 1–2–4 Portland cement concrete and cost in place in the wall per cubic yard as follows:

Cement	$ 4.80
Sand and stone	3.90
Mixing concrete	.40
Placing concrete	2.20
Forms	2.65
Total cost per cu. yd.......................................	$13.95

Bending and placing the steel cost $9.00 per ton, or $2.30 per cubic yard of concrete. There were 770 cubic yards of concrete and 185 tons of steel in the walls.

The cost of moderately large reinforced concrete grain bins is about the same in the middle west as for tile and steel bins. The advantage, if any, in most cases being in favor of the steel bins.

COST OF TILE BINS.—Tile costs from $5.00 to $6.00 per ton at the factory, while the cost of laying the tile will be from 5 to 8 cents per tile. To the cost of the tile must be added the cost of the reinforcing steel and the cement mortar.

In building the tile grain bins 21 feet diameter, for the Canadian Northern Ry., Port Arthur, Ontario, each one thousand tiles took ¾ cubic yard of mortar, and each bricklayer laid 364 tiles per day of 10 hours in the month of November. The entire cost of these bins was 19 cents per bushel of storage capacity. For a description of this elevator and quantities see Chapter XIX.

Tile grain bins cost approximately the same for moderately large bins, under average conditions, as concrete and steel bins, although the steel has the advantage where freights are any considerable item.

Cost of Reinforced Concrete Bins—1911.—The detailed costs of the concrete in the F. C. Ayres reinforced concrete grain elevator are given in Chapter XIX. The cost of building bins with moving forms is very much less than with stationary forms. The type of moving forms used on the above work are the most economical, and have made it possible to materially reduce the cost of reinforced concrete grain bins. With present prices reinforced concrete grain bins and elevators can be built for from 10 to 25 per cent less than steel grain bins and elevators.

The F. C. Ayres reinforced concrete elevator with a capacity of 190,000 bushels storage in the working house, cost $0.34 per bushel of storage capacity. The Grand Trunk reinforced concrete elevator at Fort William, Ontario, described in Chapter XIX, with a capacity of 3,500,000 bushels, cost $0.36 per bushel of storage capacity.

APPENDIX I.

CONCRETE, PLAIN AND REINFORCED.

CHAPTER I.

PLAIN CONCRETE

Introduction.—Concrete is an artificial stone, fabricated by thoroughly mixing cement, sand, and gravel or broken stone, together with sufficient water to produce a mixture of the proper consistency. The mixture is immediately deposited in molds and is well tamped, or where the concrete is wet, the mass is joggled to remove the entrained air and to cause the particles of the mixture to settle into place. Concrete is much stronger in compression than in tension, and plain concrete is well adapted for structural forms in which the principal stresses are compressive. These structures include foundations, dams, retaining walls, piers, abutments, short columns, and arches. In the design of plain concrete structures the tensile strength of the material must generally be neglected.

By the use of steel reinforcement to resist the principal tensile stresses and the stresses due to combined shear and tension or compression, concrete becomes available for use in a great variety of structures. Reinforced concrete is particularly advantageous in beams where both compression and tension exist, and other structures in which the loads cause other than compressive stresses.

The materials and the proper methods for the fabrication of concrete will first be considered, after which a general discussion of the principles and the design of reinforced concrete structures will be gone into as fully as the limited space will permit.

PLAIN CONCRETE. Materials.—The materials used in fabri-

473

cating concrete are cement, a fine aggregate commonly called sand, a coarse aggregate, and water.

CEMENT.—Hydraulic cements are divided into three classes; natural cement, Portland cement, and puzzolan cement. Natural cement concrete is used to a limited extent in unimportant structures where a large amount of masonry at a low cost is more important than strength. Natural cement is not used in reinforced concrete construction. Portland cement is used in making concrete for all important structures, and in reinforced concrete construction. Puzzolan cement is used to a limited extent for massive structures which are not to be exposed to the air, such as foundations for bridges and buildings that are below the water level.

Natural Cement.—Natural cement is the finely pulverized product resulting from the calcination of an argillaceous limestone at a temperature only sufficient to drive off the carbonic acid gas. Natural cement is never used in reinforced concrete construction, and it will not be further considered.

Portland Cement.—Portland cement is the finely pulverized product resulting from the calcination to incipient fusion of an intimate mixture of properly proportioned argillaceous and calcareous materials, to which no addition greater than 3 per cent has been made subsequent to calcination. It is composed of approximately 75 per cent lime and 25 per cent silica. Portland cement is used in reinforced concrete construction, and for all structures that will be subject to shocks or vibrations, or to stresses other than direct compression.

Puzzolan Cement.—Puzzolan, or slag cement, is a finely pulverized product resulting from grinding a mechanical mixture of granulated basic blast-furnace slag and hydrated lime. Puzzolan cement is nearly as strong as Portland cement, but is lacking in toughness, and deteriorates rapidly when exposed to the air. It should never be used in important structures.

Strength of Portland Cement.—The standard tests for Portland cement include the determination of (1) the specific gravity; (2) the fineness; (3) the time of setting; (4) the tensile strength; (5) constancy of volume; (6) a determination of the amount of sulphuric acid and magnesia.

(1) *Specific Gravity.*—The specific gravity of Portland cement, ignited at a low red heat, should not be less than 3.10, and the cement should not show a loss by ignition of more than 4 per cent. The specific gravity of first-class Portland cement will vary from 3.10 to 3.25. A specific gravity below 3.10 indicates either that the cement is underburned, or is adulterated.

(2) *Fineness.*—Portland cement should be of such fineness that it will leave by weight a residue of not more than 8 per cent on the No. 100, and not more than 25 per cent on the No. 200 sieve. In order that there may be chemical action when water is added to the cement, the cement must be finely pulverized; the more finely the cement is pulverized, other conditions being the same, the more sand it will carry and produce a mortar of a given strength. While the exact size of the cement particles required for chemical action is not known, it has been definitely proved by experiment that the residue remaining on the 100 sieve is chemically inert.

(3) *Time of Setting.*—Portland cement should not develop initial set in less than thirty minutes, and should develop hard set in not less than one hour or more than ten hours. The time of setting may be determined by (*a*) the Gilmore needles, or (*b*) the Vicat needle apparatus.

(*a*) When using the Gilmore needles, initial set has taken place when a needle weighing $\frac{1}{4}$ of a pound and having a diameter of $\frac{1}{12}$ of an inch is fully supported on a thick pat, mixed at a normal consistency. Final set is said to have taken place when a needle weighing one pound and having a diameter of $\frac{1}{24}$ of an inch is fully supported on the same pat.

(*b*) When using the Vicat needle apparatus, initial set is said to have taken place when a needle, weighing 300 grams (10.58 oz.) and having a diameter of one mm. (0.039 in.) ceases to pass a point 5 mm. (0.20 in.) above the upper surface of the glass plate. Final set is said to have taken place the moment the needle does not sink visibly into the mass. In making the test with the Vicat needle, the mortar is mixed to a normal consistency and is deposited in a conical hard rubber ring 7 cm. (2.76 in.) in diameter at the base, 4 cm. (1.57 in.) high, and resting on a glass plate.

Cement paste or mortar is mixed at normal consistency when it is mixed with the proper amount of water for molding briquettes. Moisture should just come to the surface when the paste or mortar is firmly pressed into the molds with the thumbs. A standard test for normal consistency with the Vicat needle is described in the tests of the American Society for Testing Materials.

Finely pulverized cement clinker, without the addition of a retarder, gives an initial set in from two to four minutes, and final set in from four to six minutes. To increase the time of initial and final set a retarder consisting of either raw gypsum or burned gypsum (plaster of paris) is added before final grinding. The finer the grinding the more rapid the set, and therefore the greater amount of retarder required. To give sufficient time for depositing concrete in the molds and for other necessary operations, the time of initial set should preferably be from one to two hours, and the time of final set from six to eight hours.

(4) *Tensile Strength.* — The minimum requirements for tensile strength of briquettes one inch square in section should not be less than the following, and should show no retrogression in strength within the period specified.

Age.	*Neat Cement.*	*Strength.*
24 hours in moist air		175 lbs.
7 days (1 day in moist air, 6 days in water).............		500 lbs.
28 days (1 day in moist air, 27 days in water).............		600 lbs.

One part cement, three parts standard Ottawa Sand.

7 days (1 day in moist air, 6 days in water).............		200 lbs.
28 days (1 day in moist air, 27 days in water).............		275 lbs.

The *compressive strength* of Portland cement varies from eight to eleven times the tensile strength. While concrete is used principally in compression, the practice of comparing cements on the basis of their tensile strengths is due principally to the fact that tensile tests can be made with less labor and with less expensive equipment than compression tests.

(5) *Constancy of Volume.*—When cement mortar or concrete sets in air it contracts slightly, and when it sets in water it expands slightly. Cement sets by the chemical action of water on the cement grains with a slight increase in temperature. If cement contains free lime or other chemicals that slake upon the addition of water, there will be an additional increase in the temperature and volume of the mixture. If the adulterant or free lime slakes during the time of mixing it will do little harm, while if its slaking is retarded until after the initial setting of the cement begins it will cause the cement to be unsound. In order that the cement be sound it should pass the following tests: Pats of neat cement about three inches in diameter, one-half inch thick at the center, and tapering to a thin edge, are made and are kept in moist air for a period of twenty-four hours.

(*a*) A pat is then kept in air at normal temperature (70° to 80° F.), and observed at intervals for at least twenty-eight days.

(*b*) Another pat is kept in water maintained as near 70° F. as practicable, and observed at intervals for at least twenty-eight days.

(*c*) A third pat is exposed in any convenient way in an atmosphere of steam, above boiling water, in a loosely closed vessel for five hours.

These pats, to satisfactorily pass the requirements, shall remain firm, hard and show no signs of distortion, checking, cracking, or disintegrating. The boiling test (*c*) is very severe, and cement failing to pass this test should not ordinarily be rejected, but should be held to await the results of the twenty-eight day tests (*b*). In judging the results of the above tests some experience is necessary in order that normal setting cracks which may occur near the edge of the pat shall not be confused with those cracks due to a change of volume. In making the pats the edges should slope upwards from the glass at an angle of about

45 degrees, else the thin edges of the pat will stick to the glass and cause setting cracks.

(6) Finely ground cement has a very much greater sand carrying capacity than coarsely ground cement, so that cement manufacturers are now furnishing cement more finely ground than formerly. To make cement sufficiently slow setting ground or burned gypsum is added. A large percentage of the retarder may cause the cement to be unsound or to deteriorate in the work. In order that the cement be safe, it should contain not more than 1.75 per cent of anhydrous sulphuric acid (SO_3), nor more than 4 per cent of magnesia (MgO).

AGGREGATES.—Care should be used in selecting the aggregates for concrete, and careful tests should be made to determine their qualities, and the grading necessary to secure maximum density, or a minimum percentage of voids.

(*a*) Fine aggregate consists of sand, crushed stone or gravel screenings, passing when dry a screen having ¼ in. diameter holes. It should preferably be siliceous material, clean, coarse, free from vegetable loam, or other deleterious matter. A gradation of the grains from fine to coarse is generally advantageous. Before using any natural sand as a fine aggregate very careful tests should be made to see that it is free from vegetable or organic matter that may retard the setting of the concrete and reduce the strength. Many sands that are apparently clean contain sufficient organic matter to unfit them for use as a fine aggregate.

Mortars composed of one part Portland cement and three parts fine aggregate by weight, when made into briquettes should show a tensile strength of at least 70 per cent of the strength of 1:3 mortar of the same consistency, made with the same cement and standard Ottawa sand. Standard Ottawa sand is a natural bank sand from Ottawa, Illinois, having spherical grains, all of which have passed a No. 20 screen and have been retained on a No. 30 screen.

(*b*) Coarse aggregate consists of inert material, such as crushed stone, gravel, or crushed slag, which is retained on a screen having ¼ in. diameter holes. The particles should be clean, hard, durable, and free from all deleterious material. Aggregates containing soft, flat or elongated particles should not be used. A gradation of sizes of the particles is advantageous.

The maximum size of the coarse aggregate should be such that it will not separate from the mortar in laying, and will not prevent the concrete from fully surrounding the reinforcement and filling all parts of the forms. Where concrete is used in mass, the size of the coarse aggregate may be such as to pass a 3 in. ring. For reinforced concrete members the aggregate that will pass a 1 in. ring, or a smaller size may be used.

Blast-furnace or smelter slag that is broken to the proper size by crushing, and not by granulating in water, makes a very satisfactory aggregate.

Cinder concrete is not suitable for reinforced concrete structures, and may be safely used only for filling or for fire-proofing. Cinder aggregate should be composed of hard, clean, vitreous clinker, free from sulphides, under-burned coal, or ashes.

The strength of concrete depends upon the strength and amount of cement, the strength and grading of the aggregate, and the density.

WATER.—The water used in mixing concrete should be reasonably clear, and should be free from oil, acid, alkali, or vegetable matter. When mixing concrete in cool weather the water should be heated to raise the temperature of the mixture.

PROPORTIONING CONCRETE.—The materials used in making concrete should be carefully selected, of uniform quality, and should be proportioned with a view to securing as nearly as possible the maximum density. The proportions in mixing concrete are determined by volume, the unit of measure being the barrel, which should be taken as containing 3.8 cu. ft. Four bags containing 94 pounds of cement each should be considered as the equivalent of one barrel. Fine and coarse aggregate should be measured separately as loosely thrown into the measuring vessel.

Other things being equal the strength of the concrete varies as the density. The proportions of cement, fine and coarse aggregate may be determined: (a) By arbitrary proportions, such as one part of Portland cement, two parts fine aggregate, and four parts coarse aggregate, ordinarily written 1:2:4, or 1:3:6, etc. (b) By determination of the voids in the fine and coarse aggregate; sufficient cement being used to more than fill the voids in the fine aggregate, and sufficient mortar being used to more than fill the voids in the coarse aggregate; an increase in cement and mortar being necessary on account of the coating of the particles of fine and coarse aggregate with cement or mortar, thus increasing the total volume. (c) By making trial mixtures, in order to determine a concrete of maximum density. Ordinarily the ratio of cement to fine aggregate is arbitrarily determined, and the fine and coarse aggregate are graded to determine the necessary proportions for a concrete of maximum density. (d) By a mechanical analysis of the fine and coarse aggregates, it having been found that the maximum density is obtained when the sizes follow the ordinates of a mechanical analysis curve, the amount of each size being plotted as the abscissa of the curve. The sizes of the fine and coarse aggregates may vary considerably, and care should be used to see that the proper proportions to meet the varying sizes are uniformly maintained.

In mass concrete the proportions in use vary from 1:2:4 where great strength is required, to 1:3:5 or 1:3:6 for massive work, and to 1:4:8 where concrete is used in a large mass and strength is not a requisite. For reinforced concrete construction density proportions based on 1:2:4 should generally be used, i. e., one part of cement to a total of six parts of fine and coarse aggregates, measured separately. The proper proportions should be determined by the strength or wearing qualities required in the construction at the critical period of its use. In interpreting the proportions for concrete, 1:2:4 concrete is often confused with 1:6 concrete in which a fine and coarse aggregate are measured together. A considerable portion of the fine aggregate will be included in the volume of the coarse aggregate, and 1:2:4 concrete will ordinarily be a 1:4½, and not a 1:6 mixture.

The percentage of voids in fine and coarse aggregate will vary from thirty to fifty per cent; under usual conditions being forty-five per cent of voids for each.

The amount of materials required for a cubic yard of concrete for the above proportions may be obtained by trial, or approximate quantities may be obtained by calculation. The materials required for one cubic yard of concrete, in which the voids in the fine and coarse aggregate are forty to forty-five per cent, are very closely given by the following rule, proposed by William B. Fuller and known as Fuller's rule:

Let $c =$ number parts of cement;

$s =$ number parts of sand;

$g =$ number parts of gravel or broken stone.

Then $\dfrac{11}{c+s+g} = p =$ number of barrels of Portland cement required for one cu. yd. of concrete.

$\dfrac{p \times s \times 3.8}{27} =$ number of cu. yds. of sand required for one cu. yd. of concrete.

$\dfrac{p \times g \times 3.8}{27} =$ number of cu. yds. of stone or gravel required for one cu. yd. of concrete.

The materials as calculated by Fuller's rule for one cu. yd. of concrete with different proportions are for $1:2:4$ concrete, cement 1.57 barrels, sand 0.44 cu. yd., gravel or stone 0.88 cu. yd.; $1:3:6$ concrete, cement 1.10 barrels, sand 0.46 cu. yd., gravel or stone 0.93 cu. yd.

MIXING.—The ingredients of concrete should be thoroughly mixed to the desired consistency, and the mixing should continue until the cement is uniformly distributed and the mass is uniform in color and homogeneous, since maximum density and therefore the greatest strength of a given mixture depends largely on thorough and complete mixing. A machine mixer in which the proportions are definitely determined and the mortar is forced into all interstices of the fine and coarse aggregate, will produce a concrete of greater density and strength than is ordinarily obtained by hand mixing.

31

(*a*) **Measuring Ingredients.**—Measurements of the proportions of the various ingredients, including the water, should be used which will secure separate uniform measurements at all times.

(*b*) **Machine Mixing.**—When the conditions will permit, a machine mixer of a type which insures a uniform proportioning of the materials throughout the mass should be used, since a more thorough and uniform consistency can thus be obtained. A mixer of the batch type into which the materials, including the water, have been definitely measured, and in which all parts of the batch have exactly the same treatment, will produce a more uniform concrete than can be obtained by the use of a mixer of an intermittent or continuous type. Mixers of the batch type are also more effective for mixing concrete in cold or freezing weather, where the frost may be removed from the aggregate by the addition of boiling water before adding the cement, and the entire batch can be reduced to a uniform temperature.

(*c*) **Hand Mixing.**—When it is necessary to mix concrete by hand, the mixing should be done on a water-tight platform of sufficient size for the mixing of two batches of $\frac{1}{2}$ cu. yd. or less at one time. First, spread the fine aggregate upon the mixing board, then spread the cement upon the fine aggregate, then thoroughly mix the cement and fine aggregate by turning with shovels until the mixture is of a uniform color. The coarse aggregate is then added, after first being wet down, and the entire mass is mixed by turning with shovels until the mortar and stone are thoroughly incorporated and the entire mass is of a uniform color, water being added as the mixing proceeds.

(*d*) **Consistency.**—The materials for reinforced concrete construction should be mixed wet enough to produce a concrete of such consistency as will flow into the forms, and about the metal reinforcement, and at the same time can be conveyed from the mixer to the forms without the separation of the coarse aggregate from the mortar. Where the concrete is deposited on a slope as in the case of inclined bin bottoms, or where the forms are to be removed before the concrete is hard set, as in the case of a concrete curb, care should be used to mix the concrete with sufficient water so that moisture will come to the top only when the concrete is thoroughly rammed. On most work concrete is mixed very wet, except where special requirements make the use of dry concrete necessary. It was formerly believed that concrete should be deposited in a moist condition and be thoroughly tamped, and that a wet mixture gave a porous, weak concrete. Experience and tests have shown that wet mixtures give a more uniform and denser concrete than dry mixtures, and that the cost of mixing and laying is much less. Ordinarily considerably more water is used in the mixture than is necessary for chemical action, the excess water rising to the top of the concrete in the forms. Part of this water will later be reabsorbed by the concrete and the rest will evaporate. The excess water carries a material called "laitance" to the top of the mixture, which material must be removed before depositing additional concrete. Specifications ordinarily require that concrete shall be placed in the forms within thirty minutes after it has been mixed and that retempering concrete, *i. e.*, remixing with water after it has partially set, shall not be permitted. In building reinforced concrete structures it is not possible to complete the necessary work on the mixture within thirty minutes, and a cement should be used in which the initial set is from one to one and one-half hours, in place of thirty minutes as required in standard specifications. Under ordinary conditions this will increase the length of time in which concrete may be worked after being mixed from one and one-half to two hours.

Depositing Concrete.—Concrete, after the addition of water to the mix, should be handled rapidly and in as small masses as is practicable, from the place of mixing to the forms, and under no circumstances should concrete be used that is partially set before final placing. A slow setting cement should be used when a long time is likely to occur between the mixing and the final placing. The concrete should be deposited so as to permit a thorough compacting, such as can be obtained by working with a straight shovel or slicing tool kept moving up and down until all the ingredients have settled in their proper places by gravity, and the surplus water has been forced to the surface. Where a dry mix is used, the concrete should be thoroughly tamped with a heavy rammer, in layers of from four to six inches. Before placing the concrete, care should be taken to see that the forms are substantial and thoroughly wet, and that the space to be occupied by the concrete is free from débris. When the placing of the concrete is suspended, all necessary grooves for joining future work should be made before the concrete has had time to set. When work is resumed, concrete previously placed should be roughened, thoroughly cleansed of foreign material and laitance, drenched and slushed with a mortar consisting of one part Portland cement and not more than two parts fine aggregate. The faces of concrete exposed to drying should be kept wet for a period of at least three days, when the weather is above freezing.

Concrete should not be deposited under water unless care is exercised to prevent the cement from being floated away, and to prevent the formation of laitance, which hardens very slowly and forms a poor surface on which to deposit fresh concrete. Laitance is formed in both still and running water, and should always be removed before placing fresh concrete. Concrete may be placed in water by means of a tube extending to the surface in which the concrete is to be deposited, and which is kept at all times full of concrete; by means of tight buckets with a bottom dump, or in loosely filled burlap bags.

Concrete should not be mixed or deposited at a freezing temperature, unless special precautions are taken to avoid the use of materials containing frost, and to provide means of preventing the concrete from freezing after being placed in position until it is thoroughly hardened. It has been proved that mass concrete is not seriously injured by freezing, providing it is fully protected from the air until after the frost has gone out of the mass, and the concrete has hard set. Where concrete is deposited in forms in freezing weather the frost remains largely on the surface of the concrete, causing it to scale when the forms are removed. In mass concrete the freezing temperature of the concrete may be lowered by the addition of salt, in proportions of 8 to 12 pounds to a barrel of cement. Salt is not used in reinforced concrete construction on account of the corrosive action of salt on steel. The value of salt in concrete deposited at freezing temperature is problematical, and the author has used the following specification for making and depositing concrete in cold weather for both plain and reinforced concrete structures: "When the temperature of the air is below 40° F. during the time of mixing and placing concrete, the water used in mixing concrete shall be heated to such a temperature that the temperature of the concrete mixture shall not be less than 60° F. when it reaches its final position in the forms. Care shall be used that the cement shall not be injured by boiling water." To obtain satisfactory results with hot water a batch mixer should be used. The fine and coarse aggregates should first be placed in the mixer, then practically all of the hot water should be added and the mixer should be given several turns to raise the temperature of the aggregates. The cement should then be added, together with the remainder of the water, and the mixer should be turned until the mass is thoroughly incorporated, and the frost is removed from the aggregates. The number of turns required to properly heat the aggregates will depend principally upon the maximum size of the coarse aggregate, but it will ordinarily require twice the number of turns that are made in ordinary weather for thorough mixing. In freezing weather the concrete should be carried in buckets or carts to the forms without delay. Concrete may be spouted from the mixer to the forms in ordinary weather without injury. In freezing weather, however, the concrete will be so chilled that spouting should not be permitted.

EFFECT OF SEA WATER ON CONCRETE.—Many important concrete structures built in sea water have remained in good condition after many years. A few concrete structures built in America, and many concrete structures built in Europe have been seriously damaged by the action of sea water. Injury in most of the cases is limited to the space between high and low water mark. The decomposition manifests itself in various ways; (a) the mortar may soften and finally disintegrate; (b) the mortar becomes covered with a crust which finally cracks off; (c) or more often fine white veins develop on the surface of the mortar which gradually grow large and open, and the mortar changes to a pulp-like mass. The deterioration of concrete by sea water is (1) partly chemical, due to the action of the sulphates of the water on the cement, and (2) partly mechanical, due to the formation of crystals in the concrete producing an action similar to frost. Cements which are richest in lime decompose the most quickly in sea water. While the action of sea water upon concrete is not fully understood, good results will in most cases be obtained by using the following precautions:

(a) Use a Portland cement low in aluminum, and as low as possible in lime. Puzzolanic material—ground basic slag—is a valuable addition to the cement.

(b) The cement should contain as little gypsum as possible to regulate the time of setting.

(c) The sand should not contain a large proportion of fine grains, but should preferably be coarse.

(d) The proportions of the aggregate should be such as to produce a dense, impervious concrete, and the concrete should be deposited with great care, the forms being permitted to remain in place for several weeks.

EFFECT OF ALKALI UPON CONCRETE.—The action of alkali and alkali water upon concrete is very similar to the action of sea water. In constructing concrete structures in the arid regions and other localities having alkali in the soil and water, the following precautions should be taken: (a) Chemical tests should be made of the sand and coarse aggregate to make sure that it does not carry alkali in dangerous quantities. Physical tests should be made to check the chemical analyses. (b) The water used in mixing the concrete should be free from alkali. (c) The proportions of the cement and aggregate should be such as to produce a dense, impervious concrete. Before deciding upon the proportions numerous tests should be made to determine the proportions of the cement and the aggregates that will produce a concrete of maximum density. Concrete should be rich in cement to make the concrete impervious to water and strong enough to resist the mechanical action of the alkali, which may percolate the mass. (*d*) Concrete should be deposited in tight forms from which the surface water has been removed. The forms should be permitted to remain on the concrete for several weeks or until it is thoroughly hardened.

WATER-TIGHTNESS.—Concrete under ordinary conditions is permeable to water, but may be rendered water-tight in several different ways:

(1) Use such proportions of cement and aggregate as will produce a concrete of maximum density; mix the concrete thoroughly to a wet consistency, and place the entire mixture in one continuous operation. If joints can not be avoided, the concrete should be suitably reinforced with steel to prevent cracks due to setting, expansion and contraction.

(2) After the concrete has been placed the surface may be made waterproof by a special preparation. (*a*) The surface of the concrete may be plastered with 1:1 or 1:2 Portland cement mortar. This treatment is of value only where the surface is not exposed to the air. (*b*) Before the concrete has set the surface may be given a granolithic surface of rich Portland cement mortar in a manner similar to sidewalk construction. (*c*) The surface of the concrete may be treated with a wash of alum and concentrated potash lye, mixed in proportions of one pound of lime, two to five pounds of alum, and two gallons of water. This wash should be applied several times to give satisfactory results. Or the surface may be treated with alternate washes of soft soap and alum. The soft soap wash should have one part of soap to one part of water, while the alum wash should have ½ pound of alum to four gallons of water. The soft soap wash should be applied when boiling hot. When the soap wash has become dry and hard the alum wash should be applied. The operation should be repeated until satisfactory results are obtained. With the exception of castile soap, hard soaps are made from soda and do not give satisfactory results.

(3) In a lean concrete the addition of lime or puzzolan cement makes

the concrete more dense, and therefore more nearly impermeable, and at the same time increases the strength of the concrete. In lean concrete the addition of pure clay up to five per cent has been found to make concrete more nearly water-tight. Similar results may be obtained by the addition of finely pulverized alum or other colloidal matter. There are also many patented preparations of more or less value for making concrete water-proof. The addition of an alum and soap mixture, made by taking one part of cement, two and one-half parts of sand, three-fourths pound of pulverized alum, mixed dry, to one cubic foot of sand, then adding three-fourths of a pound of soft soap to one gallon of water, has been found to make a mortar practically impervious to water without materially decreasing the strength. While the addition of the various materials mentioned above are effective in increasing the water-tightness of lean concrete, no material is as effective or as cheap for obtaining water-tightness as Portland cement, used in sufficient quantities to make a strong, dense concrete.

(4) The surface of the concrete may be made water-proof by the application of layers of water-proof material, laid with a coal tar preparation or with asphalt, in a manner similar to that employed in laying composition roofs. Where this water-proof coating is to be exposed, burlap should be used in the place of roofing felt. A $\frac{1}{4}$-in. coating of asphalt applied hot with a mop has been successfully used.

The cheapest and most satisfactory water-proof coating to be applied to the backs of concrete structures is a coal tar paint, made by mixing refined coal tar, Portland cement and kerosene in the proportions of sixteen parts coal tar, four parts Portland cement, three parts kerosene. The Portland cement should first be stirred into the kerosene, forming a creamy mixture, which is then stirred into the coal tar. The paint should be thoroughly mixed and kept well stirred. In cold weather the coal tar may be slightly heated, the quantity of kerosene being increased to make good the loss due to evaporation. This coal tar paint, applied to the dry surface of hardened concrete, has been found to sink $\frac{1}{8}$ of an inch into the mass, making it absolutely water-proof. Several coats of the coal tar paint may be required.

STRENGTH OF CONCRETE.—The strength of plain concrete depends upon the quality of the cement, the strength and character of the aggregate, the quantity of cement in a unit volume, and the density of the concrete. Other things being equal the strongest concrete is that containing the largest amount of cement in a given volume of concrete, the strength of the concrete varying directly as the amount of cement. With a given quantity of cement to a unit of volume, the strongest concrete is that in which the aggregates are proportioned so as to give a concrete of the greatest density, that is of the greatest weight per unit of volume. The strength of concrete also depends upon the methods used in mixing, upon the care taken in measuring the ingredients, and in mixing and placing the concrete. Concrete exposed to the air hardens more rapidly than protected concrete. The setting of cement is a chemical change brought about by the addition of water to the cement, the strength increasing very rapidly for the first few days, after which the mixture slowly hardens and increases in strength. Cements which show up well on twenty-eight day tests sometimes drop rapidly when tested for longer intervals. Cements showing an appreciable falling off should be rejected.

Compressive Strength.—The compressive strength of plain concrete varies between wide limits, depending upon the cement, the proportions of cement and aggregates, and the methods of mixing and depositing, and the age. With first-class Portland cement, clean sand, and stone equal to a first-class limestone or sandstone in which the percentages of voids in the sand and the stone are about 45 per cent, the average values at the age of one month and six months are given in Table I.

TABLE I.

COMPRESSIVE STRENGTH OF PORTLAND CEMENT CONCRETE IN LBS. PER SQ. IN.

Proportions.	Age, 1 Month.	Age, 6 Months.
1 cement, 2 sand, 4 broken stone......................	2,440	3,300
1 cement, 2 sand, 5 broken stone......................	2,350	3,180
1 cement, 3 sand, 5 broken stone......................	2,030	2,740
1 cement, 3 sand, 6 broken stone......................	1,950	2,630
1 cement, 3 sand, 8 broken stone......................	1,800	2,400
1 cement, 4 sand, 8 broken stone......................	1,570	2,120

A good gravel concrete may be stronger than a broken stone concrete, but may ordinarily be taken at from 75 to 80 per cent of the strength of the broken stone concrete in Table I.

The compressive strength of concrete, other things being equal, increases with the size of the aggregate. The compressive strength of concrete having a high-grade aggregate will be greater where the maximum particles of aggregate are three inches in diameter than where they are one and one-half inches in diameter, and greater when the particles are one and one-half inches in diameter than where they are three-fourths inch in diameter. The compressive strength of concrete increases very rapidly for the first 60 or 90 days, after which the strength increases very slowly.

Tensile Strength.—The tensile strength of concrete is difficult to determine by direct tensile tests, and has been for the most part determined by flexure tests on beams. The transverse tensile strength is probably somewhat greater than the direct tensile stresses. Experiments on beams give the modulus of rupture in tension as from one-sixth to one-eleventh of the compressive strength of concrete. It is commonly assumed that the tensile strength of concrete is one-tenth of the compressive strength. Since the tensile strength of concrete in reinforced concrete construction is neglected, the tensile strength of concrete is of relatively little value.

Shearing Strength.—It is difficult to determine the shearing strength of concrete, failure being due in most cases to diagonal tension, a combination of shearing stresses with tensile or compressive stresses. The recent tests would show that the shearing strength of concrete is from 60 to 80 per cent of the compressive strength. This strength of concrete in direct shear must not be confused with shearing failures due to diagonal tension, where concrete may fail with a so-called shearing stress of 10 to 15 per cent of the compressive strength.

Modulus of Elasticity.—The modulus of elasticity of concrete depends upon the proportions and ingredients of the concrete, upon the age of the concrete, and upon the stresses, the modulus of elasticity decreasing as the stress increases. Within the range of the ordinary working stresses of 600 to 800 pounds per square inch, the modulus of elasticity of any given concrete may be assumed as a constant. The moduli given in Table II may be taken as average values for a first-class Portland cement concrete.

TABLE II.

MODULUS OF ELASTICITY OF PORTLAND CEMENT CONCRETE.

Proportions.	Modulus of Elasticity, lbs. per Sq. In.
1 : 1½ : 3	4,000,000
1 : 2 : 4	3,000,000
Broken stone or gravel concretes......1 : 2½ : 5	2,500,000
1 : 3 : 6	2,000,000
1 : 4 : 8	1,500,000
Cinder Concrete............ .... 1 : 2 : 5	850,000

In the design of reinforced concrete structures it is the usual practice to assume 2,000,000 as the modulus of elasticity of 1 : 2 : 4 Portland cement concrete.

Bond Strength.—The adhesion of concrete and reinforcing bars depends upon the concrete and the surface of the steel. Tests on round or square bars give results varying from 250 to 750 lbs. per sq. in. The adhesion of concrete and deformed bars is ordinarily somewhat larger than with plain round or square bars. The adhesion of concrete and plain round or square bars is larger than with flat bars. After the initial slip the frictional resistance is about 75 per cent of the ultimate strength with plain bars, while with deformed bars and hooked bars the ultimate strength is not developed until the initial slip has taken place. It has been the practice in Germany to use plain round or square bars and to hook the ends whenever possible. The hooks are made by bending the bar 180° about a diameter of 2½ to 3 diameters, with a piece of straight bar beyond the bend. Experiments by Bach show that the initial slip is only slightly retarded but that the ultimate bond strength is increased approximately 50 per cent over a straight plain round or square bar. It would therefore appear that the working bond stress for plain round or square bars with hooked ends should be as large as for well designed deformed bars.

Expansion and Contraction.—The coefficient of expansion of concrete is practically the same as for steel, about 0.0000065. Concrete is sensitive to temperature changes and expansion joints should be provided in all concrete structures not reinforced to take temperature stresses. No amount of reinforcing steel will entirely prevent contraction cracks. The reinforcement will, however, distribute the cracks over the section, the greater the amount of reinforcement, the more uniformly the cracks will be distributed, and the smaller the individual cracks. The size and distribution of the cracks will also depend upon the bond stress of the rods.

In calculating the steel required to reinforce for expansion and contraction, the temperature stresses in the steel must be considered. If the drop in temperature in the steel be 50° the temperature stress in the steel $= 50 \times 0.0000065 \times 30,000,000 = 9,750$ pounds per sq. in. If the tensile strength of the concrete be 200 pounds per sq. in. and the elastic limit of the steel be 30,000 pounds per sq. in., the available stress $= 40,000 - 9,750 = 30,250$ pounds per sq. in., and the required percentage of steel is $p = \dfrac{200}{30,250} = 0.0066$ (0.66 per cent). If the elastic limit be 60,000 pounds per sq. in. the steel ratio $= p = 0.004$ (0.4 per cent). For temperature reinforcement bars made of high elastic limit steel are desirable.

While the calculations show that the percentage of longitudinal steel reinforcement for expansion and contraction should be from 0.4 per cent to 0.66 per cent, yet experience shows that walls reinforced with from 0.1 per cent to 0.3 per cent gives very satisfactory results where foundations are stable. Where there is a tendency for the wall to be thrown out of line the full amount of reinforcement should be used. The reinforcing steel for temperature stresses should be placed as near the exposed faces as practicable, and the rods should preferably be of small size.

The American Railway Engineering Association recommends that reinforced concrete structures be reinforced for shrinkage and temperature with not less than 0.33 per cent of reinforcement of a type of bar capable of developing high bond stress and placed near the surface of the exposed concrete.

Fireproofing.—The thickness of concrete necessary to protect the steel reinforcement from fire depends upon the quality of the concrete, and upon the member. Large members carrying maximum stresses should have a thicker covering than small bars slightly stressed. Results of fire tests show that for large members such as columns and girders $2''$ to $2\frac{1}{2}''$ furnishes ample protection, while for floor slabs from $\frac{3}{4}''$ to $1''$ is sufficient. Concrete should be thicker on corners and exposed members than on large flat surfaces.

Rust Protection.—Tests have shown that steel coated with a mortar grout are perfectly protected from corrosion. Where the concrete is mixed wet and care is used to thoroughly coat the steel reinforcement there is no danger from corrosion, even when a cinder or porous concrete is used.

CHAPTER II.

Data for the Design of Reinforced Concrete Structures.

(1) **Materials.**—The materials and workmanship for reinforced concrete shall meet the requirements of the "Specifications for Plain and Reinforced Concrete," given in Chapter IV.

The concrete recommended for general use is a mixture of one part Portland cement, two parts of fine aggregate, and four parts of coarse aggregate. A mixture of one part of Portland cement, three parts of fine aggregate, and six parts of coarse aggregate may be used in monolithic walls and foundations.

(2) **Dimensions.**—The span length for beams and slabs is to be taken as the distance from center to center of the supports, but is not to exceed a clear span plus the depth of beam or slab.

(3) **Internal Stresses.**—The internal stresses are to be calculated upon the basis of the following assumptions:

(*a*) A plane section before bending remains plane after bending.

(*b*) The distribution of compressive stresses in members subject to bending is rectilinear.

(*c*) The ratio of the moduli of elasticity of steel and concrete is $n = 15$.

(*d*) The tensile stresses in the concrete are neglected in calculating the moment of resistance of beams.

(*e*) The initial stress in the reinforcement due to contraction and expansion in the concrete is neglected.

(*f*) The depth of a beam is to be taken as the distance from the compressive face to the centroid of the tension reinforcement.

(*g*) The effective depth of a beam at any section is the distance from the centroid of the compressive stresses to the centroid of the tension reinforcement ($j.d$).

494

(*h*) Perfect adhesion is assumed between concrete and reinforcement. In compressive stress the two materials are therefore stressed in proportion to their moduli of elasticity.

(*i*) The maximum shearing unit stress in beams is to be taken as the total shear at the section divided by the product of the width of the section and the effective depth of the section considered ($v = V \div b.j.d$). This maximum shearing unit stress is to be used in place of the diagonal tension stress in calculations for web stresses.

(*j*) The bond unit stress is equal to the vertical shear divided by the product of the total perimeter of the reinforcement in the tension side of the beam and the effective depth at the section considered ($u = V \div j.d.\Sigma o$).

(*k*) In concrete columns, walls and slabs, concrete to a depth of $1\frac{1}{2}$ inches and in floor slabs 1 inch is to be considered as a protective covering, and is not to be included in the effective section.

(4) **Web Stresses.**—When the maximum shearing stresses exceed the value allowed for the concrete alone, web reinforcement must be provided to aid in carrying the diagonal tensile stresses. This web reinforcement may consist of bent-up bars or inclined or vertical members, attached to or hooked around the horizontal reinforcement. Where inclined members are used, the connection to the horizontal reinforcement shall be such as to insure against slip.

In the calculation of web reinforcement when the concrete alone is insufficient to take the diagonal tension, the concrete may be assumed to carry a shear of 40 pounds per square inch. The remainder of the shear is to be carried by metal reinforcement consisting of bent-up bars or stirrups, but preferably both. The requisite amount of such reinforcement may be estimated on the assumption that the entire shear on a section, less the amount assumed to be carried by the concrete, is carried by the reinforcement.

(5) **Working Stresses.**—The following working stresses are to be used with concrete of such a quality as to be capable of developing an average compressive strength of at least 2,000 pounds per square inch,

when tested in cylinders 6 inches in diameter and 6 inches long, after having been stored one day in air and 27 days in water, under laboratory conditions of manufacture and storage, the mixture being of the same consistency as is used in the field.

Allowable stress in pounds per square inch.

Structural steel in tension 16,000

Steel in compression, fifteen times the compressive stresses in the surrounding concrete.

Concrete in bearing, where the total surface is at least twice the bearing area 650

Concrete in direct compression without reinforcement, on a length not exceeding six times the least width 450

Columns in which the unsupported length is not more than fifteen times the least width are to be designed for the following stresses:

(*a*) Columns with not less than 1 nor more than 4 per cent of longitudinal reinforcement only 450

(*b*) Columns reinforced with bands or hoops spaced not less than $\frac{1}{4}$ the diameter of the column. The total amount of reinforcement being not less than 1 per cent of the inclosed column 540

(*c*) Columns reinforced with not less than 1 per cent nor more than 4 per cent of longitudinal bars and with bands or hoops as in (*b*)...................... 650

(*d*) Columns reinforced with structural steel column-units that thoroughly incase the concrete core 650

Concrete in compression, on extreme fiber in cross-bending ... 650

Concrete in shear not combined with tension or compression in concrete 120

Concrete in shear, where the shearing stress is used as the measure of web stress 40

Concrete in shear where part of the rods are bent up to take diagonal tension 60

Concrete in shear where the beam is completely reinforced for
shear and diagonal tension 120

Bond stress for plain round or square bars 80

Bond stress for plain round or square bars with hooked ends
bent 180° around a diameter of 3 diameters of the bar and
with a short length of bar extending beyond the bend 100

Bond stress for drawn wire 40

Bond stress for deformed bars depending upon form 80–150

CHAPTER III.

The following formulas are based upon the assumptions and principles given in Chapter II.

STANDARD NOTATION. 1. Rectangular Beams.

f_s = tensile unit stress in steel.

f_c = compressive unit stress in concrete.

ϵ_s = elongation of steel due to f_s.

ϵ_c = shortening of concrete due to f_c.

E_s = modulus of elasticity of steel.

E_c = modulus of elasticity of concrete.

$n = \dfrac{E_s}{E_c}$.

M_s = moment of resistance relative to the steel.

M_c = moment of resistance relative to the concrete.

M = moment of resistance, or bending moment in general.

A = steel area.

T = total tension.

C = total compression.

b = breadth of beam.

d = depth of beam to center of steel.

k = ratio of depth of neutral axis to depth d.

z = depth of resultant compression below top of beam.

j = ratio of lever arm to resisting couple to depth d.

$j.d = d - z$ = arm of resisting couple.

$p = \dfrac{A}{b.d}$ = steel ratio (not percentage).

$R_s = f_s.p.j$ = coefficient of strength relative to steel.

$R_c = \tfrac{1}{2}f_c.k.j$ = coefficient of strength relative to concrete.

498

2. **T-Beams.**
> $b =$ width of flange.
>
> $b' =$ width of stem or web.
>
> $t =$ thickness of flange.

3. **Beams Reinforced for Compression.**
> $A' =$ area of compressive steel.
>
> $p' =$ steel ratio for compressive steel.
>
> $f_s' =$ compressive unit stress in steel.
>
> $C' =$ total compressive stress in steel.
>
> $d' =$ depth to center of compressive steel.
>
> $z =$ depth to resultant of C and C'.

4. **Shear and Bond.**
> $V =$ total shear.
>
> $v =$ maximum shearing unit stress $= V/bjd$.
>
> $v' =$ average shearing unit stress $= V/bd$.
>
> $u =$ bond stress per unit area of bar.
>
> $o =$ circumference or perimeter of bar.
>
> $\Sigma o =$ sum of perimeters of bars.

5. **Columns.**
> $A =$ total net area of column.
>
> $A_s =$ area of longitudinal steel.
>
> $A_c =$ area of concrete.
>
> $p = \dfrac{A_s}{A} =$ steel ratio for longitudinal steel.
>
> $p' =$ steel ratio of the hoops of hooped columns.
>
> $P =$ strength of plain concrete column.
>
> $P' =$ strength of reinforced column.
>
> $f =$ average unit stress for entire cross-section.

STRESSES IN RECTANGULAR BEAMS.—In (c), Fig. 1, b is the breadth, d is the depth of the beam above the center of the reinforcing steel, $k.d$ is the distance of the neutral axis below the top of the beam, and $j.d$ is the arm of the resisting couple, k and j being ratios.

In (*a*) the deformations are shown to be proportional to the distances from the neutral axis, and in (*b*) the stress in the steel is n times the stress in the concrete at the same distance from the neutral axis.

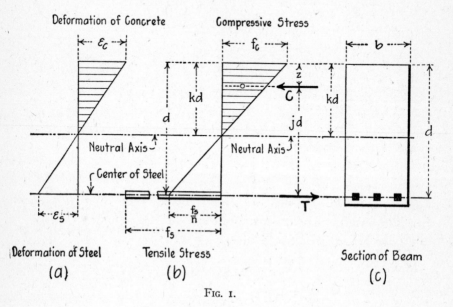

FIG. I.

Neutral Axis and Arm of Resisting Couple.—Now the sum of the horizontal compressive stresses is equal to the horizontal tensile stress, and

$$\tfrac{1}{2}f_c.b.k.d = f_s.A \tag{1}$$

Substituting the value of $A = p.b.d$, and reducing

$$\tfrac{1}{2}f_c.k = f_s.p \tag{2}$$

From (*b*) Fig. I, we have

$$f_c : f_s/n :: k.d : d(1-k),$$

and

$$f_s.k.d = f_c.n.d(1-k)$$
$$f_s.k = f_c.n(1-k) \tag{3}$$

Substituting the value of f_s in (2) in (3)

$$\tfrac{1}{2}f_c.k^2 = f_c.p.n(1-k),$$

and

$$k^2 = 2p.n(1-k)$$

$$k = \sqrt{2p.n + p^2.n^2} - p.n \tag{4}$$

This formula shows that k is a constant for all beams having a given percentage of reinforcement and the same grade of concrete. The values of k for $n = 15$ and for different values of p are given in the upper part of Fig. 2.

The centroid of the compressive stresses is $z = \tfrac{1}{3}k.d$ below the top of the beam, and the arm of the resisting couple is

$$j.d = d - \tfrac{1}{3}k.d, \text{ or } j = 1 - \tfrac{1}{3}k \tag{5}$$

Values of j for $n = 15$ and for different values of p are given in Fig. 2. It will be seen that for $f_s = 15,000$ to $16,000$ lbs. per sq. in. and $f_c = 600$ to 650 lbs. per sq. in., j may be taken as $\tfrac{7}{8}$.

Moment of Resistance.—If the beam is under-reinforced its strength will depend on the steel, and

$$M_s = T.j.d = f_s.A.j.d = f_s.p.j.b.d^2 \tag{6}$$

If the beam is over-reinforced its strength will depend on the concrete, and

$$M_c = C.j.d = \tfrac{1}{2}f_c.b.k.d.j.d = \tfrac{1}{2}f_c.k.j.b.d^2 \tag{7}$$

The resisting moment of the beam is the smaller of the two values of M. Now if $R_s = f_s.p.j$, and $R_c = \tfrac{1}{2}f_c.k.j$, equations (6) and (7) become

$$M_s = R_s.b.d^2 \tag{6a}$$

$$M_c = R_c.b.d^2 \tag{7a}$$

$$d = \sqrt{\frac{M}{R.b}} \tag{6b}$$

Fiber Stresses.—To calculate the unit fiber stresses for a given bending moment solve equations (6) and (7), and

$$f_s = \frac{T}{A} = \frac{M}{A.j.d} = \frac{M}{p.j.b.d^2} \tag{8}$$

$$f_c = \frac{2M}{b.k.j.d^2} = \frac{2f_s.p}{k} \tag{9}$$

Steel Ratio.—If k be eliminated by solving equations (2) and (3) the steel ratio will be

$$p = \frac{\frac{1}{2}}{\frac{f_s}{f_c}\left(\frac{f_s}{nf_c} + 1\right)} \tag{10}$$

If a value of p less than that given by (10) is used the steel determines the strength of the beam, while if p is greater the concrete will determine the strength of the beam.

Diagram for Rectangular Beams.—In Fig. 2 are given values of k and j for $n = 15$ and for different values of p. Values of $R_c = \frac{M}{b.d^2}$ are given for different values of f_c and p, and values of $R_s = \frac{M}{b.d^2}$ are given for different values of f_s and p. The use of the table will be shown by three problems.

Problem 1. Moment of Resistance.—Given the following data: $b = 10''$, $d = 20''$, $f_s = 16,000$ lbs., $f_c = 600$ lbs., 2 steel bars $1'' \square$ ($p = 0.01$), find M_s and M_c.

Solution.—In Fig. 2 find the value of percentage of reinforcement $p = 1$ per cent, on lower margin and follow the vertical line to curved line $f_c = 600$, then follow to the left on a horizontal line and find $R_c = 107$ on left margin. In like manner $R_s = 138$, which will over-stress the concrete. The resisting moment will then be $M = R_c.b.d^2$ $= 107 \times 10 \times 20^2 = 428,000$ in.-lbs.

Problem 2. Fiber Stresses.—Given the following data: $b = 10''$, $d = 20''$, $p = 0.009$ (0.9 per cent), $M = 360,000$ in.-lbs., find f_s and f_c.

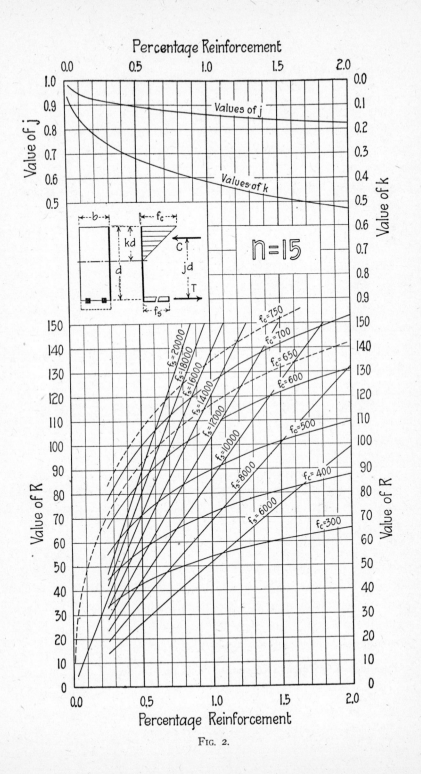

Fig. 2.

Solution.—$R = M/b.d^2 = 90$. In Fig. 2 the intersection of a vertical line through reinforcement $= 0.9$ per cent and a horizontal line through $R = 90$, gives $f_c = 520$ and $f_s = 11,700$.

Problem 3. Cross-section of Beam and Percentage of Reinforcement.—Given $M = 360,000$ in.-lbs., $f_s = 14,000$, $f_c = 500$ lbs., to find b, d and p.

Solution.—In Fig. 2 the intersection of curved line $f_c = 600$ and straight line $f_s = 14,000$ gives on the lower margin, $p = 0.0084$ (0.84 per cent), and on left margin gives $R = 102$. Then $b.d^2 = M/R = 3,530$. Now if $b = 10''$, then $d = 19''$.

STRESSES IN T-BEAMS.—There will be two cases: (1) when the neutral axis is in the flange, and (2) when the neutral axis is in the web.

Case I. The Neutral Axis in the Flange.—The formulas for a rectangular beam apply where b is the flange width and $p = A \div b.d$, not $A \div b'.d$.

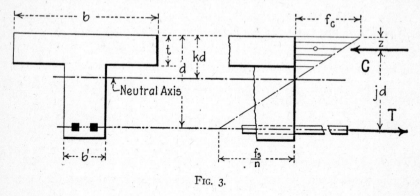

FIG. 3.

Approximate Formulas.—It will be seen in Fig. 3 that $j.d$ is always greater than $d - t/3$, and the following formulas are on the safe side. $M_s = f_s.A(d - t/3)$, and $f_s = M_s/A(d - t/3)$. There is no corresponding approximate formula for the concrete.

Case II. The Neutral Axis in the Web.—Where the thickness of the flange t is large as compared with the depth of the beam, or as compared with the width of the web, the compression in the web may be neglected.

(1) The Compression in the Web Neglected. Neutral Axis and Arm of Resisting Couple.—As in the rectangular beam

$$f_s.k = f_c.n(1-k) \tag{3}$$

and

$$k = \frac{1}{1 + f_s/n.f_c} \tag{11}$$

The average unit compressive stress in the flange is

$$\tfrac{1}{2}[f_c + f_c(1 - t/k.d)] = f_c\left(1 - \frac{t}{2k.d}\right),$$

and the total compression is

$$C = f_c\left(1 - \frac{t}{2k.d}\right)b.t$$

Now since $C = T$

$$f_s.A = f_c\left(1 - \frac{t}{2k.d}\right)b.t \tag{12}$$

Solving (3) and (12) for k we have

$$k = \frac{2n.d.A + b.t^2}{2n.d.A + 2b.d.t} \tag{13}$$

Substituting $p.b.d$ for A, we have

$$k = \frac{2n.p.d^2 + t^2}{2n.p.d^2 + 2d.t} \tag{14}$$

The arm of the resisting couple is $d - z$, where z is the distance from the top of the beam to the center of the shaded area in Fig. 3.

$$z = \frac{3k.d - 2t}{2k.d - t} \times \frac{t}{3} \tag{15}$$

Also

$$j.d = d - z \tag{16}$$

Substituting k from (14) in (15) and z from (15) in (16) we have

$$j = \frac{6 - 6t/d + 2(t/d)^2 + (t/d)^3/2p.n}{6 - 3t/d} \tag{17}$$

Moment of Resistance.—If the beam is under-reinforced the strength of the beam will depend upon the steel, and

$$M_s = f_s.A(d-z) = f_s.A.j.d \qquad (18)$$

If the beam is over-reinforced the strength of the beam will depend upon the concrete, and

$$M_c = f_c\left(1 - \frac{t}{2k.d}\right)b.t.j.d \qquad (19)$$

Unit Stresses.—The values of f_s and f_c may be obtained from (8) and (9) respectively, or from

$$C = T = M/j.d, \text{ and } f_s = \frac{T}{A} \qquad (20)$$

$$f_c = \frac{f_s}{n} \times \frac{k}{1-k} = \frac{f_s.p}{\left(1 - \frac{t}{2k.d}\right)\frac{t}{d}} \qquad (21)$$

2. **Compression in Web Considered.**—Where the flange is thin as compared with the depth of the beam, d, and width of web, b', it may become necessary to consider the compression in the web. In the same manner as in (1), we have

$$k.d = \sqrt{\frac{2n.d.A + (b-b')t^2}{b'} + \left(\frac{n.A + (b-b')t}{b'}\right)^2} - \frac{n.A + (b-b')t}{b'}$$

$$z = \frac{(k.d.t^2 - \frac{2}{3}t^3)b + \left[(k.d-t)^2\left(t + \frac{k.d-t}{3}\right)\right]b'}{b.t(2k.d-t) + b'(k.d-t)^2} \qquad (23)$$

$$j.d = d - z \qquad (24)$$

$$M_s = f_s A.j.d \qquad (25)$$

$$M_c = \frac{f_c}{2k.d}\left[(2k.d-t)b.t + (k.d-t)^2b'\right]j.d \qquad (26)$$

Design of T-Beams.—Where the dimensions and reinforcement of the beam are given the safe load can be calculated by the preceding formulas. If the value of $k.d$ is less than t the problem comes under Case I, and the formulas for rectangular beams may be used.

In designing a T-beam the value of b' will be determined by the space required for the reinforcing rods and to give the required shearing strength. The thickness of the flange t will be governed by the width of flange b; standard specifications require that the overhang of the flange shall not be greater than $4t$, or that $b \leq 8t + b'$, also that the total flange width shall not exceed one-fourth the span.

STRESSES IN BEAMS REINFORCED FOR COMPRESSION.—The beam is reinforced with steel on both the compression and tension sides.

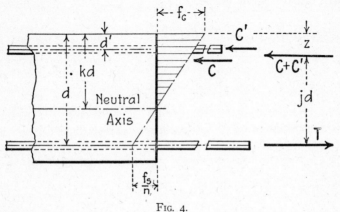

FIG. 4.

Neutral Axis and Arm of Resisting Couple.—From Fig. 4, as in Fig. 1, we have

$$f_s.k = f_c.n(1 - k) \tag{3}$$

Also

$$f_s'.k.d = f_c.n(k.d - d'),$$

and

$$f'_s = f_c.n\left(1 - \frac{d'}{k.d}\right) \tag{27}$$

For simple flexure $T = C + C'$, and $f_s.A = \frac{1}{2}f_c.b.k.d + f_s'.A' \quad (28)$
Substituting values of f_c and f_s' from (3) and (27) in (28), we have

$$k^2 + 2n(p + p')k = 2n(p + p'.d'/d)$$

and solving for k,

$$k = \sqrt{2n(p + p'd'/d) + [n(p + p')]^2} - n(p + p') \qquad (29)$$

The arm of the resisting couple is

$$j.d = d - z \qquad (30)$$

where z is given by the equation

$$z = \frac{\frac{1}{3}k^3.d + 2p'.n.d'\left(k - \dfrac{d'}{d}\right)}{k^2 + 2p'.n\left(k - \dfrac{d'}{d}\right)} \qquad (31)$$

Moment of Resistance.—If the beam is under-reinforced on the tension side the strength of the beam is determined by the steel, and

$$M_s = f_s.A.j.d = f_s.p.j.b.d^2 \qquad (32)$$

If the beam is over-reinforced on the tension side, the strength of the beam is determined by the compressive resistance and

$$M_c = \frac{1}{2}f_c.k(1 - \frac{1}{3}k)b.d^2 + f_s'.p'.b.d(d - d') \qquad (33)$$

If the value of f_s' from (27) be substituted in (33), then

$$M_c = f_c.b.d^2[k(\tfrac{1}{2} - \tfrac{1}{6}k) + n.p'(k - d'/d)(1 - d'/d)/k] \qquad (34)$$

Fiber Stresses.—The stress f_s for a moment M is

$$f_s = \frac{M}{A.j.d} = \frac{M}{p.j.b.d^2} \qquad (35)$$

while the compressive stresses may be calculated by equations (3) and (27).

Approximate Formulas.—For approximate calculations assume that $k = 0.45$ and $j = 0.85$, and then

$$M_s = 0.85p.f_s.b.d^2 \qquad (36)$$

$$M_c = (0.19 + 10.5p')f_c.b.d^2 \qquad (37)$$

$$f_s = 1.18M/p.b.d^2 \qquad (38)$$

FLEXURE AND DIRECT STRESS.—When a member carries direct stress and at the same time acts as a beam, there are both direct stresses and bending stresses at any section. A common example is where the resultant of the external forces on a beam acting on one side of the section is not normal to the beam. There are two cases: (1) where the neutral axis is entirely outside of the beam and the combined stresses are all tension or all compression, and (2) where the neutral axis is inside the section and the stresses on the section are both tension and compression.

The following additional notation is required:

$P =$ resultant of all external forces acting on a beam on either side of the section.

$N =$ component of P normal to section.

$e =$ eccentric distance of P.

$M =$ bending moment on section $= N.e$.

$A' =$ area of steel near face most highly stressed.

$d' =$ distance from upper face to center of steel A'.

$A =$ area of steel near other face.

$d =$ distance from upper face to center of steel A.

$h =$ height of section.

$p' =$ steel ratio $A'/b.h$.

$p =$ steel ratio $A/b.h$.

$y =$ distance from upper face to center of the transformed section.

$A_t =$ area of the transformed section.

$I_t =$ moment of inertia of transformed section with reference to its centroidal axis.

$I_c =$ moment of inertia of the concrete with reference to the same axis.

$I_s =$ moment of inertia of the steel with reference to the same axis.

Case I. Stresses all Compression.—(*a*) The unit stresses in the concrete and steel can be calculated by transforming the section, the steel being assumed to be equal to concrete, having n times the area of the steel, and acting with its center of gravity in the same line.

$$A_t = b.h + n(A + A') \tag{39}$$

$$y = \frac{h/2 + n.p.d + n.p'.d'}{1 + n.p + n.p'} \tag{40}$$

$$I_c = \tfrac{1}{3}[y^3 + (h - y)^3]b \tag{41}$$

$$I_s = A(d - y)^2 + A'(y - d')^2 \tag{42}$$

$$I_t = I_c + n.I_s \tag{43}$$

If the reinforcement is symmetrical and equal, $y = h/2$, and $I_c = \tfrac{1}{12}b.h^3$, and $I_s = 2A(\tfrac{1}{2}h - d')^2$.

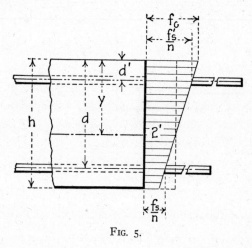

FIG. 5.

Now in Fig. 5 the direct unit stress in the concrete will be N/A, and the maximum flexural unit stress in the concrete is $\dfrac{M.y}{I_t}$, and the combined stresses are

$$f_c = \frac{N}{A_t} + \frac{M.y}{I_t} \tag{44}$$

$$f'_s = n\frac{N}{A_t} + \frac{n.M(y - d')}{I_t} \tag{45}$$

$$f_s = n\frac{N}{A_t} - \frac{n.M.(d - y)}{I_t} \tag{46}$$

(b) The stresses may be calculated directly from Fig. 6 without using the transformed sections. From Fig. 6

$$f_s' = n.f_c(1 - d'/k.h) \tag{47}$$

$$f_s = n.f_c(1 - d/k.h) \tag{48}$$

$$f_c' = f_c(1 - 1/k) \tag{49}$$

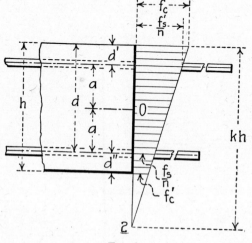

FIG. 6.

Now since the resultant normal stress equals N, we have

$$N = \tfrac{1}{2}(f_c + f_c')b.h + f_s'.A' + f_s.A \tag{50}$$

and since $M =$ moment of all forces about the neutral axis

$$M = \tfrac{1}{2}(f_c + f_c')b.h \frac{h}{6(2k-1)} + f_s'.A'\left(\frac{h}{2} - d'\right) - f_s.A\left(\frac{h}{2} - d\right) \tag{51}$$

The unit stresses may be calculated by means of the formulas above.

If the reinforcement is symmetrical, and $A = A'$, k is given by the equation

$$12k(1 + 2n.p)e/h = 1 + 24n.p.a^2/h^2 + 6(1 + 2n.p)e/h \tag{52}$$

and

$$M = f_c.b.h^2(1 + 24n.p.a^2/h^2)/12k \tag{53}$$

If $e/h = \tfrac{1}{10}$ and $p = 1.0$ per cent, $k = 2.07$.

Case II. Stresses, Both Tension and Compression.—(*a*) If the tension as calculated by the formula $f'_e = \dfrac{N}{A} - \dfrac{M.y}{I_t}$ does not exceed, say 60 lbs. per sq. in. it will be sufficient to use the formulas of Case I.

(*b*) If the tensile stresses in the concrete are too large to be neglected the stresses may be calculated as follows:

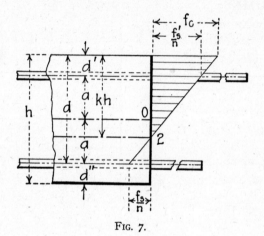

FIG. 7.

From Fig. 7 we have

$$f_s = n f_c \left(\frac{d}{k.h} - 1 \right) \tag{54}$$

and

$$f'_s = n f_c \left(1 - \frac{d'}{k.h} \right) \tag{55}$$

The resultant fiber stress may be obtained from

$$N = \tfrac{1}{2} f_c.b.k.h + f'_s.A' - f_s.A \tag{56}$$

The moment of the fiber stresses about the horizontal axis through O is M, and

$$M = \tfrac{1}{2} f_c.b.k.h \left(\frac{h}{2} - \frac{k.h}{3} \right) + f'_s.A' \left(\frac{h}{2} - d' \right) + f_s.A \left(d - \frac{h}{2} \right) \tag{57}$$

If the reinforcement is equal on both sides and symmetrical we have

$$k^3 - 3\left(\frac{1}{2} - \frac{e}{h}\right)k^2 + 12n.p\frac{e}{h}k = 6n.p\left(\frac{e}{h} + 2\frac{a^2}{h^2}\right) \quad (58)$$

The greatest compression in the fiber is then obtained from

$$M = f_c.b.h^2\left[\frac{1}{12}k(3 - 2k) + \frac{2p.n}{k}\frac{a^2}{h^2}\right] \quad (59)$$

5. **COLUMNS.** For short columns the ratio of length to least width not exceeding 15,

$$f_s = n.f_c \quad (60)$$

$$P' = f_c.A_c + f_s.A_s \quad (61)$$

$$= f_c.A_c[1 + (n-1)p] \quad (62)$$

$$\frac{P'}{P} = 1 + (n-1)p \quad (63)$$

French Commission's formula for hooped columns:

$$P' = f_c.A(1 + 15p + 32p') \quad (64)$$

For long columns:

$$f = \frac{f_c[1 + (n-1)p]}{1 + \dfrac{1}{20,000}\left(\dfrac{l}{r}\right)^2} \quad (65)$$

Where f is the average unit stress on the column, and l and r are the length and radius of gyration of the column respectively, both measured in the same units.

Bond or Resistance to Slipping of Reinforcing Bars.—where there is no web reinforcement the shear is taken by the concrete and the shear increments are transferred to the bars by the adhesion of the concrete to the bars. The solution is the same as that for finding the pitch of rivets in the flanges of a plate girder.

Now in (b), Fig. 1, take two right sections at a distance dx apart. Equilibrium of these two sections is maintained by the resisting moment of the bond which is equal and opposite to the moment of the vertical shear, a couple with an arm dx.

33

Taking moments about center of gravity of compressive forces we have

$$V.dx = o.u.dx.j.d \tag{66}$$

where $o =$ surface of bar for one inch in length and $\Sigma o =$ surface of all the bars one inch in length, $u =$ bond developed per square inch of surface of bar, and V is the vertical shear in the beam.

Solving for u, we have

$$u = \frac{V}{j.d.\Sigma o} \tag{67}$$

Equation (67) applies to the case of horizontal bars. For inclined bars, $j.d$ will be a variable and u will be the horizontal component of the bond resistance.

Vertical and Horizontal Shearing Stresses.—At any point in a beam the vertical unit shearing stress is equal to the horizontal unit shearing stress. The horizontal shearing stress transmits the increments of tension to the reinforcing bars by bond stresses, as explained in the preceding discussion.

The amount of this horizontal stress transmitted to the reinforcing bars is by equation (67)

$$\Sigma o.u = \frac{V}{j.d}$$

Now if the horizontal shear just above the plane of the bars is v, the total horizontal shearing stress will be $v.b$, which equals $\Sigma o.u$, and

$$v = \frac{V}{b.j.d} \tag{68}$$

As an approximate formula j may be taken equal to $\frac{7}{8}$, and

$$v = \frac{8}{7} \frac{V}{b.d}$$

As no tension is assumed to exist in the concrete, the horizontal shear will be constant up to the neutral axis, above which point it decreases to zero at the top of the beam. It will be seen that lean or poor concrete lacking in shearing strength should not be placed below the neutral axis of beams with the idea that it may be satisfactory for the reason that the concrete is assumed to take no tension.

The same formulas apply to beams reinforced for compression as regards shear and bond stress on tensile steel.

For T-Beams.

$$u = \frac{V}{j.d.\Sigma o} \tag{69}$$

$$v = \frac{V}{b'.j.d} \tag{70}$$

Diagonal Tension in Concrete.—In Mechanics of Materials (Merriman's Mechanics of Materials, p. 265, 1905 edition) it is shown that shear and tensile stresses combine to cause diagonal tensile stresses.

$$t = \tfrac{1}{2}s + \sqrt{\tfrac{1}{4}s^2 + v^2} \tag{71}$$

where t is the diagonal tensile unit stress, s is the horizontal tensile unit stress, and v is the horizontal or vertical shearing unit stress. The direction that stress t makes with the horizontal is one-half the angle whose cotangent is $\tfrac{1}{2}s/v$. If there is no tension in the concrete this reduces to

$$t = v \tag{72}$$

and t makes an angle of 45° with the horizontal.

Stresses due to diagonal tension may be carried (1) by bending the reinforced bars, or by strips sheared from them, into a diagonal position, or (2) by means of stirrups to take the vertical component of the diagonal tension, or (3) by both bent-up bars and stirrups.

Stresses in Stirrups.—The following analysis is approximate but gives results that agree closely with experiments. From formula (72) it will be seen that for no tension below the neutral axis the diagonal tension will make an angle of 45° with the horizontal; the plane of failure will then be normal to the diagonal tension and will also make an angle of 45° with the horizontal. Let V be the shear in the beam not carried by the concrete. Also assume that the shear is uniform over the cross-section. Then $v' = V/b.d = t$.

From Fig. 8, if s is the spacing of the vertical stirrups the stress in one stirrup is

$$P = v'.b.s = \frac{V}{d}.s \tag{73}$$

Stirrups inclined at an angle of 45° will carry the diagonal tension on a section $s.b.\cos 45°$. Then for diagonal stirrups

$$P = v'.b.s \cos 45° = 0.7 \frac{V}{d}.s \tag{74}$$

To be effective the stirrups should be spaced so that at least one stirrup will intersect the line of rupture (45° line) below the center of the

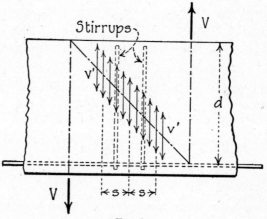

Fig. 8.

beam, which requires that s never be greater than $d/2$. Rods spaced farther apart than d are of no value.

Inclined stirrups should be rigidly fastened to the horizontal reinforcement, and all stirrups should pass around the horizontal reinforcement, and have hooked ends at the top.

To calculate the stress in a rod bent up at 45° in a beam with a uniform load the method shown in Fig. 9 may be used. The average shear at the support, $v' = V/b.d$, is laid off as shown. The shear that may be carried by the concrete, $v = 40$ lbs., or $v' = 35$ lbs., is subtracted. The stress in the bent-up rod is then equal to area 1-2-3-4 $\times b$. If the bar is bent-up at some angle other than 45° the shear v' should be laid off parallel to the bent-up bar. If stirrups are used the stress carried by them should be subtracted before calculating the stresses in the bent-up rods.

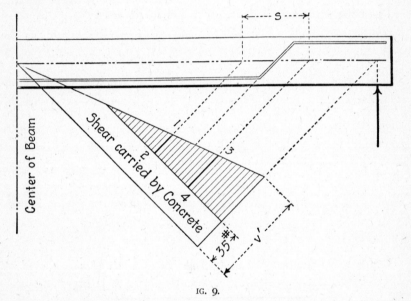

IG. 9.

Spacing of Bars.—The lateral spacing of parallel bars should not be less than $2\frac{1}{2}$ diameters, center to center, nor should the distance from the side of the beam to the center of the nearest bar be less than 2 diameters. The clear spacing between two layers of bars should not be less than $\frac{1}{2}$ inch, but the distance center to center of bars in the different layers should not be less than $2\frac{1}{2}$ diameters.

T-Beams.—In beam and slab construction, an effective bond should be provided at the junction of the beam and the slab. When the principal slab reinforcement is parallel to the beam, transverse reinforcement should be used extending over the beam and well into the slab.

Where the slab and beam are well bonded the slab may be considered as part of the beam, but the effective width should not exceed $\frac{1}{4}$ of the span length of the beam, or its overhanging width on either side of the web should not exceed four times the thickness of the slab. Unless an efficient mechanical bond is provided the beam and slab should be cast in one operation. In the design of continuous T-beams due consideration should be given to the compressive stresses at the supports.

Floor Slabs.—Floor slabs should in general be made continuous over the supports. Square slabs should be reinforced in both directions with each system of reinforcement designed to take one-half of the load. For rectangular slabs reinforced in both directions the proportion of the load taken by the transverse reinforcement should be taken as equal to the quotient obtained by dividing the fourth power of the length by the sum of the fourth power of the length and the fourth power of the breadth, and the longitudinal reinforcement designed to take the remainder of the load. The loads carried to beams by slabs which are reinforced in two directions may be assumed to vary in accordance with the ordinates of the triangle formed by the main diagonals of the rectangle, and the moments in the beams calculated accordingly.

Bending Moments.—When the beam or slab is continuous over its supports, reinforcement should be fully provided at points of negative moment. In computing the bending moments in beams and slabs due to uniformly distributed loads the following rules should be used:

(*a*) For floor slabs the bending moments at center and supports may be taken as $w.l^2/12$ for slabs continuous over the supports; $w.l^2/10$ for slabs with one end continuous and the other end supported; and $w.l^2/8$ for slabs supported at the ends, for both dead and live loads, where w represents the loads per linear foot and l the length of the span.

(*b*) For beams the bending moment at center and supports for interior spans may be taken at $w.l^2/12$; and for end spans may be taken at $w.l^2/10$ for the center and adjoining supports for both dead and live loads. In the case of floor slabs, beams and girders designed as above the reinforcing steel should be rigidly fastened at the ends, or the bending moments may be taken as $w.l^2/8$. Where beams are reinforced on the compression side, the steel may be assumed to carry its proportion of compressive stress. In the case of continuous beams, tensile and compressive reinforcement over supports should extend sufficiently beyond the support to develop the required bond strength, or the bars should be bent around the flanges of beams or other frame work with bends not less than 6 inches long.

For a more complete discussion of the design of reinforced concrete structures, see Turneaure and Maurer's " Principles of Reinforced Concrete Construction."

CHAPTER IV.

Specifications for Plain and Reinforced Concrete and Steel Reinforcement.

Concrete Materials.

1. **Cement.**—The cement shall be Portland and shall meet the requirements of the standard specifications of the American Society for Testing Materials.

2. **Fine Aggregates.**—Fine aggregate shall consist of sand, crushed stone, or gravel screenings graded from fine to coarse, and passing when dry a screen having ¼ in. diameter holes; it shall preferably be of siliceous material, clean, coarse, free from vegetable loam or other deleterious matter, and not more than 6 per cent shall pass a sieve having 100 meshes per linear inch.

3. **Strength of Mortar.**—Mortars composed of one part Portland cement and three parts fine aggregate by weight when made into briquettes shall show a tensile strength of at least equal to 70 per cent of the strength of 1 : 3 mortar of the same consistency made with the same cement and standard Ottawa sand.

4. **Coarse Aggregates.**—Coarse aggregate shall consist of crushed stone or gravel, graded in size, and which is retained on a screen having ¼ in. diameter holes; it shall be clean, hard, durable, and free from all deleterious material. Aggregates containing soft, flat or elongated particles shall not be used.

5. **Water.**—The water used in mixing concrete shall be free from oil, acid and injurious amounts of alkalies or vegetable matter.

Steel Reinforcement.

6. **Manufacture.**—Steel shall be made by the open-hearth process. Rerolled material will not be accepted.

7. Plates and shapes used for reinforcement shall be of structural steel only. Bars and wire may be of structural steel or high carbon steel.

8. **Schedule of Requirements.**—The chemical and physical properties shall conform to the following limits:

Elements Considered.	Structural Steel.	High Carbon Steel.
Phosphorus, max... { Basic.........	0.04 per cent	0.04 per cent
{ Acid	0.06 per cent	0.06 per cent
Sulphur, maximum..	0.05 per cent	0.05 per cent
Ultimate tensile strength.	Desired.	Desired.
Pounds per square inch.............	60,000	88,000
Elong., min. % in 8″, Fig. 1... {	$\dfrac{1,500,000*}{\text{Ult. tensile strength}}$	$\dfrac{1,000,000}{\text{Ult. tensile strength}}$
Character of fracture.................	Silky	Silky or finely granular.
Cold Bends without Fracture......	180° flat †	180° $d = 4t$.‡

* See paragraph 15. † See paragraphs 16 and 17. ‡ "d = 4t" signifies "around a pin whose diameter is four times the thickness of the specimen."

9. Yield Point.—The yield point for bars and wire, as indicated by the drop of the beam, shall be not less than 60 per cent of the ultimate tensile strength.

10. Allowable Variations.—If the ultimate strength varies more than 4,000 lbs. for structural steel or 6,000 lbs. for high carbon steel, a retest shall be made on the same gage, which, to be acceptable, shall be within 5,000 lbs., for structural steel, or 8,000 lbs. for high carbon steel, of the desired ultimate.

11. Chemical Analyses.—Chemical determinations of the percentages of carbon, phosphorus, sulphur and manganese shall be made by the manufacturer from a test ingot taken at the time of the pouring of each melt of steel, and a correct copy of such analysis shall be furnished to the engineer or his inspector.

12. Form of Specimens. Plates, Shapes and Bars.—Specimens for tensile and bending tests for plates and shapes shall be made by cutting coupons from the finished product, which shall have both faces rolled and both edges milled to the form shown by Fig. 1; or with both edges parallel; or they may be turned to a diameter of ½ in. with enlarged ends, Fig. 2.

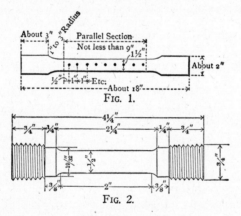

FIG. 1.

FIG. 2.

13. Bars shall be tested in their finished form.

14. Number of Tests.—At least one tensile and one bending test shall be made from each melt of steel as rolled. In case steel differing ⅜ in. and more in thickness is rolled from one melt, a test shall be made from the thickest and thinnest material rolled.

15. Modifications in Elongation.—For material less than ⅝ in. and more than ¾ in. in thickness the following modifications will be allowed in the requirements for elongation:

   (a) For each ⅛ in. in thickness below ⅝ in. a deduction of 2½ will be allowed from the specified percentage.

   (b) For each ⅛ in. in thickness above ¾ in., a deduction of 1 will be allowed from the specified percentage.

16. Bending Tests.—Bending tests may be made by pressure or by blows. Shapes and bars less than one inch thick shall bend as called for in paragraph 8.

17. **Thick Material.**—Test specimens one inch thick and over shall bend cold 180 degrees around a pin, the diameter of which, for structural steel, is twice the thickness of the specimen, and for high carbon steel, is six times the thickness of the specimen, without fracture on the outside of the bend.

18. **Finish.**—Finished material shall be free from injurious seams, flaws, cracks, defective edges or other defects, and have a smooth, uniform and workmanlike finish.

19. **Stamping.**—Every finished piece of steel shall have the melt number and the name of the manufacturer stamped or rolled upon it, except that bar steel and other small parts may be bundled with the above marks on an attached metal tag.

20. **Defective Material.**—Material which, subsequent to the above tests at the mills, and its acceptance there, develops weak spots, brittleness, cracks or other imperfections, or is found to have injurious defects, will be rejected and shall be replaced by the manufacturer at his own cost.

21. All reinforcing steel shall be free from excessive rust, loose scale, or other coatings of any character, which would reduce or destroy the bond.

WORKMANSHIP.

22. **Unit Measure.**—The unit of measure shall be the cubic foot. A barrel containing 4 bags weighing not less than 94 lbs. each shall be assumed as containing 3.8 cubic feet of cement. Fine and coarse aggregates shall be measured separately as loosely thrown into the measuring receptacle.

23. **Relation of Fine and Coarse Aggregates.**—The fine and coarse aggregates shall be used in such relative proportions as will insure maximum density.

24. **Proportions.**—The proportions of materials for the different classes of concrete shall be as follows:

Class.	Use.	Cement.	Aggregates.	
			Fine.	Coarse.

25. **Proportions.**—For plain concrete, a proportion of 1 : 9 (unless otherwise specified) shall be used, i. e., one part of cement to a total of nine parts of fine and coarse aggregates *measured separately;* for example, 1 cement, 3 fine aggregate, 6 coarse aggregate.

26. For reinforced concrete a proportion of 1 : 6 (unless otherwise specified) shall be used, i. e., one part of cement to a total of six parts of fine and coarse aggregates *measured separately.*

27. **Mixing.**—The ingredients of concrete shall be thoroughly mixed to the desired consistency, and the mixing shall continue until the cement is uniformly distributed and the mass is uniform in color and homogeneous.

28. **Measuring Proportions.**—The various ingredients, including the water, shall be measured separately, and the methods of measurement shall be such as to secure the proper proportions at all times.

29. **Machine Mixing.**—A machine mixer, preferably of the batch type, shall be used wherever the volume of the work will justify the expense of installing the plant. The requirements demanded are that the product delivered shall be of the specified proportions and consistency and thoroughly mixed.

30. **Hand Mixing.**—When it is necessary to mix by hand, the mixing shall be on a watertight platform of sufficient size to accommodate men and materials for the progressive and rapid mixing of at least two batches of concrete at the same time. Batches shall not exceed one-half cubic yard each. The mixing shall be done as follows: The fine aggregate shall be spread evenly upon the platform, then the cement upon the fine aggregates, and these mixed thoroughly until of an even color. The coarse aggregates which, if dry, shall first be thoroughly wetted down shall then be added to the mixture. The mass shall then be turned with shovels until thoroughly mixed and all of the aggregate covered with mortar, water being added as the mixing proceeds. Or, at the option of the engineer, the coarse aggregate may be added after, instead of before, adding the water.

31. **Consistency.**—The materials shall be mixed wet enough to produce a concrete of such consistency that it will flow into the forms and about the metal reinforcement, and which, on the other hand, can be conveyed from the place of mixing to the forms without separation of the coarse aggregate from the mortar.

32. **Retempering.**—Retempering mortar or concrete, i. e., remixing with water after it has partially set, will not be permitted.

33. **Placing of Concrete.**—Concrete after the addition of water to the mix shall be handled rapidly from the place of mixing to the place of final deposit, and under no circumstances shall concrete be used that has partially set before final placing.

34. The concrete shall be deposited in such a manner as will prevent the separation of the ingredients and permit the most thorough compacting. It shall be compacted by working with a straight shovel or slicing tool kept moving up and down until all the ingredients have settled in their proper place and the surplus water is forced to the surface. In general, except in arch work, all concrete should be deposited in horizontal layers of uniform thickness throughout.

35. In depositing concrete under water, special care shall be exercised to prevent the cement from floating away, and to prevent the formation of laitance.

36. Before depositing concrete in forms, the forms shall be thoroughly wetted except in freezing weather, and the space to be occupied by the concrete cleared of debris.

37. Before placing new concrete on or against concrete which has set, the

surface of the latter shall be roughened, thoroughly cleansed of foreign material and laitance, drenched and slushed with a mortar consisting of one part Portland cement and not more than two parts fine aggregate.

38. The faces of concrete exposed to premature drying shall be kept wet for a period of at least three days.

39. **Freezing Weather.**—The concrete shall not be mixed or deposited at a freezing temperature, unless special precautions, approved by the engineer, are taken to avoid the use of materials containing frost or covered with ice crystals, and to provide means to prevent the concrete from freezing.

When the temperature of the air is below 40° F. during the time of mixing and placing concrete, the water used in mixing concrete shall be heated to such a temperature that the temperature of the concrete mixture shall not be less than 60° when it reaches its final position in the forms. Care shall be used that the cement shall not be injured by boiling water.

40. **Rubble Concrete.**—Where the concrete is to be deposited in massive work, clean, large stones, evenly distributed, thoroughly bedded and entirely surrounded by concrete, may be used, at the option of the engineer.

41. **Forms.**—Forms shall be substantial and unyielding and built so that the concrete shall conform to the designed dimensions and contours, and so constructed as to prevent the leakage of mortar.

42. **Removing Forms.**—The forms shall not be removed until authorized by the engineer.

43. **Form Lumber.**—For all important work, the lumber used for face work shall be dressed to a uniform thickness and width; shall be sound and free from loose knots and secured to the studding or uprights in horizontal lines.

44. For backings and other rough work undressed lumber may be used.

45. Where corners of the masonry and other projections liable to injury occur, suitable moldings shall be placed in the angles of the forms to round or bevel them off.

46. Lumber once used in forms shall be cleaned before being used again.

Details of Construction.

47. **Splicing Reinforcement.**—Wherever it is necessary to splice the reinforcement otherwise than as shown on the plans, the character of the splice shall be decided by the engineer on the basis of the safe bond stress and the stress in the reinforcement at the point of splice. Splices shall not be made at points of maximum stress. The reinforcement shall be carefully placed in accordance with the plans, and adequate means shall be provided to hold it in its proper position until the concrete has been deposited and compacted.

48. **Joints in Concrete.**—Concrete structures, wherever possible, shall be cast at one operation, but when this is not possible, the resulting joint shall be formed where it will least impair the strength and appearance of the structure.

49. Girders and slabs shall not be constructed over freshly formed walls or columns without permitting a period of at least four hours to elapse to provide for settlement or shrinkage in the supports. Before resuming work, the tops of such walls or columns shall be cleaned of foreign matter and laitance.

50. A triangular-shaped groove shall be formed at the surface of the concrete at vertical joints in walls and abutments.

51. **Surface Finish.**—Except where a special finish is required, a spade or special tool shall always be worked between the concrete and the form to force back the coarse aggregates and produce a mortar face.

52. **Top Surfaces.**—Top surfaces shall generally be "struck" with a straight edge or "floated" after the coarse aggregates have been forced below the surface.

53. **Sidewalk Finish.**—Where a "sidewalk finish" is called for on the plans, it shall be made by spreading a layer of 1:2 mortar at least ¾ in. thick, troweling the same to a smooth surface. This finishing coat shall be put on before the concrete has taken its initial set.

APPENDIX II.

DEFINITIONS OF MASONRY TERMS APPLIED TO RAILROAD CONSTRUCTION.*

Masonry.—All constructions of stone or kindred substitute materials in which the separate pieces are either placed together, with or without cementing material to join them, or where not separately placed, are encased in a matrix of firmly cementing material.

Riprapping and paving are not masonry construction.

CLASSIFICATION OF MASONRY.

Kinds of Masonry.	Sub-division into Classes of Material.	Manner of Work.	Dressing.	Face or Surface Finish.
Stone.	Dimension.	In courses.	Fine-pointed. Crandalled. Axed or Pean-hammered. Tooth-axed. Sawed. Rubbed.	
	Arch.	In courses.	Fine-pointed. Crandalled. Axed or Pean-hammered. Tooth-axed. Sawed.	Quarry-faced. Pitch-faced. Drafted.
	Ashlar.	Range. Broken Range.		
	Squared stone.	Range. Broken range. Random.	Rough-pointed. Fine-pointed. Crandalled.	
	Rubble.	Coursed. Uncoursed.	None.	Quarry-faced.
	Dry.	No mortar.	May be any of the above.	May be any of the above.
Concrete.	Broken stone. Gravel. Other material.			
Brick.	Face. No. 1 paving. No. 2 " Common.	English bond. Flemish bond.		

* Recommended by American Railway Engineering and Maintenance of Way Association.

Dimension Stone.—A block of stone cut to specified dimensions.

Coping.—A top course of stone or concrete, generally slightly projecting, to shelter the masonry from the weather, or to distribute the pressure from exterior loading.

Arch Masonry.—That portion of the masonry in the arch ring only, or between the intrados and the extrados.

Ashlar Masonry.—Masonry built of ashlar blocks.

Range Masonry.—Masonry in which the various courses are laid up with continuous horizontal beds.

Broken Range Masonry.—Masonry in which the bed joints are parallel but not continuous.

Square-Stone Masonry.—Masonry in which the stones are roughly squared and roughly dressed on beds and sides.

Rubble Masonry.—Masonry composed of squared or roughly squared stones, or rubble of irregular size or shape.

Dry Wall.—A masonry wall in which stones are built up without the use of mortar.

CONCRETE.

Concrete.—A compact mass of broken stone, gravel or other suitable material assembled together with cement mortar and allowed to harden.

Rubble Concrete.—Concrete in which rubblestone are imbedded.

Reinforced Concrete.—Concrete which has been reinforced by means of metal in some form, so as to give the concrete elasticity and increased strength.

BRICK.

Brick.—No. 1.—Hard burned brick, absorption not to exceed 2 per cent by weight.

Brick.—No. 2.—Softer and lighter brick than No. 1, absorption not to exceed 6 per cent by weight.

CEMENT.

Cement.—A preparation of calcined clay and limestone, or their equivalents, possessing the property of hardening into a solid mass when moistened with water. This property is exercised under water, as well as in the air. Cements are divided into four classes: Portland, Natural, Puzzolan and Silica cement. (See each.)

Portland Cement.—This term is applied to the finely pulverized product resulting from the calcination to incipient fusion of an intimate mixture of properly proportioned argillaceous and calcareous materials, and to which no addition greater than 3 per cent has been made subsequent to calcination.

Natural Cement.—This term shall be applied to the finely pulverized product resulting from the calcination of an argillaceous limestone at a temperature only sufficient to drive off the carbonic acid gas.

Puzzolan.—An intimate mixture of pulverized granulated furnace slag and slaked lime without further calcination which possesses the hydraulic qualities of cement.

Silica Cement (sand cement).—A mixture of clean sand and Portland cement ground together.

DESCRIPTIVE WORDS.

Arris.—An external angle, edge or ridge.

Ashlar.—A squared or cut block of stone with rectangular dimensions.

Axed.—Dressed so as to cover the surface of a stone with chisel marks which are nearly or quite parallel.

Backing.—That portion of a masonry wall or structure built in the rear of the face. It must be attached to the face and bonded with it. It is usually of a cheaper grade of masonry than the face.

Batter.—The slope or inclination of the face from a vertical line.

Bed.—The top and bottom of a stone. (See Course Bed; Natural Bed; Foundation Bed.)

Bed Joint.—A horizontal joint, or one perpendicular to the line of pressure.

Beton.—(See Concrete.)

Block Rubble.—Large blocks of building stone as they come from the quarry. (See Rubble.)

Bond.—The mechanical disposition of stone, brick or other building blocks by overlapping to break joints.

Build.—A vertical joint.

Bush-Hammered.—A surface produced by removing the roughness of stone with a bush-hammer.

Centering.—A temporary support used in arch construction. (Also called Centers.)

Course.—Each separate layer in stone, concrete or brick masonry.

Course Bed.—Stone, brick or other building material in position, upon which other material is to be laid.

Crandalled.—Dressed with a crandalling tool, producing the same effect as fine-pointed.

Draft.—A line on the surface of a stone cut to the breadth of the chisel.

Draft Stones.—Stones on which the face is surrounded by a draft, the space inside the draft being left rough.

Dressing.—The finish given to the surface of stones or to concrete.

Expansion Joint.—A vertical joint or space to allow for temperature changes.

Extrados.—The upper or convex surface of an arch.

Face.—The exposed surface in elevation.

Facing.—In concrete: (1) A rich mortar placed on the exposed surfaces to make a smooth finish. (2) Shovel facing by working the mortar of concrete to the face.

Final Set.—A stage of the process of setting marked by certain hardness. (See Cement Specifications.)

Fine Pointed.—Dressed by fine point to smoother finish than by rough point.

Flush.—(Adj.) Having the surface even or level with an adjacent surface. (Verb.) (1) To fill. (2) To bring to a level. (3) To force water to the surface of mortar or concrete by compacting or ramming.

Footing.—A projecting bottom course.

Forms.—Temporary structures for holding concrete in desired shape.

Foundation.—(1) That portion of a structure, usually below the surface of the ground, which distributes the pressure upon its support. (2) Also applied to the natural support itself; rock, clay, etc.

Foundation Bed.—The surface on which a structure rests.

Grout.—A thin mortar either poured or applied with a brush.

Header.—A stone which has its greatest length at right angles to the face of the wall, and which bonds the face stones to the backing.

Initial Set.—An early stage of the process of setting, marked by certain hardness. (See Cement Specifications.)

Intrados.—The inner or concave surface of an arch.

Joint.—The narrow space between adjacent stones, bricks or other building blocks, usually filled with mortar.

Lagging.—Strips used to carry and distribute the weight of an arch to the ribs or centering during its construction.

Leveller.—A small rectangular stone, not less than four to six inches thick, used in broken range work to complete the bed for a stone in

34

the course above and give it proper bond. Sometimes called jumper or dutchman.

Lock.—Any special device or method of construction used to secure a bond in work.

Mortar.—A mixture of sand, cement or lime and water, used to cement the various stones or brick in masonry or to cover the surface of same.

Natural Bed.—The surface of a stone parallel to its stratification.

Paving.—Regularly placed stone or brick forming a floor.

Pean-Hammered.—(See Axed.)

Pinner.—A spall or small stone used to wedge up a stone and give it better bearing.

Pitched-Faced.—Having the arris clearly defined by a line beyond which the rock is cut away by the pitching chisel so as to make approximately true edges.

Pointing.—Filling joints or defects in the face of a masonry structure.

Quarry-Faced.—Stone faced as it comes from the quarry.

Random Range Masonry.—(See Broken Range Masonry.)

Riprap.—Rough stone of various sizes placed compactly or irregularly to prevent scour by water.

Rough Pointed.—Dressed by pick or heavy point until the projections vary from one-half to one inch.

Rubbed.—A fine finish made by rubbing with grit or sandstone.

Rubble.—Field stone or rough stone as it comes from the quarry. When it is of large or massive size it is termed block rubble.

Set (noun).—The change from a plastic to a solid or hard state.

Soffit.—The under side of a projection.

Spall (noun).—A chip or small piece of stone broken from a large block.

Stretcher.—A stone which has its greatest length parallel to the face of the wall.

Tooth-Axed.—Dressed by a method of fine pointing.

Voussoirs.—The stones, blocks of concrete or other material forming the arch ring.

APPENDIX III.

SPECIFICATIONS FOR STONE MASONRY.*

RECOMMENDED STANDARD SPECIFICATIONS.

GENERAL.

1. **Standard Specifications.**—The classification of Masonry and the requirements for cement and concrete shall be those adopted as the recommended practice of the American Railway Engineering Association.

2. **Engineer Defined.**—Where the term "Engineer" is used in these specifications, it refers to the engineer actually in charge of the work.

GENERAL REQUIREMENTS.

3. **Stone.**—Stone shall be of the kinds specially designated and shall be hard and durable, free from seams or other imperfections, of approved quality and shape, and in no case shall have less bed than rise. When liable to be affected by freezing, no unseasoned stone shall be laid.

4. **Dressing.**—Dressing shall be the best of the kind specified.

5. Beds and joints or builds shall be square with each other, and dressed true and out of wind. Hollow beds shall not be allowed.

6. Stone shall be dressed for laying on natural beds.

7. Marginal drafts shall be neat and accurate.

8. Pitching shall be done to true lines and exact batter.

9. **Mortar.**—Mortar shall be mixed in a suitable box and kept clean and free from foreign matter. Sand and cement shall be mixed dry and in small batches in proportions as directed by the engineer; water shall then be added; and the whole mixed until the mass of mortar is thoroughly homogeneous and leaves the hoe clean when drawn from it. Mechanical mixing, to produce the same results, may be permitted. Mortar shall not be retempered after it has begun to set.

10. **Laying.**—The arrangement of courses and bond shall be as indicated on the drawings, or as directed by the engineer. Stone shall be laid to exact lines and levels, to give the required bond and thickness of mortar in beds and joints.

11. Stone shall be cleansed and dampened before laying.

12. Stone shall be well bonded, laid on its natural bed and solidly settled into place in a full bed of mortar.

13. Stone shall not be dropped or slid over the wall, but shall be placed without jarring stone already laid.

* Adopted by American Railway Engineering Association.

14. Heavy hammering shall not be allowed on the wall after a course is laid.

15. Stone becoming loose after the mortar is set shall be relaid with fresh mortar.

16. Stone shall not be laid in freezing weather, unless directed by the engineer. If laid, it shall be freed from ice, snow or frost by warming; the sand and water used in the mortar shall be heated.

17. With precaution, a brine may be substituted for the heating of the mortar. The brine shall consist of one pound of salt to eighteen gallons of water, when the temperature is 32 degrees Fahrenheit; for every degree of temperature below 32 degrees Fahrenheit, one ounce of salt shall be added.

18. **Pointing.**—Before the mortar has set in beds and joints, it shall be removed to a depth of not less than one (1) in. Pointing shall not be done until the wall is complete and mortar set; nor when frost is in the stone.

19. Mortar for pointing shall consist of equal parts of sand, sieved to meet the requirements, and Portland cement. In pointing, the joints shall be wet, and filled with mortar, pounded in with a " set-in " or calking tool and finished with a beading tool the width of a joint, used with a straight-edge.

BRIDGE AND RETAINING WALL MASONRY.

Ashlar Stone.

20. **Bridge and Retaining Wall Masonry.**—The stone shall be large and well proportioned. Courses shall not be less than fourteen (14) in. or more than thirty (30) in. thick, thickness of courses to diminish regularly from bottom to top.

21. **Dressing.**—Beds and joints or builds of face stone shall be fine-pointed, so that the mortar layer shall be not more than one-half (½) in. thick when the stone is laid.

22. Joints in face stone shall be full to the square for a depth equal to at least one-half the height of the course, but in no case less than twelve (12) in.

23. **Face or Surface.**—Exposed surfaces of the face stone shall be rock-faced, and edges pitched to true lines and exact batter; the face shall not project more than three (3) in. beyond the pitch line.

24. Chisel drafts one and one-half (1½) in. wide shall be cut at exterior corners.

25. Holes for stone hooks shall not be permitted to show in exposed surfaces. Stone shall be handled with clamps, keys, lewis or dowels.

26. **Stretchers.**—Stretchers shall not be less than four (4) ft. long and have at least one and a quarter times as much bed as thickness of course.

27. **Headers.**—Headers shall not be less than four (4) ft. long, shall occupy one-fifth of face of wall, shall not be less than eighteen (18) in. high, width of face shall not be less than height of course.

28. Headers shall hold in heart or wall the same size shown in face, so arranged that a header in a superior course shall not be laid over a joint, and a joint shall not occur over a header; the same disposition shall occur in back of wall.

29. Headers in face and back of wall shall interlock when thickness of wall will admit.

30. Where the wall is three (3) ft. thick or less, the face stone shall pass entirely through. Backing will not be allowed.

31-*a**. **Backing.**—Backing shall be large, well-shaped stone, roughly bedded and jointed; bed joints shall not exceed one (1) in. At least one-half of the backing stone shall be of same size and character as the face stone and with parallel ends. The vertical joints in back of wall shall not exceed two (2) in. The interior vertical joints shall not exceed six (6) in. Voids shall be thoroughly filled with $\begin{cases} concrete. \\ spalls,\ fully\ bedded\ in\ cement\ mortar. \end{cases}$

31-*b**. **Backing.**—Backing shall be of $\begin{cases} concrete. \\ headers\ and\ stretchers,\ as\ specified \end{cases}$ in paragraphs 26 and 27, and heart of wall filled with concrete.

32. Where the wall will not admit of such arrangement, stone not less than four (4) ft. long shall be placed transversely in heart of wall to bond the opposite sides.

33. Where stone is backed with two courses, neither course shall be less than eight (8) in. thick.

34. **Bond.**—Bond of stone in face, back and heart of wall shall not be less than twelve (12) in. Backing shall be laid to break joints with the face stone and with one another.

35. **Coping.**—Coping stone shall be full size throughout, of dimensions indicated on the drawings.

36. Beds, joints, and top shall be fine-pointed.

37. Location of joints shall be determined by the position of the bed plates, and as indicated on the drawings.

38. **Locks.**—Where required, coping stone, stone in the wings of abutments, and stone on piers shall be secured together with iron clamps or dowels, in the position indicated on the drawings.

BRIDGE AND RETAINING WALL MASONRY.

RUBBLE STONE.

39. The stone shall be roughly squared, and laid in irregular courses. Beds shall be parallel, roughly dressed, and the stone laid horizontal to the wall. Face joints shall not be more than one (1) in. thick. Bottom stone shall be large, selected flat stone.

40. The wall shall be compactly laid, having at least one-fifth the surface back and face headers arranged to interlock, having all voids in the heart of the wall thoroughly filled with $\begin{cases} concrete. \\ suitable\ stones\ and\ spalls,\ fully\ bedded\ in\ cement\ mortar. \end{cases}$

* Paragraphs 31-*a* and 31-*b* are so arranged that either may be eliminated according to requirements. Optional clauses printed in italics.

534

APPENDIX III.

ARCH MASONRY.

Ashlar Stone.

41. Arch Masonry. Ashlar Stone.—Voussoirs shall be full size throughout and dressed true to templet, and shall have bond not less than thickness of stone.

42. Dressing.—Joints of voussoirs on the intrados shall be fine-pointed Mortar shall not exceed three-eighths (⅜) in.

43. Face or Surface.—Exposed surfaces of the ring stone shall be $\begin{cases} smooth. \\ rock- \end{cases}$ *faced, with a marginal draft.*

44. Courses.—Number of courses and depth of voussoirs shall be as indicated on the drawings.

45. Voussoirs.—Voussoirs shall be placed in the order indicated on the drawings.

46. Backing.—Backing shall consist of $\begin{cases} concrete. \\ large\ stone, shaped\ to\ fit\ the\ arch, \end{cases}$ *bonded to the spandrel and laid in full bed of mortar.*

47. Waterproofing.—Where waterproofing is required, a thin coat of mortar or grout shall be applied evenly for a finishing coat, upon which shall be placed a covering of approved waterproofing material.

48. Centers.—Centers shall not be struck until directed by the engineer.

49. Bench Walls and Piers. Spandrels, etc.—Bench walls, piers, spandrels, parapets, wing walls and copings shall be built under the specifications for Bridge and Retaining Wall Masonry, Ashlar Stone.

ARCH MASONRY.

Rubble Stone.

50. Arch Masonry. Rubble Stone.—Voussoirs shall be full size throughout, and shall have bond not less than thickness of voussoirs.

51. Dressing.—Beds shall be roughly dressed to bring them to radial planes.

52. Joints.—Mortar joints shall not exceed one (1) in.

53. Face or Surface.—Exposed surfaces of the ring stone shall be rock-faced, and edges pitched to true lines.

54. Voussoirs.—Voussoirs shall be placed in the order indicated on the drawings.

55. Backing.—Backing shall consist of $\begin{cases} concrete. \\ large\ stone, shaped\ to\ fit\ the\ arch, \end{cases}$ *bonded to the spandrel, and laid in full bed of mortar.*

56. Waterproofing.—Where waterproofing is required, a thin coat of mortar or grout shall be applied evenly for a finishing coat, upon which shall be placed a covering of approved waterproofing material.

57. Centers.—Centers shall not be struck until directed by the engineer.

58. Bench Walls, Piers, Spandrels, etc.—Bench walls, piers, spandrels parapets, wing walls and copings shall be built under the specifications for Bridge and Retaining Wall Masonry, Rubble Stone.

CULVERT MASONRY.

59. **Culvert Masonry.**—Culvert Masonry shall be laid in cement mortar. Character of stone and quality of work shall be the same as specified for Bridge and Retaining Wall Masonry, Rubble Stone.

60. **Side Walls.**—One-half the top stone of the side walls shall extend entirely across the wall.

61. **Cover Stones.**—Covering stone shall be sound and strong, at least twelve (12) in. thick, or as indicated on the drawings. They shall be roughly dressed to make close joints with each other, and lap their entire width under high embankments, as indicated on the drawings.

62. **End Walls Coping.**—End walls shall be covered with suitable coping, as indicated on the drawings.

DRY MASONRY.

63. **Dry Masonry.**—Dry Masonry shall include dry retaining walls and slope walls.

64. **Retaining Walls.**—Retaining Walls of Dry Masonry shall include all walls in which rubble stone laid without mortar is used for retaining embankments or for similar purposes.

65. **Dressing.**—Flat stones at least twice as wide as thick shall be used. Beds and joints shall be roughly dressed square to each other and to face of stone.

66. **Joints.**—Joints shall not exceed three-quarters (¾) in.

67. **Disposition of Stone.**—Stone of different sizes shall be evenly distributed over entire face of wall, generally keeping the largest stone in lower part of wall

68. **Bond.**—The work shall be well bonded and present a reasonably true and smooth surface, free from holes or projections.

69. **Slope Walls.**—Slope walls shall be built of such thickness and slope as directed by the engineer. Stone shall not be used in this construction which does not reach entirely through the wall. Stone shall be placed at right angles to the slopes. The wall shall be built simultaneously with the embankment which it is to protect.

APPENDIX IV.

SPECIFICATIONS FOR MATERIAL AND WORKMANSHIP FOR STEEL STRUCTURES.*

MATERIAL.

1. **Process of Manufacture.**—Steel shall be made by the open-hearth process.

2. **Schedule of Requirements.**

Chemical and Physical Properties.	Structural Steel.	Rivet Steel.	Steel Castings.
Phosphorus Max.. { Basic ... Acid..... Sulphur maximum............	0.04 per cent. 0 08 " " 0.05 " "	0.04 per cent. 0.04 " " 0.04 " "	0 05 per cent. 0.08 " " 0.05 " "
Ultimate tensile strength.. Pounds per square inch......	Desired 60000	Desired 50000	Not less than 65000
Elongation: min. % in 8" {	1,500,000 †	1,500,000	
	Ult. tensile strength	Ult. tensile strength.	
Elongation: min. % in 2"... Character of fracture......... Cold bends without fracture.	22 Silky 180° flat ‡	Silky 180° flat §	18 Silky or fine granular 90°, $d = 3t$

The yield point, as indicated by the drop of beam, shall be recorded in the test reports.

3. **Allowable Variations.**—If the ultimate strength varies more than 4,000 lbs. from that desired, a retest shall be made on the same gage, which, to be acceptable, shall be within 5,000 lbs. of the desired ultimate.

4. **Chemical Analyses.**—Chemical determinations of the percentages of carbon, phosphorus, sulphur and manganese shall be made by the manufacturer from a test ingot taken at the time of the pouring of each melt of steel and a correct copy of such analysis shall be furnished to the engineer or his inspector. Check analyses shall be made from finished material, if called for by the purchaser, in which case an excess of 25 per cent above the required limits will be allowed.

* Adopted by American Railway and Maintenance of Way Association, and the American Society for Testing Materials.

† See paragraph 11.   ‡ See paragraphs 12, 13 and 14.   § See paragraph 15.

5. **Form of Specimens.** PLATES, SHAPES AND BARS.—Specimens for tensile and bending tests for plates, shapes and bars shall be made by cutting coupons from the finished product, which shall have both faces rolled and both edges milled to the form shown by Fig. 1; or with both edges parallel; or they may be turned to a diameter of ¾ inch for a length of at least 9 inches, with enlarged ends.

6. RIVETS.—Rivet rods shall be tested as rolled.

7. PINS AND ROLLERS.—Specimens shall be cut from the finished rolled or forged bar, in such manner that the center of the specimen shall be 1 inch from the surface of the bar. The specimen for tensile test shall be turned to the form shown by Fig. 2. The specimen for bending test shall be 1 inch by ½ inch in section.

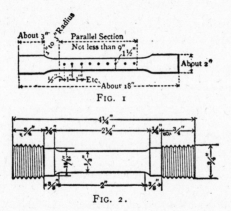

FIG. 1

FIG. 2.

8. STEEL CASTINGS.—The number of tests will depend on the character and importance of the castings. Specimens shall be cut cold from coupons molded and cast on some portion of one or more castings from each melt or from the sink heads, if the heads are of sufficient size. The coupon or sink head, so used, shall be annealed with the casting before it is cut off. Test specimens to be of the form prescribed for pins and rollers.

9. **Annealed Specimens.**—Material which is to be used without annealing or further treatment shall be tested in the condition in which it comes from the rolls. When material is to be annealed or otherwise treated before use, the specimens for tensile tests representing such material shall be cut from properly annealed or similarly treated short lengths of the full section of the bar.

10. **Number of Tests.**—At least one tensile and one bending test shall be made from each melt of steel as rolled. In case steel differing $\frac{3}{8}$ inch and more in thickness is rolled from one melt, a test shall be made from the thickest and thinnest material rolled.

11. **Modifications in Elongation.**—For material less than $\frac{5}{16}$ inch and more than $\frac{3}{4}$ inch in thickness the following modifications will be allowed in the requirements for elongation:

(*a*) For each $\frac{1}{16}$ inch in thickness below $\frac{5}{16}$ inch, a deduction of $2\frac{1}{2}$ per cent will be allowed from the specified elongation.

(*b*) For each $\frac{1}{8}$ inch in thickness above $\frac{3}{4}$ inch, a deduction of 1 per cent will be allowed from the specified elongation.

(*c*) For pins and rollers over 3 inches in diameter the elongation in 8 inches may be 5 per cent less than that specified in paragraph 2.

12. **Bending Tests.**—Bending tests may be made by pressure or by blows. Plates, shapes and bars less than 1 inch thick shall bend as called for in paragraph 2.

13. **Thick Material.**—Full-sized material for eye-bars and other steel 1 inch thick and over, tested as rolled, shall bend cold 180 degrees around a pin the diameter of which is equal to twice the thickness of the bar, without fracture on the outside of bend.

14. **Bending Angles.**—Angles $\frac{3}{4}$ inch and less in thickness shall open flat and angles $\frac{1}{2}$ inch and less in thickness shall bend shut, cold, under blows of a hammer, without sign of fracture. This test will be made only when required by the inspector.

15. **Nicked Bends.**—Rivet steel, when nicked and bent around a bar of the same diameter as the rivet rod, shall give a gradual break and a fine, silky, uniform fracture.

16. **Finish.**—Finished material shall be free from injurious seams, flaws, cracks, defective edges, or other defects, and have a smooth, uniform, workmanlike finish. Plates 36 inches in width and under shall have rolled edges.

17. **Stamping.**—Every finished piece of steel shall have the melt number and the name of the manufacturer stamped or rolled upon it. Steel for pins and rollers shall be stamped on the end. Rivet and lattice steel and other small parts may be bundled with the above marks on an attached metal tag.

18. **Defective Material.**—Material which, subsequent to the above tests at the mills, and its acceptance there, develops weak spots, brittleness, cracks or other imperfections, or is found to have injurious

defects, will be rejected at the shop and shall be replaced by the manufacturer at his own cost.

19. **Allowable Variation in Weight.**—A variation in cross-section or weight of each piece of steel of more than $2\frac{1}{2}$ per cent from that specified will be sufficient cause for rejection, except in case of sheared plates, which will be covered by the following permissible variations, which are to apply to single plates.

20. **When Ordered to Weight.**—Plates $12\frac{1}{2}$ pounds per square foot or heavier:

(*a*) Up to 100 inches wide, $2\frac{1}{2}$ per cent above or below the prescribed weight.

(*b*) One hundred inches wide and over, 5 per cent above or below.

21. Plates under $12\frac{1}{2}$ pounds per square foot:

(*a*) Up to 75 inches wide, $2\frac{1}{2}$ per cent above or below.

(*b*) Seventy-five inches and up to 100 inches wide, 5 per cent above or 3 per cent below.

(*c*) One hundred inches wide and over, 10 per cent above or 3 per cent below.

PLATES ¼ INCH AND OVER IN THICKNESS.

Thickness Ordered.	Nominal Weight.	Width of Plate.			
		Up to 75 Inch.	75″ and up to 100″.	100″ and up to 115.″	Over 115.″
1–4 inch.	10.20 lbs.	10　per cent.	14　per cent.	18　per cent.	
5–16 "	12.75 "	8　"　"	12　"　"	16　"　"	
3–8 "	15.30 "	7　"　"	10　"　"	13　"　"	17 per cent.
7–16 "	17.85 "	6　"　"	8　"　"	10　"　"	13 " "
1–2 "	20.40 "	5　"　"	7　"　"	9　"　"	12 " "
9–16 "	22.95 "	4½ " "	6½ " "	8½ " "	11 " "
5–8 "	25.50 "	4　"　"	6　"　"	8　"　"	10 " "
Over 5–8 "		3½ " "	5　"　"	6½ " "	9 " "

PLATES UNDER ¼ INCH IN THICKNESS.*

Thickness Ordered.	Nominal Weights Lbs. per Square Ft.	Width of Plate.		
		Up to 50.″	50″ and up to 70″	Over 70.″
1–8 ″ up to 5–32″	5.10 to 6.37	10　per cent.	15　per cent.	20 per cent.
5–32 " " 3–16	6.37 " 7.65	8½ " "	12½ " "	17 " "
3–16 " " 1–4	7.65 " 10.20	7　"　"	10 " "	15 " "

*Withdrawn but was adopted by American Society for Testing Materials, September 1, 1905.

22. **When Ordered to Gage.**—Plates will be accepted if they measure not more than .01 inch below the ordered thickness.

23. An excess over the nominal weight, corresponding to the dimensions on the order, will be allowed for each plate, if not more than that shown in the preceding tables, one cubic inch of rolled steel being assumed to weigh 0.2833 pounds.

Special Metals.

24. **Cast-Iron.**—Except where chilled iron is specified, castings shall be made of tough gray iron, with sulphur not over 0.10 per cent. They shall be true to pattern, out of wind and free from flaws and excessive shrinkage. If tests are demanded they shall be made on the " Arbitration Bar " of the American Society for Testing Materials, which is a round bar, $1\frac{1}{4}$ in. in diameter and 15 in. long. The transverse test shall be on a supported length of 12 in. with load at middle. The minimum breaking load so applied shall be 2,900 lbs., with a deflection of at least $\frac{1}{10}$ inch before rupture.

25. **Wrought-Iron Bars.**—Wrought-iron shall be double-rolled, tough, fibrous, and uniform in character. It shall be thoroughly welded in rolling and be free from surface defects. When tested in specimens of the form of Fig. 1, or in full-sized pieces of the same length, it shall show an ultimate strength of at least 50,000 lbs. per sq. in., an elongation of at least 18 per cent in 8 in., with fracture wholly fibrous. Specimens shall bend cold, with the fiber through 135°, without sign of fracture, around a pin the diameter of which is not over twice the thickness of the piece tested. When nicked and bent the fracture shall show at least 90 per cent fibrous.

Inspection and Testing at the Mills.

26. The purchaser shall be furnished complete copies of mill orders, and no material shall be rolled, nor work done, before the purchaser has been notified where the orders have been placed, so that he may arrange for the inspection.

27. The manufacturer shall furnish all facilities for inspecting and testing the weight and quality of all material at the mill where it is manufactured. He shall furnish a suitable testing machine for testing the specimens, as well as prepare the pieces for the machine, free of cost.

28. When an inspector is furnished by the purchaser to inspect mate-

rial at the mills, he shall have full access, at all times, to all parts of mills where material to be inspected by him is being manufactured.

WORKMANSHIP.

29. **General.**—All parts forming a structure shall be built in accordance with approved drawings. The workmanship and finish shall be equal to the best practice in modern bridge works.

30. **Straightening Material.**—Material shall be thoroughly straightened in the shop, by methods that will not injure it, before being laid off or worked in any way.

31. **Finish.**—Shearing shall be neatly and accurately done and all portions of the work exposed to view neatly finished.

32. **Rivets.**—The size of rivets, called for on the plans, shall be understood to mean the actual size of the cold rivet before heating.

33. **Rivet Holes.**—When general reaming is not required, the diameter of the punch for material not over $\frac{5}{8}$ inch thick shall be not more than $\frac{1}{16}$ inch, nor that of the die more than $\frac{1}{8}$ inch larger than the diameter of the rivet. The diameter of the die shall not exceed that of the punch by more than $\frac{1}{4}$ the thickness of the metal punched. Material over $\frac{5}{8}$ inch thick, except minor details, and all material where general reaming is required, shall be sub-punched and reamed as per paragraph 62, or drilled from the solid. Holes in flanges of rolled beams and channels used in floors of railroad bridges shall be drilled from the solid. Those in webs of same shall be so drilled or sub-punched and reamed.

34. **Punching.**—Punching shall be accurately done. Slight inaccuracy in the matching of holes may be corrected with reamers. Drifting to enlarge unfair holes will not be allowed. Poor matching of holes will be cause for rejection at the option of the inspector.

35. **Assembling.**—Riveted members shall have all parts well pinned up and firmly drawn together with bolts before riveting is commenced. Contact surfaces to be painted (see paragraph 66).

36. **Lattice Bars.**—Lattice bars shall have neatly rounded ends, unless otherwise called for.

37. **Web Stiffeners.**—Stiffeners shall fit neatly between flanges of girders. Where tight fits are called for the ends of the stiffeners shall be faced and shall be brought to a true contact bearing with the flange angles.

38. **Splice Plates and Fillers.**—Web splice plates and fillers under stiffeners shall be cut to fit within $\frac{1}{8}$ inch of flange angles.

39. **Web Plates.**—Web plates of girders, which have no cover plates, shall be flush with the backs of angles or project above the same not more than $\frac{1}{8}$ inch, unless otherwise called for. When web plates are spliced, not more than $\frac{1}{4}$ inch clearance between ends of plates will be allowed.

40. **Connection Angles.**—Connection angles for floor girders shall be flush with each other and correct as to position and length of girder. In case milling is required after riveting, the removal of more than $\frac{1}{16}$ inch from their thickness will be cause for rejection.

41. **Riveting.**—Rivets shall be driven by pressure tools wherever possible. Pneumatic hammers shall be used in preference to hand driving.

42. Rivets shall look neat and finished, with heads of approved shape, full and of equal size. They shall be central on shank and grip the assembled pieces firmly. Recupping and calking will not be allowed. Loose, burned or otherwise defective rivets shall be cut out and replaced. In cutting out rivets great care shall be taken not to injure the adjacent metal. If necessary they shall be drilled out.

43. **Turned Bolts.**—Wherever bolts are used in place of rivets which transmit shear, the holes shall be reamed parallel and the bolts turned to a driving fit. A washer not less than $\frac{1}{4}$ inch thick shall be used under nut.

44. **Members to be Straight.**—The several pieces forming one built member shall be straight and fit closely together, and finished members shall be free from twists, bends or open joints.

45. **Finish of Joints.**—Abutting joints shall be cut or dressed true and straight and fitted close together, especially where open to view. In compression joints depending on contact bearing the surfaces shall be truly faced, so as to have even bearings after they are riveted up complete and when perfectly aligned.

46. **Field Connections.**—Holes for floor girder connections shall be sub-punched and reamed with twist drills to a steel template 1 inch thick. Unless otherwise allowed, all other field connections shall be assembled in the shop and the unfair holes reamed; and when so reamed the pieces shall be match-marked before being taken apart.

47. **Eye-Bars.**—Eye-bars shall be straight and true to size, and shall be free from twists, folds in the neck or head, or any other defect. Heads shall be made by upsetting, rolling or forging. Welding will not be allowed. The form of heads will be determined by the dies in use at the works where the eye-bars are made, if satisfactory to the engineer, but the manufacturer shall guarantee the bars to break in the body with a silky fracture, when tested to rupture. The thickness of head and neck shall not vary more than $\frac{1}{16}$ inch from the thickness of the bar.

48. **Boring Eye-Bars.**—Before boring, each eye-bar shall be properly annealed and carefully straightened. Pin holes shall be in the center line of bars and in the center of heads. Bars of the same length shall be bored so accurately that, when placed together, pins $\frac{1}{32}$ inch smaller in diameter than the pin holes can be passed through the holes at both ends of the bars at the same time.

49. **Pin Holes.**—Pin holes shall be bored true to gages, smooth and straight; at right angles to the axis of the member and parallel to each other, unless otherwise called for. Wherever possible, the boring shall be done after the member is riveted up.

50. The distance center to center of pin holes shall be correct within $\frac{1}{32}$ inch, and the diameter of the hole not more than $\frac{1}{50}$ inch larger than that of the pin, for pins up to 5 inches diameter, and $\frac{1}{32}$ inch for larger pins.

51. **Pins and Rollers.**—Pins and rollers shall be accurately turned to gages and shall be straight and smooth and entirely free from flaws.

52. **Pilot Nuts.**—At least one pilot and driving nut shall be furnished for each size of pin for each structure, and field rivets 10 per cent in excess of the number of each size actually required.

53. **Screw Threads.**—Screw threads shall make tight fits in the nuts and shall be U. S. standard, except above the diameter of $1\frac{3}{8}$ inch, when they shall be made with six threads per inch.

54. **Annealing.**—Steel, except in minor details, which has been partially heated shall be properly annealed.

55. **Steel Castings.**—All steel castings shall be annealed.

56. **Welds.**—Welds in steel will not be allowed.

57. **Bed Plates.**—Expansion bed plates shall be planed true and smooth. Cast wall plates shall be planed top and bottom. The cut of the planing tool shall correspond with the direction of expansion.

58. **Shipping Details.**—Pins, nuts, bolts, rivets, and other small details shall be boxed or crated.

59. **Weight.**—The weight of every piece and box shall be marked on it in plain figures.

60. **Finished Weight.**—Payment for pound price contracts shall be by scale weight. No allowance over 2 per cent of the total weight of the structure as computed from the plans will be allowed for excess weight.

Additional Specifications When General Reaming and Planing are Required.

61. **Planing Edges.**—Sheared edges and ends shall be planed off at least $\frac{1}{4}$ inch.

62. **Reaming.**—Punched holes shall be made with a punch $\frac{3}{16}$ inch smaller in diameter than the nominal size of the rivets and shall be reamed to a finished diameter of not more than $\frac{1}{16}$ inch larger than the rivet.

63. **Reaming after Assembling.**—Wherever practicable, reaming shall be done after the pieces forming one built member have been assembled and firmly bolted together. If necessary to take the pieces apart for shipping and handling, the respective pieces reamed together shall be so marked that they may be reassembled in the same position in the final setting up. No interchange of reamed parts will be allowed.

64. **Removing Burrs.**—The burrs on all reamed holes shall be removed by a tool countersinking about $\frac{1}{16}$ inch.

Shop Painting.

65. Steel work, before leaving the shop, shall be thoroughly cleaned and given one good coating of pure linseed oil, or such paint as may be called for, well worked into all joints and open spaces.

66. In riveted work, the surfaces coming in contact shall each be painted before being riveted together.

67. Pieces and parts which are not accessible for painting after erection, including tops of stringers, eye-bar heads, ends of posts and chords, etc., shall have a good coat of paint before leaving the shop.

68. Painting shall be done only when the surface of the metal is perfectly dry. It shall not be done in wet or freezing weather, unless protected under cover.

69. Machine finished surfaces shall be coated with white lead and tallow before shipment or before being put out into the open air.

Inspection and Testing at the Shops.

70. The manufacturer shall furnish all facilities for inspecting and testing weight and the quality of workmanship at the shop where material is manufactured.   He shall furnish a suitable testing machine for testing full-sized members if required.

71. The purchaser shall be furnished complete shop plans, and must be notified well in advance of the start of the work in the shop, in order that he may have an inspector on hand to inspect material and workmanship.   Complete copies of shipping invoices shall be furnished to the purchaser with each shipment.

72. When an inspector is furnished by the purchaser, he shall have full access, at all times, to all parts of the shop where material under his inspection is being manufactured.

73. The inspector shall stamp each piece accepted with a private mark.   Any piece not so marked may be rejected at any time, and at any stage of the work. If the inspector, through an oversight or otherwise, has accepted material or work which is defective or contrary to the specifications, this material, no matter in what stage of completion, may be rejected by the purchaser.

Full-sized Tests.

74. Full-sized parts of the structure may be tested at the option of the purchaser.   Such tests on eye-bars and similar members to prove the workmanship, shall be made at the manufacturer's expense, and shall be paid for by the purchaser, at contract price, if the tests are satisfactory.   If the tests are not satisfactory, the members represented by them will be rejected.   The expense of testing members, to prove their design, shall be paid for by the purchaser.

75.   In eye-bar tests the ultimate strength, true elastic limit and the elongation in 10 feet, unless a different length is called for, shall be recorded.

76. In transverse tests the lateral and vertical deflections shall be recorded.

35

Unit Stresses.*

All parts of the structure shall be so proportioned that the sum of the maximum stresses shall not exceed the following amounts in pounds per square inch of cross-section:

Tension......................16,000

Compression................16,000 $- 70 \dfrac{l}{r}$

where $l =$ length of the member in inches and $r =$ the least radius of gyration in inches.

Rivets and pins, bearing 22,000
Rivets and pins, shear 11,000
Pins, bending on extreme fiber 24,000
Plate girder webs, shearing on net section 10,000
Bearing on granite masonry 500
Bearing on sandstone, limestone, and Portland
   cement concrete masonry 300
Expansion rollers per lineal inch .... 600 D

where $D =$ diameter of roller.

* Recommended by the American Railway Engineering and Maintenance of Way Association, but not formally adopted.

INDEX.

INDEX TO APPENDIX I.